submission, to our
Father's will, the
life, has been taken away.
I shall always feel most
grateful, to your Noble Husband,
for his unwavering friendship
& faithful support of the
President, which was highly
appreciated, I assure you, by
his grateful heart....

My son Robert, has entered
a law office, to read & study for
the summer, going into C- in
the morning & returning in the
evening. We occupy three very
pleasant rooms & how gladly
we would welcome, our Eastern
friends, to see us, those who have
known & loved my darling Husband

Mrs. Donn Corp

MR. LINCOLN'S WIFE

Mr. Lincoln's Wife

By Anne Colver

FARRAR & RINEHART, Inc.
New York Toronto

The endpaper is a portion of a letter from Mary Lincoln to a friend in Washington in June, 1865. It is reproduced through the courtesy of The Pierpont Morgan Library, New York.

PRINTED IN THE UNITED STATES OF AMERICA

For

Mary Cleveland Huntington

MR. LINCOLN'S WIFE

Part One

1

ELIZABETH EDWARDS WAS HAVING A FAMILY DINNER. BUT not for the Edwards family. The only Edwards at the long oval table in the candlelit dining room was Elizabeth's husband Ninian, who sat at the head and carved the roast, and saw that the wine was poured properly. All the others at the table were Todds. Elizabeth had been a Todd before she married.

"When you marry a Todd," Ninian had said once, in his careful, unemphatic way, "it's a little like joining a religious cult. You renounce all other worldly claims and become simply a Todd."

Not that Ninian resented it. There were very few things Ninian went so far as to resent, least of all anything connected with Elizabeth, whom he regarded with admiration as an example of all that a wife should be. But it was true that when Elizabeth spoke of The Family she was referring to her own. On the occasions when she had reason to bring an Edwards into the conversation, she made the distinction clear by saying "one of Mr. Edwards's connections."

Which was natural enough, really. By sheer force of numbers, the Todds made other families seem trifling and unmemorable in comparison. Robert Todd of Kentucky, Elizabeth's father, had fourteen children. Six by his first wife, and the second round, still presumably incomplete, by Elizabeth's stepmother. Adding three sets of grandparents, an assortment of aunts and cousins, and a battery of uncles who ran to senators and judges, the Todds summed up to a quite magnificent display.

"Being a Todd in Lexington is like being an angel in

heaven," a visitor to Kentucky had said. "All the best people are."

Along with so many other Kentuckians, a number of the Todds had migrated to Illinois, and nowadays there were enough of them in Springfield to represent the family adequately at Elizabeth's table.

"Virtually a quorum," Ninian said.

To the scraggly, growing, raw prairie town of Springfield, the Todds had brought an atmosphere of their own, thick with culture and bluegrass, that served as buffer between them and the cruder, bleaker aspects of frontier society.

"*It is scarcely necessary,*" they wrote home, "*to associate with the native Yankees, except in matters of business, for wherever one goes one finds plenty of congenial Kentuckians.*"

Elizabeth had been the first of the Todds to move from Lexington, and shortly after her marriage she was writing back enthusiastic invitations for others in her family to follow. The rapidly expanding prairie communities offered opportunities in business and politics that were not dreamed of in Kentucky, she said. Judge Hardin, one of the uncles, had come next, bringing his law practice and his nephew John Todd Stuart to Springfield with him.

Elizabeth had been careful to point out, delicately, that the advantages of pioneering were not confined to the gentlemen of the family. There were probably, she observed, more eligible bachelors to be found in Springfield alone than in the whole state of Kentucky. It was a fact that Elizabeth, with seven younger sisters, all unmarried, bore well in mind.

One by one, beginning with the oldest and working downward systematically, Elizabeth had brought her sisters to Springfield and seen to it that they were properly introduced into a society that abounded in young and ambitious gentlemen, all on the very brink of brilliant success, and nearly all, seemingly, starved for the affection and guidance of a suitable wife.

It was an act of simple kindness.

Nevertheless, Ninian Edwards was puzzled at first by this obligation to the younger Misses Todd.

"I can't see why so much planning should be necessary," he said mildly. "After all, Elizabeth, you married without any undue influence, I hope—"

Yes, Elizabeth conceded, that was true. But her case had been different. It had happened that shortly before her eighteenth birthday Ninian had come to Lexington to study at Transylvania University. His father, who was at that time governor of Illinois, as well as one of the wealthiest men in the state, had thoughtfuly provided Ninian with a letter of introduction to his friend Robert Todd. His son, the governor explained, was a serious, rather suggestible boy, not apt to make friends readily in a strange city. Mr. Edwards would be most grateful if Mr. Todd, for old time's sake, would be kind enough to see that Ninian's sojourn at the university was not too lonely.

Such a happy combination of circumstances, Elizabeth felt, could not be expected to recur with any degree of frequency. Merely because a watchful providence had performed one miracle unassisted was no reason to sit back with folded hands and assume that opportunity would knock seven more times at the Todd's front door.

"And besides," Elizabeth said thoughtfully, "none of the younger girls seem to have much initiative—unless perhaps Mary—but *she's* apt to be difficult for other reasons."

Mr. Edwards unfolded his newspaper.

"I expect you know best, my dear," he said. "Certainly you have never given me any reason to doubt your judgment."

Accordingly, in due time, Frances Todd had arrived to make her home in Springfield with the Edwards. There was no time limit on the invitation—but it was tacitly assumed that she would remain until she had either gladdened some eligible Springfield heart or exhausted the possibilities offered. It could not be said, certainly, that Frances outstayed her welcome. She was a mildly pretty girl, with a wholesome practical streak beneath a rather sentimental exterior, and at the end of five months she obligingly said yes to a young physician, already well established in Springfield, and promptly became Mrs. Wallace, in the Edwards parlor, by candlelight.

Ann, the next in order, arrived after a short breathing spell, and presented a rather more complex problem. Ann had a sallow complexion and slightly prominent teeth, and was not a good dancer. These minor defects might have been quite easily overcome, however, had it not been for the far more serious fact that Ann had a sharp wit, and an unfortunate tendency to view the world with an eye as jaundiced as her complexion. All in all it was a relief, when, at the end of a year and a half, a well-to-do Springfield merchant named Smith reached the conclusion, one evening in the Edwards sitting room, that Miss Ann was the object of his deepest desire.

During off moments in the course of these momentous happenings, Elizabeth found time to manage one of the largest houses in Springfield, to entertain regularly and attend the Episcopal church, and to produce three children, at appropriate intervals, without ever seriously dislocating the even tenor of the household.

Small wonder that Ninian Edwards was often told, with emphasis, that his wife was a remarkable woman. It was an opinion he heartily seconded; indeed, there were moments when he was positively overwhelmed by the spectacle of so much virtue and efficiency concentrated in one person. Elizabeth herself took a more modest view of her activities.

"Life," Elizabeth was fond of saying, "is precisely what one chooses to make of it."

The family dinner at the Edwards was a sort of double celebration, it being Ninian's birthday and also the occasion of welcoming Mary Todd, who had just arrived from Lexington to visit.

They were all present. The judge, bald and pleasantly pontifical after three glasses of port and an excellent meal, John Todd Stuart with his wife and daughters, Judge Logan, another of the uncles, Cousin Lizzie Grimsley, who had been a Todd—and of course Frances and Ann with their husbands.

Mary Todd, seated on Ninian's right, said she felt as though she hadn't left home at all.

Elizabeth smiled speculatively at the newest sister. Not precisely pretty, but there was a quality of freshness and sparkle in her round, pert face that Elizabeth approved. It was plain, too, that at eighteen Mary had already learned the trick of looking her best. Her light-brown hair was parted in the center and dressed in becoming curls behind her ears, and her summer frock of starched embroidered muslin had short puffed sleeves and touches of blue at the waist and throat in just the proper shade to show off her eyes. She carried her head well, had a lively, animated way of talking, and could express herself with wit (though not too much, Elizabeth hoped, remembering Ann).

A few weeks before, Mary had graduated from Madame Mentelle's classes in Lexington, and in the autumn she was planning to return—to enter Ward's Academy for two years of postgraduate study. Her visit to Springfield was not, therefore, in the nature of an official one. It was merely, so to speak, a sort of warming up. Still, Elizabeth felt, it could do no harm to consider the ultimate possibilities, and on the whole she was inclined to regard Mary as definitely the most promising of the sisters to date.

At the moment, unconscious of Elizabeth's speculations, Mary was listening to an account by John Stuart of the curious antics of his new law partner—a man by the name of Lincoln. John had, it seemed, first met Lincoln when they shared a room in a boardinghouse up in Vandalia, during a session of the state legislature of which they were both members. John had persuaded his lanky, easygoing roommate to take up law, and had lent him the books and kept after him so diligently that within six months Lincoln had been admitted to the bar.

"Don't see how you ever did, John," Judge Logan said. "I've known Abe Lincoln ever since he used to pilot a flatboat on the river, and I'd have staked my life he'd never stick to one thing or one place long enough to amount to anything. Abe's smart enough—and he's got a real knack for politics. I've seen him get up to speak in the Assembly, looking like a scarecrow in those clothes of his, and before he was finished he'd have the whole house on his side. But then, as likely as not, he wouldn't even show up when the question was put to vote. He'd be out fishing, or swapping yarns down at the post office. The trouble with Abe is, he doesn't care about anything enough to stay with it."

"Well, he's staying with the law—so far, at least," John said. "He was trying a case last week up in Decatur, and while he was summing up, a man in the back of the courtroom kept interrupting. The judge reprimanded him two or three times, but the man kept right on, and every time Abe would get ready to make a point, the man would heckle him again. Abe didn't seem to notice, but all of a sudden he stopped speaking and took off his coat. Then he walked back to where the man was sitting, picked him up like a sack of meal, carried him to the door, and threw him out. Calm as you please, he brushed off his hands, put on his coat, said 'Excuse me, your Honor,' and went on to finish his speech. I don't know but what it was that, as much as anything, that won the case for us."

Mary laughed with the others.

"I'd like to meet your Mr. Lincoln sometime, John," she said. "He sounds interesting."

Ninian rose to pass the gentlemen segars. "I'm afraid you'd be disappointed, Mary. Abe's hardly what you'd call a ladies' man—"

"Oh, I don't know, Ninian—" Judge Logan leaned back in his chair. "Maybe that's just what Abe needs—a little feminine influence to make up his mind for him, and polish off the rough corners—"

Elizabeth stood up rather abruptly, murmuring something about leaving the gentlemen to their segars, and there was a rustle of skirts as the other women rose to follow.

Mary was the last to push back her chair. She would have liked to stay, instead of going into the sitting room and listening to the latest exchange of gossip about clothes and servants. But Elizabeth's eye was on her. As she crossed the hall, the sound of the men's voices trailed after her. They were still talking, Mary noticed, about this curious Mr. Lincoln.

During the two months she stayed in Springfield, it seemed to Mary that she heard the name Lincoln mentioned more often than any other. Wherever she went the conversation was certain, sooner or later, to get around to some anecdote involving Mr. Lincoln. And the strange part was that no two people appeared to agree about him. If one said he was the homeliest man on earth, another was sure to protest.

"I don't see how you can call Abe homely. He's plain, I suppose—but there's something about his eyes that makes you forget the rest of his face."

There were stories about his strength. He could throw any man in the county in a wrestling match. Stories about his uncouth, back-country manners. And yet they said he could match wits with the smartest lawyers on the circuit—and win. There were jokes about the schoolbooks he carried around in his pockets, and was forever studying.

"I asked Abe what he was reading one day," Judge Logan said, "and he showed me an old first-year grammar. Said he was trying to figure out how you'd go about parsing a sentence."

And yet he'd read all of Shakespeare and could argue theories of philosophy with any man in town. He was sad, they said. To look at him sometimes, you'd think he'd lost his last friend. John Stuart said there were hours on end when Abe would sit in the office and hardly look up—just sit with his head in his hands, staring at nothing in particular, as if all the gloom in the world were settled on him. But ten minutes later, you'd likely see him down at Diller's drugstore with the boys—telling one of his stories that was comical enough to make a cat laugh.

"Trouble with Abe is, he doesn't take anything really seriously. Whatever comes up—he'll twist it into a joke somehow."

Once, someone said, when one of Lincoln's old friends had died, back in New Salem, he'd been asked to say a few words at the funeral. He stood right up in front of everybody, in that awkward way of his, with the tears rolling down his cheeks. And when he'd finished speaking, there wasn't a man in the room that was ashamed to admit he was crying.

No matter what they said about Abe Lincoln, the tone, Mary noticed, was always a trifle condescending. They were very sure, these Kentucky ladies and gentlemen, very certain that this odd fellow was not quite one of them. He was able—yes. But he was uncouth, ill-bred, uneducated. He'd been born in a log cabin somewhere, and had no family anyone had ever heard of. When someone had asked him where his people came from, he said they were Virginians, but he reckoned you wouldn't call them one of the first families—more like the third or fourth.

It seemed odd that with so much talk about him, Mary never actually got to meet Mr. Lincoln. When she asked Elizabeth why she didn't have him at the house, Elizabeth was vague.

"There's no call to, particularly. He's been up at Vandalia most of the summer, at the Assembly. And besides—Mr. Lincoln doesn't take any interest in young ladies."

Mary sighed. "Don't they take any interest in him?"

"Oh, heavens no!" Elizabeth shook her head. This was more of John's doing, she thought impatiently. What on earth did John Stuart mean, filling the child's head full of nonsense about a man like Abe Lincoln? "I've no doubt Mr. Lincoln sounds interesting enough to hear about, but actually he's shy and dull and he doesn't dance at all or have the faintest notion how to treat girls. I expect you'd find him a great bore. Tell me," she switched the subject briskly, "did you enjoy talking to Stephen Douglas last evening? Cousin Lizzie tells me he danced with you at least half a dozen times—and I can assure you Mr. Douglas is considered the best dancer in Springfield, as well as being very brilliant . . ."

Nevertheless, when the time came for Mary to go home to Lexington she was still a little disappointed not to have met Abe Lincoln.

2

IT WAS TWO YEARS BEFORE MARY CAME BACK TO SPRINGfield—two years during which she studied the classics in French and English, history, poetry and a smattering of the sciences. She gave enough attention to her lessons to stand well in her class at the academy, and devoted the rest of her time to dancing parties, picnics, riding horseback, and quarreling with her stepmother. There were afternoon promenades in the Botanical Gardens, musical evenings, when the young ladies, modest and self-conscious, rendered sentimental ballads or played dashing airs on the pianoforte, for the polite edification of audiences gathered in candlelit drawing rooms. There were lectures, for the more seriously minded, delivered at the weekly meetings of the Lyceum—and there was the new model planetarium at the university to be visited and marveled at.

Dr. Holly, the venerable, white-haired president of Transylvania, was fond of telling visitors that Lexington offered as varied and stimulating a cultural life as could be found in any city in America. Others, of less scholarly taste, were likely to point out that there were more pretty girls in Kentucky than there were stars in the sky. On one point all Kentuckians were agreed—that there was no place in the world like Kentucky.

"I daresay there are gentlemen to be found everywhere," Mary's grandmother Parker admitted, "but in Kentucky even the farmers are gentlemen."

It seemed odd, really, that anyone should want to leave such a paradise. But Mary, though she fitted pleasantly enough into the pattern of social life, was not sorry when the time came for her promised return to Springfield. For one thing, the girls with whom she had grown up suddenly began to seem rather tiresome and sentimental with their eternal confidences about their love affairs. Peg Breckinridge, for instance, was forever going into raptures over the charms of some newly discovered gentleman. A visiting lecturer from the East, or somebody's older brother home from college—or, if all else failed, one of the younger university professors, or the new minister, who had presided so graciously at the Literary Festival, sponsored by the Episcopal church.

"I can't see what earthly use there is in fluttering over someone who probably doesn't even know you're alive," Mary said, at the end of one of Peg's palpitating recitals.

Peg was hurt. "You don't *understand,*" she said. "But, oh—the way he looked at me, Mary, when he said good night. My heart turned to butter!"

Mary sniffed. "I should think that must have felt quite nasty," she said.

Peg sighed. "Haven't you ever been in love, Mary? Not even the least tiny bit? When someone held your hand—and told you he thought you were the prettiest girl he'd ever seen?"

Mary shook her head. The truth was, she realized a trifle uncomfortably, that no one had ever seemed moved to quite these sentiments in her presence. It was odd, really, because she was quite as pretty as Peg, and danced a good deal better.

"I just don't care for boys," Mary said airily. "If I ever *were* in love—it would be with a man. Someone who was clever, brilliant and ambitious and could make speeches and do things—" She stopped suddenly, surprised at having said so much.

But Peg didn't seem to have noticed anything strange. "Well, I expect it's because you've always been clever," she said. "All the same—you'll be like the rest of us when the time comes. Just you wait and see . . ."

Two years had wrought a good many changes in the breezy, sprawling town of Springfield. It was still growing, by leaps and bounds—new houses had sprung up everywhere, and the streets were pushing out in all directions, pushing the cornfields farther and farther back, into the flat brown prairies. There were new shops around the square, and now the State House, massive and somber, cast an impressive solemnity over everything.

The old sign that had read *Stuart and Lincoln* was gone, Mary saw, and there was a new one, farther up the block, with glittering gold letters: *Logan and Lincoln, Attorneys at Law.*

So, Mary thought, Judge Logan must have been persuaded after all that the odd Mr. Lincoln could stick at his trade.

Elizabeth pointed out the new developments proudly, but she made no mention of Judge Logan's new partner. "You'll find the town quite different nowadays," she said. "Since they moved the capital here from Vandalia, we have all sorts of interesting young men coming and going. And by the way—" she smiled significantly—"Mr. Douglas has been inquiring for you, Mary. I told him you'd be here in time for the Assembly Ball next week. I do hope you've brought plenty of new frocks . . ."

The ball was a great success. It was remarkable, Mary thought, the way one's popularity seemed to increase merely because one happened to be a visitor from out of town.

Mary wore a white dress, with a sash of deep-pink satin that matched her slippers, and a cluster of late roses from Elizabeth's garden fastened in her curls. When one young legislator, whose name she had failed to catch, murmured in her ear that she was like the spirit of all roses, captured from heaven, Mary marveled. No one, certainly, in Lexington would have dreamed of saying such a thing.

It was midway through the evening that Mary found a moment for a word with Elizabeth.

"Are you having a good time, Mary?" Elizabeth's smile was fond, and her glance was sharp. No less than three women had confided in her that her latest little sister was really too charming. And had she noticed that Mr. Douglas seemed to be quite smitten? He'd already had three quadrilles and a waltz with Miss Mary, by actual count.

"Everything is lovely, Elizabeth," Mary said. She sat down for a minute, fanning herself. "I was just wondering—" she paused—"who is that gentleman over there by the door? The tall one, in the black coat—talking to Uncle. He doesn't seem to be dancing—though he looks quite young enough—"

Elizabeth looked. Then she settled back.

"Oh—that's only Mr. Lincoln," she said. "He's gone into partnership with your uncle recently. I expect you may have heard his name—though I really can't remember whether you met him when you were here before."

"No," Mary said, "I haven't met Mr. Lincoln yet . . ."

3

ON A BLUSTERY EVENING IN FEBRUARY, ELIZABETH AND Ninian were driving home from a church supper at Cousin Lizzie's house. It had snowed and sleeted for two days, without signs of letting up, and the roads were so rutted with icy drifts that the horses slithered helplessly, and the carriage swayed like a ship tossed on a stormy sea.

Ninian was tired. He disliked church suppers in general, and those under Cousin Lizzie's fluttering and nervous eye most particularly. He was chilled, his shoes were wet from the snow, and he wished nothing more than that he were at home, before his own fire, instead of being joggled along in a miserably drafty carriage.

Elizabeth seemed quite unmindful of the disagreeable elements. With that total disregard of discomfort which Ninian had learned to recognize in women whose minds were on something else, she sat beside him, apparently oblivious to the howling wind and the angry clatter of sleet that whipped against the windows.

"The thing that troubles me about Mary," Elizabeth said suddenly, quite as though they had been discussing the matter, "is that she's got her head full of notions. Where she ever got them, I'm sure I don't know. I never had any such difficulty with Frances—or even Ann."

Mr. Edwards nodded, suppressing a shiver as a vicious gust of wind whipped through the carriage. Having already lived through two courtships, he was familiar with the peculiar difficulties that seemed to be the natural prelude to matrimony.

"The strange part of it is," Elizabeth went on thoughtfully, "that Mary really started out so well. Much better than either of the others. There was Mr. Douglas, for instance. If Mary had given him an ounce of proper encouragement, he'd have proposed long ago. But he might be a fly on the wall, for all the attention Mary ever gives him. And then there was Mr. Tyre—and that young clergyman from Decatur—he could perfectly easily have come to something—" Elizabeth paused, sighing. "Really, I can't understand Mary."

It might be, Ninian suggested, trying to keep his teeth from chattering audibly, that Mary just didn't want to get married after all.

To this absurdity, Elizabeth naturally paid no attention.

"I suppose the trouble is," she said, "that Mary has a mind of her own—and that's always so difficult where men are concerned. It's a pity though—"

When they drew up at last before the front door, Ninian saw that the parlor lights were still burning.

"Who's the victim tonight?" he asked.

Elizabeth stepped out of the carriage briskly.

"Really, Mr. Edwards—you do speak vulgarly sometimes," she said. "It's no one of any consequence. Only Mr. Lincoln again. Why Mary persists in letting him come to call, I can't think. If she has any notion of making Mr. Douglas jealous, she's overdoing it—and I've told her so plainly. But of course she doesn't listen. She never does. She says—" Elizabeth shook the snow from her mantle energetically—"she enjoys Mr. Lincoln's mind."

When they came into the parlor, Mary was alone. Looking at her sister, Elizabeth could scarcely fail to feel a certain satisfaction. A bright fire—a pleasant room. A girl in a blue dress, with her small, pretty feet resting on the brass fender. A storm outside—and a whole evening of solitude. From experience, Elizabeth had learned that one might sell all other commodities short, in favor of solitude. Such a pity, really, to think it had all been wasted on Abe Lincoln.

"Well—did you enjoy your evening?"

Mary looked up, smiling.

"Mr. Lincoln has just gone," she said. "He said to tell you he was ever so sorry not to have seen you—but he's leaving for Decatur in the morning, to try a case, and he has a brief to finish."

Elizabeth walked over to the mantel and straightened an ornament. Running a finger, with practiced inquisitiveness, along the underside, she inspected it for dust.

"Tell me—" Elizabeth's tone was crisp—"what do you and your rough diamond talk about when you're alone?"

"Not very much." Mary's smile deepened. "A good deal of the time he just sits and looks at the fire."

"That seems rather a waste, doesn't it?" Ninian came in from the hall, stretching his hands, elegant and tapering, toward the warm hearth. "Especially when you're so charmingly gotten up for his benefit."

Mary flushed. "Mr. Lincoln doesn't care for clothes and such things," she said quickly. "He's very serious."

"Really?" Ninian raised his pale brows. "I shouldn't have thought Abe was altogether bent on the intellectual life—judging from some of his stories."

"All the same, Mary," Elizabeth cut in, "you do well to appeal to his mind, since there's so little else one could appeal to in Mr. Lincoln." She suppressed a yawn. "Well, I daresay we'd better get to bed."

From the stairway she looked back, a touch of impatience in her glance.

"For pity's sake don't sit there mooning, Mary. Come to bed."

One morning Elizabeth came to Mary's room with a letter in her hand. It was from a niece of Ninian's who lived in Maryland, she explained; and, of all things, the girl had suddenly taken it into her head to come to Springfield.

"I never supposed Mr. Edwards was especially fond of her," Elizabeth said, frowning, "but for some reason he quite insists on our having her, though he knows perfectly well it will crowd us—with only one guest room for the two of you. He says"—Elizabeth bit her lip—"that it will be a refreshing novelty to have a member of his family visit us. The worst of it is, Matilda doesn't give any idea how long she intends to stay, which means, I daresay, a month at the very least. So I expect there's nothing to be done but try to make the best of it—"

Mary looked up quickly. "What's she like?"

"Oh—quite plain, I think." Elizabeth's tone was reassuring. "As I remember, she was a gawky sort of child—

all arms and legs. She used to have notions about being a writer, or some such thing. At any rate, she's probably interested in books, and won't expect to go about much. I daresay she won't be troublesome—but all the same, it *is* upsetting, having her come just now."

Matilda arrived two weeks later, and it was at once apparent that she had changed considerably since the last time Elizabeth had seen her. There was, certainly, no trace of gawkiness in her slim, graceful figure, and from the number of party frocks that emerged from her trunk it was evident that she did, most definitely, expect to spend her time at something besides reading.

"I hope I haven't brought too many things," Matilda said at once, with engaging frankness. "I expect it looks as though I intended to stay forever—but after all, Mamma and I decided it was better to bring too much than not enough. Especially as Uncle Ninian wrote Mamma that there were so many parties in Springfield nowadays."

Mary and Elizabeth exchanged glances.

"I'm afraid your uncle Ninian exaggerated our gaiety, dear." Elizabeth's smile was slightly strained. "But I hope you won't find us too dull."

Matilda laughed, tipping her head so that the honey-colored curls over her ears fell back prettily.

"There's not much fear of *that,*" she said. "After the plantation where nothing ever happens, it's exciting enough just to be here. And besides, it's going to be nice sharing a room with Mary. Such a change from home—where I've got nothing but brothers to plague me."

It wasn't going to be so bad after all, having Matilda, Mary thought. She was pleasant and friendly, and for all her prettiness, there wasn't a scrap of self-consciousness about her. Her brown eyes were direct, under level brows, and she seemed to travel on the amiable assumption that everyone was going to like her as much as she liked them.

Going down to lunch, Matilda slipped her arm through Mary's.

Elizabeth watched them come into the dining room together, with mingled feelings. It was plain that they were getting on well, and that was a relief. On the other hand, Matilda was altogether too pretty for Elizabeth's peace of mind. One thing, at least, she was thankful for. Matilda wasn't the flirting kind—on that Elizabeth would stake her life.

It wasn't long, however, before Elizabeth discovered that there were things far worse than being a flirt. It was true—Matilda made not the slightest effort to attract attention. Her manner toward the young gentlemen she met was precisely the same candid, pleasant friendliness she showed for everyone. But, most unexpectedly, the gentlemen seemed, without exception, to respond to this good-naturedly impartial treatment with a quite alarming degree of interest. Matilda became the center of every gathering. Matilda was the most popular girl on picnics. Matilda had a dozen young men begging for the privilege of escorting her to every dance.

Wherever she went, Elizabeth heard nothing but compliments for Matilda. Matilda was so sweet, so charmingly unaffected. And *so* pretty. Senator Robinson's wife confided to Elizabeth that her husband was quite captivated by dear Ninian's little niece.

"You must let us plan a party for her," Mrs. Robinson said. "The senator says she's the first young girl he's met in years who doesn't make him feel like an old fogy . . . And, of course," she added, "your sister Mary will come too . . ."

"You might think," Elizabeth said to Ann and Frances, with some bitterness, "that Matilda Edwards was the first girl who had ever visited Springfield."

At the end of ten days, Ninian asked his niece whether she was enjoying her stay. They were at the dinner table, and Matilda looked up with her quick, friendly smile.

"Why, of course I am, uncle. How could I help it—when Aunt Elizabeth and Mary are being so lovely to me?"

It wasn't until nearly a week later that Matilda met Mr. Lincoln.

He had been out of town, attending to some business in Vandalia, and on the first day after his return he sent around a note asking Mary if he might come to call the following evening.

"I've never known Mr. Lincoln to be so formal," Elizabeth said, when Mary showed her the note. "All the same"—she smiled with rather unexpected warmth—"it goes to show how well he thinks of you, Mary."

It was arranged that Matilda would go with Elizabeth and Ninian to a supper party at Ann's house, while Mary stayed home to receive Mr. Lincoln.

"After all," Elizabeth said, "I'm sure Mr. Lincoln would find an evening of conversation with Matilda quite tiresome."

But when Mr. Lincoln arrived, rather more carefully dressed than usual, he glanced around inquiringly.

"I thought I heard your cousin was visiting," he said.

All during the evening, Mr. Lincoln was a great deal more conversational than usual. Indeed, he found so many things to tell Mary about his trip that at ten-thirty, when Matilda came in, he was still there. Nor did he, even then, show the slightest inclination to go home, though more than once Elizabeth glanced rather pointedly at the clock—and Mary, who had laughed so appreciatively at Mr. Lincoln's anecdotes earlier, lapsed into an unaccountable silence from which his most amusing sallies failed to rouse her.

"I declare," Ninian said later, "I never saw Abe in better spirits than he was tonight."

Elizabeth, busy before the mirror, gave one of her curlpapers an extra vicious yank. She said nothing.

It wasn't long before others besides Ninian observed the odd metamorphosis of Mr. Lincoln's behavior.

"I don't know what's got into Abe these days," John Stuart said. "He's as cheerful as a cricket. Always whistling around the office—and he's had his boots shined twice this week."

"It looks as though Elizabeth had made another match," said Mrs. Stuart. "Mr. Lincoln is over there nearly every evening—and, from all I hear, he seems to be really smitten this time. They say he has no eyes for anyone since Matilda Edwards came to town."

Meanwhile, in the Edwards house, a sort of armed neutrality existed. Night after night Mary and Matilda shared the guest-room bed. When Mary's temper grew noticeably short, Matilda cheerfully overlooked it, and maintained an accommodating and friendly silence. Only once had the subject of Mr. Lincoln been mentioned between them. That was a few days after he had come home, when Mary inquired, being careful to keep her tone casual, whether Matilda liked him.

"Oh, yes, ever so much," Matilda said warmly. "I like everyone I've met in Springfield."

Elizabeth kept silent until one evening when Mary had excused herself from a party, saying she had a headache, and Mr. Lincoln had gone off with Matilda. Then Elizabeth faced her husband squarely.

"It's a shame," she said. "Matilda ought to be spoken to, Mr. Edwards. But if *I* say anything, of course it will only look as though I were taking Mary's part—"

"I can't see what Matilda has done. . ." Ninian glanced up mildly.

"She hasn't done anything." Elizabeth's tone was bitter. "She never does do anything—that's just the trouble. But she knows quite well that Mr. Lincoln was interested in Mary before she came. I've as good as told her so. And yet she goes on, accepting his attentions as though it were the most natural thing in the world . . ."

Ninian spread his hands.

"It's all beyond me, Elizabeth," he said. "Until a few weeks ago, you were complaining that Mary was wasting her time on Mr. Lincoln. Now—simply because he seems to find Matilda agreeable company—"

"There's a great deal more in it than that, Mr. Edwards," Elizabeth said darkly. "It's plain to be seen that the girl has designs on him."

"I can't see that she treats him one bit differently than she does any of the others who seem to be taken with her."

"That's precisely my point, Mr. Edwards. It simply isn't natural for a girl to like *every* man who comes her way. It—" she groped helplessly for a moment—"it isn't decent."

The winter thawed itself into spring, and spring melted into summer, and Mr. Lincoln's presence in the Edwards parlor did not diminish.

Matilda showed no signs of going home. Not all Elizabeth's hints, to the effect that Matilda's family must by now be quite frantic for a glimpse of her, had the slightest effect.

"Mamma was so worried at first for fear I might be homesick," Matilda said cheerfully, "but when I wrote how wonderful you were all being to me, she said she and Papa were perfectly willing for me to stay just as long as you and Uncle Ninian wanted me."

There was a night in July when the girls came home late from a picnic supper, and Mary found Elizabeth downstairs sewing by the lamplight. Matilda had gone straight upstairs.

"I can't stand it any longer," Mary said suddenly. "I'm going home."

Elizabeth put down her sewing, startled by the white, set look on Mary's face.

"I can't stand it, I tell you!"

"Sh-sh—dear, Matilda will hear you."

"I don't care who hears me. I'm going back to Lexington. I never liked it here anyway. The men are hateful. They have no manners—and I—"

"*Mary*—" Elizabeth's voice was sharp. Then it softened soothingly. "If Mr. Lincoln has done something, dear . . . if Matilda—"

Mary took off her wide-brimmed straw hat and flung it on a chair.

"Mr. Lincoln has nothing to do with this," she said, "nor Matilda either. It's just—" her words broke on a flood of bitter, unexpected tears—"it's just—everything."

Elizabeth rose, thoroughly alarmed. If there was anything she disliked and avoided, it was weeping.

"Now, Mary," she said sensibly, "stop and think. What would you be going home to? A stepmother who never thinks of anything but her own babies. You know quite well how unhappy you were in Lexington—"

Mary's sobs, dry and frightening, cut her short.

"I couldn't be any more unhappy than I am here—I couldn't—possibly—"

The next morning, at breakfast, Matilda observed quite matter-of-factly that she must be going home.

"I just hate to think of it, really." Matilda's smile, warm and affectionate, embraced them all. "I'm going to miss you just awfully—especially Mary."

In the silence, tense and strained, that followed her announcement, Matilda went on placidly. She was going, she said, to be married. There was a Mr. Ramsey at home—he was a lot older than she was, but ever so kind. The wedding was planned for October, and Mamma thought she really ought to be planning her trousseau.

For a moment no one said anything. Then Elizabeth spoke.

"Well—" Her tone, for once, was strangely flat. "I'm sure we're all very happy for you, Matilda. But I should have thought, if you had anything like this in mind, you might have taken us into your confidence a trifle sooner."

Matilda buttered a hot biscuit. She hadn't dreamed, truly, of keeping anything from them. But she hadn't supposed it made any particular difference.

"Not make any *difference*—well, really—" Elizabeth set her cup down with a smart click. Her glance swept the table, as though appealing for support in the face of this extraordinary observation. But Mary was staring fixedly at her plate and Ninian appeared to be, for the moment, wholly preoccupied with the business of lighting his segar.

"I must say, Matilda," Elizabeth went on, "your attitude strikes me as peculiar—to say the least. Whether or not you chose to confide in us, there are certain standards of proper conduct for an engagement. One hardly expects a girl who is about to be married to go about as though she were entirely free to accept the attentions of other young men. Aside from the fact that it's undignified—it scarcely seems decent deliberately to lead a man on—"

Seeing the small, puzzled frown that gathered between Matilda's wide-set eyes, Ninian cleared his throat.

"Your aunt is intending to say, my dear—" he brushed the ash from the tip of his segar delicately—"that we had ventured to hope, in these weeks, that your fancy might quite possibly settle on one of the local gentlemen who seem to have been competing so earnestly for your favor."

"Oh!" Matilda's brow cleared. Then, quite startlingly, she threw back her head and laughed. "Oh, goodness no, uncle." Her smile dimpled with amusement. "I never even thought of such a thing—though your friends here have been ever so kind to me."

"Rather more than kind, in a few cases, I should say," Elizabeth put in dryly. Such matters, her tone implied, were hardly the occasion for mirth.

Matilda looked thoughtful for a moment. Then she helped herself to another biscuit. "I suppose," she said, "they were nice to me mostly because they rather liked

meeting someone who wasn't expecting to marry one of them."

Ninian, quite suddenly, was taken with a fit of coughing. It must have been, he explained, that some smoke had got down his throat.

That night Mary lay awake for a long time. It wasn't the first time she had lain so—listening to the wind that rustled faintly in the dark trees outside the window, hearing the dry, monotonous count of the crickets' chirping.

Usually Matilda went to sleep as soon as she had said good night. But tonight, although Matilda lay still beside her, Mary sensed that she was awake. Mary's hands were clenched tightly at her sides. She wanted to speak. All day, since Matilda's astonishing revelation at the breakfast table, one question had been circling in her mind, wearing a sharp and weary pattern. Now, in the darkness, she drew her breath.

"Matilda—?"

"Yes?"

Mary shut her eyes. In the blackness, the circle swirled narrower and narrower—until it was like a fiery pin point.

"Matilda—have you ever thought—has Mr. Lincoln ever said—that he was in love with you?"

There was an instant's silence. Then Matilda's voice, calm and matter-of-fact, cut through the dark, spinning void.

"Why, no."

Mary waited. Waited while the pounding, surging tide subsided. She heard the wind again, and the vague familiar sounds of the summer night, coming back into focus.

"I thought perhaps—" she kept her voice level, carefully—"since he seemed to like you so much—and you liked him . . ."

"Yes," Matilda said, "I like him very much. If it weren't for—" there was just a shade of hesitation—"for other things . . ." Her voice trailed away. "He talked to

me a great deal—mostly about the things he wants to do. I think perhaps he liked to talk to me, because I've always wanted to do something too—only I never knew quite what it was."

"Yes."

"But as for love," Matilda said, "I don't suppose he knows the meaning of the word."

4

IT WAS AMAZING, MARY'S SISTERS AGREED, THE WAY MARY had taken Mr. Lincoln back without a murmur. Matilda's tracks had scarcely cooled, so to speak, before he was calling on Mary again—with never so much as a word of explanation or apology.

"I can't understand it," Frances said. "Mary, of all people—who's always had so much spirit—"

"Yes, exactly—" Ann nodded. "And now—to see her making a perfect doormat of herself, after the way Mr. Lincoln has acted. I don't wonder people are talking about her."

"Really, Elizabeth, you must speak to her plainly."

Speaking to Mary plainly, however, was not without its difficulties. Whatever lack of spirit she may have displayed toward Mr. Lincoln's shortcomings was more than made up for in her response to Elizabeth's suggestions.

"It's perfectly plain to everyone," Elizabeth said angrily, "that you're making a fool of yourself—not to mention of me, which I presume you never consider. If you go on like this, throwing yourself at Mr. Lincoln's head, you'll soon find yourself in a position where no other gentleman will consider it possible to entertain any feelings toward you at all."

Mary set her chin. It was of no interest to her, she

said, what other gentlemen might entertain in the way of feelings.

"It's beyond me," Elizabeth said despairingly to Ninian, "why Mary should fasten on Abe Lincoln. But since she has—I suppose there's nothing to do but to see that she gets him."

There was no question, in Elizabeth's mind, but that marrying the wrong man was infinitely preferable to marrying none at all. With this in view, she brought her best technique to bear.

Mr. Lincoln, however, remained peculiarly impervious to technique. He called, he was pleasant. He squired Mary to local parties with reasonable faithfulness. He consumed large quantities of Elizabeth's food, and smoked dozens of Ninian's excellent segars. But on the subject of matrimony he was as mute as if the holy estate were nonexistent.

Elizabeth was reduced at last to telling Mary she'd better go home to Lexington.

"Let him see that you don't care," she said. "That will bring him to terms quickly enough."

Mary was not so sure. Something warned her that it was foolish to force an issue where it might very well turn out that there was no issue to force.

"The plain fact is, Mr. Edwards," Elizabeth said, "that Mary is in love. And that always makes these things so difficult."

It was a good year for Whig politics. William Harrison was running for president, and from the looks of things he had a good chance of being elected. The local party members in Springfield were rallying their forces.

"Reckon this is where Abe gets a chance," they said. "He's one of old Tippecanoe's best rooters around these parts. If Harrison gets in, Abe's sure to get some plum out of it."

One evening there was an item in the paper saying that Mr. Lincoln, esteemed local attorney, had been invited to make a speech at a campaign rally in Missouri, early in October.

The next morning Mary walked into the nursery, where Elizabeth was feeding the baby. She sat down for a minute, absently observing the diligent process by which the infant was being stuffed with porridge.

"I've been thinking, Elizabeth," Mary said. "You know the Judge Todds down in Columbia have been asking me to visit for ever so long. I think maybe I ought to go."

Elizabeth glanced up, between spoonfuls.

"All the way to Missouri?" she asked.

"Well—it really isn't so far. And you know I haven't seen any of them since Cousin Ann was just a little girl. I didn't care much about going in the summer—when it was so hot—but now that it's cooler . . ."

Elizabeth set down the empty porridge bowl and raised the baby to her shoulder, bouncing him up and down. Over the top of his bobbing head, she contemplated her sister.

"Just when were you thinking of going?"

"Well—I hadn't decided really." Mary picked up the baby's flannel nightrobe. She folded it neatly, pressing the edges together with a thoughtful air. "I thought perhaps toward the end of the month—if that's convenient for you."

Elizabeth was silent. She joggled the baby more briskly, churning him until his small face puckered with distress, and there were warning gurgles from the region of his full stomach. Presently, after a particularly vigorous bounce, the baby opened his round pink mouth and disgorged a sizable portion of the porridge he had just consumed. Elizabeth laid him on the bed and mopped a stray dribble from his chin.

"I never can see," Mary said, "why you go to all the trouble of feeding him—and then shake half of it up again."

Elizabeth flopped the baby over expertly and adjusted a pin.

"The only way to get the acid out of a baby's stomach is to make him spit up after he eats," she said. "It keeps them from having the colic." She popped the baby into his cradle, where he lay, gorged and amiable, staring up out of vague, blue eyes. "There now—go to sleep like a good boy."

Gathering up the empty bowl and an armful of clothes, Elizabeth started toward the door.

"If you want to go traipsing down to Missouri next month, Mary," she said, "I'm sure I have no objection."

When Ninian heard of the projected trip, he raised his eyebrows.

"Isn't this rather sudden?"

"It seems," Elizabeth said dryly, "that Mary has been planning to go for some time."

"Well—the weather in Missouri ought to be pleasant at this season."

Elizabeth shrugged. "For all Mary cares about the weather, I daresay it could be hailing pitchforks and she'd never notice—so long as Mr. Lincoln was going to be there."

Ninian studied the tip of his boot thoughtfully.

"I expect we ought to remember," he said, "that all's fair in love or war. Only in this case, I wonder sometimes —which it is."

If the Judge Todds were startled by the abruptness with which their niece announced that she was about to favor them with a visit, they managed to conceal their surprise. And once Mary was there, she exerted herself so diligently at being charming and agreeable that the judge said, upon his word, he believed she'd turned out the best of any of Robert's children so far.

Mrs. Todd agreed.

"I declare though—" she shook her head—"I never saw

a girl so taken up with politics. She's been at me since the first moment she got here about going up to that Whig rally in Rocheport. She's even got Ann all excited—though I don't suppose before she'd listened to Mary's talk Ann could so much as tell the difference between a Whig and a Democrat."

On the morning of the rally, Mary was up and dressing before seven. She combed her hair carefully, and laid out her best hat and a fresh pair of gloves. It was going to be a fair day, thank goodness—which meant there would surely be no last-minute indecision about going. The judge had said only the night before that he was willing enough to take the girls if the weather was good, but, by heaven, he wasn't going to risk an attack of rheumatism by sitting five hours in the rain just to hear a lot of political windbags spout.

No danger of rheumatism today, Mary thought, as she slipped on three starched petticoats and fetched her new blue watered silk frock from the wardrobe. The October sky was serene and cloudless, and the early mist would surely burn off long before they got to the river. The excursion boats were due to leave at ten.

Promptly at seven-thirty, Mary knocked at her aunt's door.

Was there anything she could do to help get ready? she inquired sweetly. She'd already wakened Ann and got her started dressing.

Mrs. Todd blinked. "Heavens and earth, child—whatever have you put on your best dress for? No one will be gotten up much for this sort of outing."

Later, when Mary had gone, Mrs. Todd turned to her husband thoughtfully.

"You know, Mr. Todd, I wonder if that child isn't in love."

The judge, bending over to pull on his boots, only grunted.

"I do believe that's it." Mrs. Todd narrowed her eyes. "When a girl gets up before seven and puts on her best dress—there's something more than politics on her mind. I do hope she isn't planning any mischief." She frowned anxiously. "There's no telling what she might lead Ann into. The child seems positively hypnotized by Mary . . ."

"Now, Sophie, for the love of God stop fretting." The judge straightened up, puffing. "It won't do Ann a bit of harm to get waked up a little—and Mary's all right."

Mrs. Todd shook her head.

"I'm sure I hope so," she said, "but all the same, it's not like a Todd to be as sugary as all that without some good reason behind it. Mind you keep a sharp eye on both of them today."

For all the judge's grumbling protests that they were starting entirely too early, there was already a crowd at the docks when they arrived. Mary stood with Ann while her uncle went to see about tickets.

"Don't you think it might be rather fun to get on the speakers' boat?" Mary asked. "Of course, it doesn't really matter—but if you'd just mention it, I'm sure Uncle would be willing."

Ann looked a trifle bewildered. She admired Mary tremendously—it was really wonderful the way she seemed to know all about speakers and rallies and such things.

"Well, I don't know, Mary . . ." Ann's dark eyes were vague.

Mary took her cousin's arm confidentially.

"It's always interesting to watch the bigwigs, don't you think? Besides, don't breathe a word of it to Uncle, but there *may* be one or two gentlemen I know among the speakers."

When the judge came back, he found Ann standing alone.

"Where's Mary?"

Ann shook her head. Mary had gone to find out about something. She wanted to know which boat the speakers were taking.

What difference, the judge inquired testily, did that

make? He took off his hat and mopped his forehead. It was all very well, taking the girls on an outing, but damn it, what did Mary think she was doing—running the election?

"She'll be right back, papa," Ann said nervously.

It was impossible, after all, to take the speakers' boat, which was being held till later. When Mary came back, they went aboard. The steamboat whistled—a long and ear-splitting shriek, and everyone leaned over the rail, shouting, waving their handkerchiefs.

"Tippecanoe and Tyler too!"

"Hurray for Harrison!"

A brass band was blaring noisily, playing the campaign song. Voices took it up, raising above the din.

> Have you forgot your fathers' mouldering clay?
> And has their blood been absorbed in sand
> and sunk away . . .

Mary turned to Ann.

"Isn't it exciting?"

The whistle shrieked again, and the side-wheel paddles bit into the muddy river with a dogged, shuddering strength.

It was pretty going up the river. The low shores, green and rolling, moved slowly past, and the boat's engine throbbed like a laboring heart against the swift, downstream current. Sitting between Ann and the judge, Mary kept up a lively conversation. She gave them the latest news from Springfield, and bits of gossip out of letters from Lexington. She was charming, gay, and prettily attentive to the judge's comfort. And her blue eyes, beneath the brim of her new hat, were bright with expectancy.

By midafternoon, Ann felt her new-found enthusiasm for politics beginning to wane. It had been thrilling at first—being part of the crowd, cheering and applauding as one speaker after another was introduced, came forward to bow, then laid aside his coat and settled down to business.

But as hour after hour passed, the long-winded phrases, the magnificent, sweeping gestures began to take on a certain wearisome monotony. The sun was unexpectedly hot, beating down on their heads relentlessly, and the benches were certainly most uncommonly hard.

Ann glanced at her father.

He was dozing comfortably, his arms folded, his head sunk onto his chest. A long career in politics had inured him to interminable hours of heated oratory.

Ann leaned hopefully toward Mary, sitting very straight and still at her side.

"Do you think, Mary, we might go and get some lemonade?" Ann whispered. "They're selling it—right over there—"

"Sh-sh, no. Not now." Mary frowned, her glance never leaving the platform, where a group of new speakers, in frock coats and tall silk hats, were just arriving.

At that very moment, a short stout gentleman was coming forward.

"Ladeeez and gentlemen—your attention please. The next speech this afternoon was to have come from our distinguished and eloquent brother from Illinois—known and revered by all his fellow countrymen, Mr. Abraham Lincoln—"

The stout gentleman paused. Mary leaned forward.

"But—due to an unforeseen concatination of events, the forces of nature, over which not even the Whig party has complete control—*as yet* [scattered laughter and applause]—our good friend Mr. Lincoln has been *delayed* . . ."

Mary's hands tightened. Scarcely daring to breathe, she heard the stout gentleman bellowing on. One of the later boats had been grounded in the shallows—and Mr. Lincoln's appearance was unavoidably prevented. Meanwhile, craving the indulgence of his amiable listeners, the stout gentleman begged the honor of presenting that incomparable patriot, that prince among statesmen, the senator from . . .

Mary stood up.

"All right," she said, with a suddenness that made Ann blink, "let's go and get some lemonade."

It was long after the speeches were over that Mary saw him. At first she could scarcely believe her eyes. But there he was, unmistakably. No one else, surely, could be so tall, could look quite like that, his face so tanned and weather-beaten under the shock of dark hair, rumpled and uncombed. He was standing near the empty platform, with his coat hanging over one arm, talking to some men gathered around him.

"Look," someone in the crowd said, "ain't that Abe Lincoln over there?"

Remembering it later, Ann couldn't help thinking it was strange the way Mary had changed so, all of a sudden. One minute she'd been so cross and queer, not a bit like herself, complaining about the crowd, and acting almost as if she wished she hadn't come. And then, the very next moment, she was all cheerful, smiling at Ann and saying it didn't really matter a bit about the lemonade getting spilled on her new frock. And then the way she'd taken Papa's arm, and said, oh, by the way, she'd almost forgotten, but there was a friend of Mr. Edwards's here she'd promised to look up and introduce the judge to. Someone from Springfield that Mr. Edwards was most particularly anxious to have them meet . . .

Before she really knew what was happening, Ann found herself being towed along through the jostling crowd, and Mary talking all the while, explaining how fond Mr. Edwards was of his friend Mr. Lincoln. As a matter of fact, Mary was saying, she thought Mr. Edwards had said something about Mr. Lincoln staying in Columbia for a few days, and it might be nice if they could ask him for dinner.

"If Auntie wouldn't mind, that is?"

Taken by surprise, the judge gruffled something by way

of an answer. If Ninian set such store by the fellow, he guessed it'd be all right.

But when they finally made their way to the platform, Mary hesitated. She had never seen Mr. Lincoln like this, surrounded by people who were stepping up to shake his hand, greeting him respectfully, asking how things looked for the Whigs up Illinois way. He seemed almost like a stranger—pleasant and self-assured. There was no awkwardness about him now, none of the familiar half-apologetic diffidence she had seen so often in Springfield.

Waiting her turn to greet him, Mary was aware of an odd feeling of shyness. He hadn't seen her yet—there was a broad-shouldered man in front of her, and she hung back, wondering suddenly whether she ought to speak after all.

There was only a moment. The large gentleman stepped aside, and Mary found herself looking straight up into Mr. Lincoln's eyes. For an instant he only stared, as though he couldn't quite credit what he saw—and then wonderfully, unbelievably, his long, sober face lighted up.

"Miss Mary—" He put out his hands to take both of hers, and held them so firmly that the rings bit into her fingers. "I—didn't know you were here."

He smiled down so warmly, with such a hungry welcome in his eyes, that Mary felt the shyness go out of her in a wave of sudden, exultant tenderness.

Her hat, she realized, was all askew. The blue frock, so fresh and pretty that morning, was sadly bedraggled now, and stained with lemonade. She knew her face must be flushed and shiny from the heat—and yet, strangely, for the first time since she could remember, Mary was conscious of being really pretty. She drew her hands away gently.

"Yes—" she said, laughing a little—breathlessly. "Yes, Mr. Lincoln, I'm here . . ."

On the boat going home that evening, Mary stood alone for a while by the rail. She was bareheaded, and the sharp breeze that blew her hair whipped the muddy surface of the river below. Out here alone, the voices and band music from the cabin were lost and there was only the rush of wind in the darkness and the steady, laborious churning of the paddle wheels.

While she watched the wake, sweeping out behind them like a shining path in the black water, Mary saw a stray log, drawn suddenly from its aimless, drifting course into the swirl of the wake. She saw how the log struggled, bobbing and twisting helplessly against the relentless strength that pulled it along, until at length it was left behind, and vanished in the dimness of the river.

It had been, for that little while, like something caught up by a fate—strange and exciting—that drew it without meaning or destination, and would not let it go.

5

"I RECKON YOU WERE WRONG AFTER ALL ABOUT MARY being in love," the judge said when he was undressing that night. "She wasn't out of my sight all day—and I'll vow she never so much as spoke to a single person, outside of that lawyer friend of Ninian's from Springfield."

"Well—maybe not." Mrs. Todd shook her head reluctantly. "Though I wouldn't put it past a smart one like Mary to pull the wool over your eyes, Mr. Todd. And whether she saw him today or not—I tell you that child is in love with someone, just as sure as the Lord made little apples. And sooner or later you'll find out I was right."

At dinner the next evening, it was plain to be seen that Mr. Lincoln was making a most favorable impression on the Todds. For the most part, Mary was silent during the meal. Watching her guest, hearing the easy, agreeable way he talked to the judge, and the pleasant courtesy with which he addressed Mrs. Todd, Mary felt a sudden, rather unexpected pride. Why was it, she wondered, that he was so seldom like this in Springfield? Only when Matilda had been there had she seen him so charming—so completely without his usual air of reserve, aloof and melancholy. But she put that thought aside hastily. Matilda was far away now—and Mr. Lincoln was smiling at her across the table.

Mary looked down at her plate, hardly daring to meet that smile for fear her eyes would say too much.

"You see—" Mrs. Todd said later to her husband. "I *am* right about Mary. Anyone would suppose she might have put herself out a little to entertain that nice Mr. Lincoln, especially since he's Ninian's friend and she asked us to invite him here. But no—she's so taken up with her own thoughts that, for all she noticed, he might as well have been a fly on the wall. I declare, if she were my child, I'd give her a good talking to for being so rude."

"Well, I guess it didn't make much difference to Mr. Lincoln," the judge said comfortably. "He seemed to be enjoying himself well enough. I don't wonder Ninian's so taken with him. He's got a likable way with him—and plenty of good horse sense. I reckon a man as smart as that has too much to think about to worry over whether the girls notice him or not."

When he bade them good night at the door, Mr. Lincoln had said he expected to stay in Columbia until Friday morning.

By noon on Thursday, Mrs. Todd was beginning to be positively alarmed about Mary. From having been so bright and friendly, the child had suddenly taken the queerest streak. Ever since breakfast, she'd wandered around the house as though she didn't know what to do with herself. She'd take up a book, frown at it for a minute or two, and then throw it aside to go and stand at the window—staring out at the street and hardly answering when she was spoken to. Once, when she was holding a skein of wool for Mrs. Todd to wind and someone had knocked at the front door, Mary had jumped as though she'd been shot—and barely apologized for dropping the wool and getting it all tangled.

At lunch, Mary made the merest pretense of toying with her food. She sat scowling at her plate—and when Ann ventured to speak to her, she answered with such scornful impatience that poor Ann's eyes filled with tears.

Mrs. Todd put down her fork. She wondered anxiously if she could have been mistaken about Mary. Perhaps she wasn't in love at all—but only coming down with something. Dear heaven—Mrs. Todd frowned—she did hope not. It would be so awkward, particularly if Mary were going to be difficult like this—and sickness in the house always put the judge into such a wretched humor.

"Don't you like omelet, dear?" Mrs. Todd said kindly. "You've hardly eaten a mouthful—but if you'd rather have something else—"

Mary pushed back her plate.

"I just don't feel like eating," she said. "I—have sort of a headache. I think I'll go lie down for a while."

There was no escaping Mrs. Todd's solicitude. She and Ann followed Mary upstairs, and hovered about, drawing the blinds, fetching an extra cover, and offering various remedies, until Mary felt certain that in another moment she would scream.

But when, at last, they had tiptoed away and Mary was alone, she found she couldn't lie still. The darkened room made her nervous, and she felt half smothered by the compress on her forehead. Perhaps if she were to get up and write a letter to Peg Breckinridge . . .

Halfway through the first page, she tore it in two. It was no use. No use. No use. She came back to the bed and sat down, pressing her hands against her eyes. He wasn't coming. He wasn't even going to write—or send any message. She'd been stupid to think he would. Doubtless by this time he'd forgotten she was even in Columbia.

She should have realized that he'd have far too many important things to do even to think of bothering about someone he could see any day in the week in Springfield. It was stupid to keep on hoping like this . . . *stupid* . . .

Angrily she dug her hands tighter, until sharp darts and wheels spun against the blackness of her eyelids. Suddenly, out of the forlorn, choking misery, she saw herself standing at the rail of the excursion steamer. She remembered the night wind, and the river, swift-flowing and relentless . . . and the moment when Mr. Lincoln had smiled as he took her two hands in his.

After supper that evening, Mrs. Todd settled herself by the sitting-room lamp with her mending. It was a mercy, she thought, that Mary's headache hadn't developed into anything after all. Mary had quite insisted on putting on one of her prettiest frocks and coming down for supper —and from the way she'd chattered and laughed all through the meal, it was plain that at least she wasn't going to be ill. All the same, there was something about the child that made Mrs. Todd a trifle uneasy. The way she'd stop right in the middle of saying something, for no reason at all—and look toward the door, for all the world as though she expected to see someone standing there. If Mary was often like this, Mrs. Todd thought, it was a miracle Elizabeth could stand it, month after month.

Well, young girls were apt to be trying. Mrs. Todd sighed. Particularly nowadays, when they had such notions about being independent and heaven only knew what other strange ideas. She ought to be thankful, really, that Ann showed so few signs of having any ideas at all.

Ann was at the piano now, aimlessly picking out tunes with one finger from a book of new songs. As she hit the fourth wrong note in succession, her mother looked up.

"Why don't you let Mary play awhile, dear? She reads so prettily."

Ann rose, willingly enough, but Mary shook her head. She didn't feel like playing. Catching Mrs. Todd's eye, she forced herself to smile quickly. She mustn't let them see anything—but, dear God, she couldn't stand it much longer. She couldn't just keep on sitting there—staring at the clock, watching the gilt hand creep its way toward eight, past eight, down toward the half hour—ticking away the evening into nothingness.

Mary jumped up. "How about a game of checkers, uncle?"

At nine-thirty Mrs. Todd put away her mending.

"Time for bed, girls."

In spite of her aunt's objections, Mary managed to coax the judge into one more game. The evening mustn't end yet, she thought desperately. Please—please, not yet. Even though there wasn't any hope now . . . She bit her lip, trying not to let herself notice the curious, whistling sound of the judge's breathing as he bent over the board, pondering his next move with nerve-racking deliberation.

"Well—mind you remember to lock up then." Mrs. Todd stifled a yawn. "And don't let Mary sit up too late, Mr. Todd. She ought to have a good night's sleep . . . Come along, Ann."

Ten minutes later, when someone knocked at the front door, Mary didn't raise her eyes from the board. It couldn't be, she thought. Of course it couldn't. It was absurd to think anyone would be calling at this hour. But still—she fought down the fierce surge of pounding hope—still, if she just didn't look up, if she pretended not to notice at all—perhaps . . .

She could hear old Peter's step, shuffling and slow, going down the hall toward the door. A pause—endless—unbearable—and then, quite unmistakably, a gentleman's voice asking if Miss Todd was at home.

Mary looked up.

"I'm afraid I've won this time, uncle." She began to clear away the checkers, careful to keep her fingers steady. "But I'm sure you won't mind too much—for here's Mr. Lincoln come to see you."

Outside it was cool, and the night air, after the stuffy, lighted parlor, smelled sharp and sweet.

"I hope you didn't mind my asking you to come for a walk," Mr. Lincoln said. "I've had to be indoors so much these past few days, it seemed kind of a shame to miss such a pretty night."

Mary shook her head.

"As a matter of fact, I've been in all day too. I was wishing just before you came I could get a breath of air."

"Which way shall we go?"

"I don't know—" Mary laughed. "I haven't had much chance to walk since I've been here. That road looks pretty—over toward the hill—"

They walked rapidly at first, Mary having almost to run in order to keep up with Mr. Lincoln's long strides. Once, in the darkness, she stumbled over a loose stone. Mr. Lincoln stopped and took her arm.

"You're not tired, Miss Mary? You don't want to go back, do you?"

"Oh, no—not a bit," she said quickly. "Only—you go so fast. You forget what long legs you have, Mr. Lincoln."

"That's right, I guess I do." He started on again, more slowly, still holding her arm. "The trouble is, I reckon," he said seriously, "that I'm not much used to walking with ladies. If I forget and start to gallop again—you just call *whoa*—"

At the end of the road they turned onto a side path that led up the hill. They went in silence until they reached the top, then they stood for a minute looking back, over the trees and rooftops that lay below. Overhead, the sky arched clear and starry, and the scent of autumn was in the still air.

"When I get up on a hill like this," Mr. Lincoln said, "it makes me feel kind of important. Makes it easier to think."

Mary said nothing. She had never been alone with him—

never quite like this. Always before there had been that sense of his pulling away—of a wall, high and guarded, that cut him off. But now there was no wall, no pulling back. She stood quietly, her hand resting on his arm.

"How old are you, Mary?"

She turned a little, startled by the abruptness of the question. It was the first time he had called her Mary.

"Twenty-one."

"I'm thirty-one."

He was silent for a moment, seeming to ponder something. Looking up, Mary could see the outline of his head, brooding and shadowed, in the dimness.

"There's a big difference between us," he said slowly. "I used to think, a long time ago, that by the time I was thirty I'd know what I really wanted to do. But I guess I don't know any more now than I ever did. Maybe"—he hesitated, seeming to laugh a little—"the answer is I'm not going to do anything after all."

"But you have your work, Mr. Lincoln. Judge Logan says you're doing wonderfully at law—"

"I didn't mean that exactly." He paused a moment. "I suppose the trouble with me is I'm always too full of my own mistakes. Other people seem to know just what they want—but I can't ever make myself be sure. There was a time, a long while back, when I used to think I'd like to try preaching. I gave that up though, because I couldn't decide what it was I wanted to preach. Then I thought some about studying to be a doctor—but that didn't seem just right either. I reckon what I want most is just to be around—" he hesitated again. "Only—nobody else seemed to think much of that idea. They were always asking me, 'What are you going to be, Abe? What are you aiming to make yourself?' Finally I started on law—just to please them."

Mary glanced up. "You're not sorry, are you?"

"No—I don't think so. Not most of the time, anyway. Only—there are an awful lot of questions I haven't answered yet. Some, I guess I never will." He stopped then. After a little he turned and looked down. "I reckon I don't make much sense," he said, "but it's hard for me to say what I mean. Right now, for instance, I suppose anybody else would be talking about you—instead of me. They'd be saying how pretty you looked, wouldn't they?"

"I—don't know."

"I mean," he said slowly, "if they felt like I do. They'd want to ask you whether someday you might be willing to think about—getting married."

Mary stood perfectly still. The moment had come so suddenly, she was afraid to speak. Afraid that the least whisper, a single breath drawn too deep, might somehow break the spell. The silence was like a spun thread, fragile and shining, between them. A thread drawn taut and quivering, all but breaking with the weight of all that hung suspended.

"I can't say much, Mary. Maybe I oughtn't to mention it at all—when I've got so little to offer. But would you, Mary? Sometime?"

"If—you wanted it—" Her words were soft and light, scarcely a murmur in the deep, dark stillness.

She felt his arm beneath her hand. The solid strength of it. Somewhere, above her head, she heard him sigh. Then, a little awkwardly, he took her in his arms—and for a minute they were close, not speaking.

At the door, when they said good-bye, Mr. Lincoln took her hand. In the light from the window she could see his face, and the strange sadness in his eyes.

"If you ever feel you've made a mistake, Mary, you must tell me. Will you promise that?"

"Yes—I promise."

The thread, shining and tenuous, trembled between them.

"Good night, Mary."

"Good night."

He put her hand down gently.

While she still watched from the doorway, he turned the corner at the end of the street, and was gone.

6

BACK IN SPRINGFIELD EVERYBODY WAS TALKING ABOUT the elections. It was beginning to look as though the Whigs had it for sure. The whole West was behind Harrison and the National Road—and Van Buren was out just as sure as the sun rose Thursdays. They'd heard Abe Lincoln hadn't got to make his speech down in Missouri after all, but he'd said he guessed it didn't matter much. Everybody at the rally was going to vote Whig anyway.

Elizabeth looked Mary over with an experienced weather eye.

"I must say the trip seems to have done you good," she said; "I've never seen you look so well."

Privately to Ninian, however, Elizabeth reported that the trip had apparently not accomplished much.

"I'd hoped it might bring things to a head with Mr. L.—one way or another." She sighed. "You'd think, in all conscience, that having her chase him all the way to Missouri would wake any man up to speak his mind. But I can't get a word out of Mary—though it's plain from the way she acts that *something* happened."

For a week—two weeks—nothing was said. Mr. Lincoln was out of town, making a last round of campaign speeches, and whenever his name was mentioned, Mary was vague and evasive.

At length, weary of hints and innuendoes that got nowhere, Elizabeth came straight to the point.

"I know perfectly well, Mary, that there is something

between you and Mr. Lincoln. And since you are living in my home—"

"For the purpose of finding a husband—"

"Please don't be vulgar, Mary. I am responsible for you while you are here, and I have a right to know what your intentions are."

Mary was silent. Caught thus, in the full cold light of Elizabeth's good sense, the slender gossamer thread seemed perilously threatened. But if she still refused to speak, Elizabeth might question Mr. Lincoln. He'd be back in a few days now. If Elizabeth or Ninian said anything—the frail, sweet thread would surely break.

Mary drew a breath. Briefly, hating with her whole soul the necessity of putting wordless things into words, she told what had happened the night on the hill.

"Well—" Elizabeth laid aside her sewing and folded her hands. "I'm sure I don't see why you couldn't have told me this sooner, Mary. However, we won't bother with that now. I must say I'm surprised that he actually got to the point—" She paused a moment, thoughtfully. "Of course he did ask you to marry him?"

"We—spoke of it—yes." Mary twisted her hands. "But nothing is really decided yet."

Elizabeth nodded.

"Naturally not. After all, Mr. Lincoln has had no chance to speak to Mr. Edwards. But as soon as he returns—"

"Oh, *no*—" Mary stopped quickly, aware of the look in Elizabeth's eyes. "I mean, we'd rather not have anything said. Until we're both quite sure, that is. Just for now, we must keep everything secret."

"Secret?" Elizabeth raised her brows. "Why, for pity's sake? There's nothing disgraceful, I hope, about being engaged."

Well—no, of course not. But there was much to be decided.

"I—can't explain, Elizabeth, but you *must* let me do this my way. Don't you see? There are reasons—"

Elizabeth did not see.

"I never had this trouble with your sisters," she said. "When Ann and Frances were engaged they—"

"I am not my sisters," Mary said bitterly. "And besides, I'm tired of eternally hearing about what you did for Ann and Frances. You sound like a matrimonial bureau."

"*Mary!*"

"I don't care. You do."

For one speechless, outraged moment, Elizabeth stared. Then, rising, she swept her sewing from the table.

"We won't discuss this any further, Mary. Now or ever. Heaven knows, I've tried to be patient with your foolishness, I've tried to help you—but since you seem determined to insult me, I don't know what more I can possibly be expected to do."

"You can let me alone," Mary said, choking back the hot, miserable tears that rose suddenly in her throat. "Just . . . let me alone . . . that's all . . ."

It was all very difficult when Mr Lincoln came back. Elizabeth said nothing more on the subject of the engagement, but there was a reserve in her manner, an air of silent, martyred patience, that made the atmosphere electric with her waiting.

And Mary waited too. In the days and the nights she waited always for a return of that moment when they had stood on the hill. But everything seemed so different here in Springfield. Mr. Lincoln was very busy, for one thing. Mary reminded herself of that when he was late for appointments—or forgot them altogether. No doubt, she told herself, it was only because he was tired that he seemed so distraught and far away when they were together. After the elections were over—surely it would be better . . .

Elections came and went, and the Whigs swept triumphantly into office. And still Mr. Lincoln's grave and melancholy abstraction did not lift. He was kind. He continued to be reasonably attentive. But when he came to call now he was more and more often silent—staring into the fire, his eyes lost in some unreachable sadness that left Mary helpless and frightened.

She began to make new excuses for him. He was working too hard. He was overtired—perhaps he was even ill. Or it might be that he was worried for fear she had regretted her promise. Lying awake in the night, she could think of a thousand reasons to explain his strange, unfathomable silence. Then, in the darkness, she could still call back the moment on the hill. It seemed real then—and she could believe it would come back again, living and real, between them.

But in the morning there was only another day to face—and the cool, unspoken question in Elizabeth's eyes.

Near Christmastime, around the stove at Diller's store, they said Abe was looking kind of seedy lately.

"Don't know what ails him—but he don't drop in here like he used to, and chew the fat. You'd think he might perk up a little, since the elections. But he looks as peaked as a cat in a cistern. You don't reckon he's sick, do you?"

"No, Abe's not sick," Mr. Diller said. "Josh Speed was in a couple of days ago, and he says it's nothing to worry about. He says back in New Salem when Abe got like this they used to call it the Lincoln Blues."

"Well, Josh ought to know if anybody does. All the same, Abe's got a mighty bad case this time. What's eating him, do you suppose?"

Mr. Diller rubbed his chin.

"I wouldn't want to say for sure," he said. "But judging from a few remarks I've heard dropped lately, I guess maybe Abe's got Todd trouble."

On Christmas Eve, John Stuart dropped by the Edwards' with a bundle of packages for the children's tree. It was a mean night out—raw and sharp, with a rain that had been trying all day to turn into snow.

"It doesn't look much like a white Christmas," John

said, taking off his wet coat. "Unless the winds pulls around north before morning, we'll have nothing but mud."

He started toward the fire, rubbing his hands briskly, and then, as he caught sight of Mary, he stopped short.

"Hello—what's Mary doing here? I thought all the young people had gone to the dance over at Mrs. Browning's."

There was an awkward silence. Ninian coughed slightly.

"As a matter of fact, Mary was expecting to go. But it seems that Mr. Lincoln has been—detained. I daresay he's had trouble finding a carriage, on such a bad night." Ninian was careful to avoid Elizabeth's eye. "What about a spot of brandy, John, just to celebrate the holiday?"

"I don't mind if I do," John said. He stood with his back to the fire, looking at Mary thoughtfully. "I declare it seems a shame to deprive all the other gentlemen of your company, Mary. Especially when you look so charming. I'll tell you what—my carriage is right outside. Why not let me drive you over to the Brownings'? Then if Abe shows up later—"

Mary stood up suddenly. There were bright spots of color in her cheeks, and the folds of her white moiré skirt crackled stiffly.

"Thank you," she said, "but it's not necessary, John. I—didn't want to go to the dance anyway. Mrs. Browning's parties are always stupid. And I wish you'd all stop pretending to be sorry Mr. Lincoln forgot to come for me —when I know quite well you're actually delighted."

"Oh, now come, Mary—" John's smile was tolerant. "You mustn't take it so hard. You know how thoughtless these Yankees are—and Abe's worse than most. Why, I daresay Abe will forget his head one of these days, if the Lord doesn't keep it fastened on his shoulders. I still think it's a pity, though, to let that handsome dress go to waste—"

Mary turned away.

"I hate the dress," she said. "I wish I'd never seen it. I

wish I'd never seen any of you—or Springfield—or—or anyone."

"Mary—be still," Elizabeth's tone warned her sharply. "You're upset. You don't know what you're saying."

"What if I am upset?" Mary said. "A precious lot you care. You don't care how I feel—so long as you get your way. So long as you can meddle, and manage everything—the way you did with Ann and Frances."

"Now, Mary"—John's smile grew a shade less bland—"there's no reason to turn on Elizabeth like that. She's not responsible if Abe takes exception to some of the things people are saying."

Mary turned on him. "And just what *are* people saying?"

"Well—nothing much." John shrugged. "Only you know how talk gets around. And there seems to be a general opinion that your family doesn't look very kindly on Abe as a match for you. I don't know just how the idea got started, but—"

"There—you see?" Mary flung the words at Elizabeth furiously. "You see what you've done with your wicked meddling? You've ruined everything—just because you couldn't hold your tongue. And after you promised not to tell—"

"I'm sure I don't know what John is talking about," Elizabeth said. "I've told no one anything."

"Except Ann and Frances, I suppose."

"Don't be a fool, Mary. I hope I still have the right to speak to my own sisters confidentially."

A queer, choked sound came from Mary's throat.

"You might as well have told the whole town and been done with it. Don't you suppose I know why you're all scheming and plotting to keep me from marrying Mr. Lincoln? You pretend it's because he's not good enough for me. Because he's poor—and you think his manners aren't elegant enough to suit your fine Kentucky taste. Well, I know the real reason—it's because you're jealous, all of you. You're jealous because you know I love him—

and he loves me—and that's something that never happened in this family before. It never happened to Ann or Frances, with their silly, smug little marriages. It never happened to you either!"

"*Mary!*" Elizabeth's voice cut like a knife. She went over and took her sister by the shoulders. "You'll stop this hysterical nonsense *at once!*"

Mary shook her head, half sobbing, twisting her shoulders angrily against Elizabeth's grip.

"I won't stop. You can't make me be quiet just because you're afraid to hear the truth. Because you know Mr. Lincoln will be a great man someday. Everybody says so—everybody believes it. And that makes you jealous—doesn't it? You and Ninian and John and Frances—"

"I warn you, Mary—if you go on like this I shall send Ninian for a doctor. I'll tell him you are out of your mind."

With one last effort Mary wrenched herself free. Half laughing now, her breath coming in strangling gasps, she pushed back the curls that had tumbled across her face.

"Very well—" her voice dropped, toneless and dull—"I'll stop." She went slowly toward the door, stumbling a little over the hem of her white frock. "It doesn't matter anyway."

Later, when Elizabeth went upstairs to see to the children, she came down to report that Mary was in bed, apparently asleep.

"I'm sure *I* don't know what to do with her." Elizabeth set her lips grimly. "Mary's always had a temper, but I must say I never expected her to make any such exhibition of herself as she did tonight."

John sighed.

"It's all most unfortunate, certainly." He helped himself to the brandy, frowning a little. "Still—it may not do any harm to have Mary realize the way people are talking about her. If she has any pride, after all—"

"Well, she hasn't," Elizabeth said. "I should think that

was plain enough. Mary's made up her mind she's going to marry Abe Lincoln—and when she sets her mind on a thing there's nothing in heaven or earth that will stop her."

"I don't know about that, Elizabeth." John shook his head. "Abe can be pretty stubborn himself. Especially when he gets an idea that other people are trying to make up his mind for him. I've no doubt he's fond of Mary—but all the same, you can't blame him for being skittish. A man doesn't exactly relish hearing the opinion of his future in-laws before he's got around to asking for it."

Ninian, twirling the stem of his brandy glass thoughtfully, said nothing.

It was New Year's afternoon when Mr. Lincoln came to the house again.

Elizabeth and Ninian had gone out to make a round of calls, and Mary was alone in the sitting room. At half past four the winter dusk was already deepening. Through the long windows, Mary watched the fading twilight, cold and blue. In a minute now, Joseph would be coming in to draw the curtains and light the lamp on the center table. Hearing his step in the hall, she straightened.

"You-all expecting company this evening, Miss Mary?"

"I—don't think so, Joseph."

He lingered a moment, stooping to put fresh coal on the fire. In the flickering light, Mary's dress of scarlet wool glowed softly. Didn't seem right, Joseph reflected uneasily, for Miss Mary to set here all by herself.

"Mis' Edwards didn't say nothing about tea," Joseph said. "Wouldn't you like me to bring you a nice hot cup?"

Mary shook her head.

"No, thank you, Joseph. I—think I'll wait."

"Yes, ma'am."

When Mr. Lincoln came in, shortly after five, he said he couldn't stay for tea.

"As a matter of fact, Mary," he blurted out abruptly,

almost as though he were afraid to hesitate, "I've got to talk to you about something."

"Yes, Mr. Lincoln?" Mary felt her smile go suddenly stiff, like cold wax. Looking up, she saw such a depth of misery in his eyes that she stretched out her hand in quick alarm. "Mr. Lincoln—what is it?"

He only stared at her, not speaking, his face marked with shadows, deep-cut and brooding. Then he drew a long breath.

"I don't know how to say this, Mary. I wish I could make it easy—but I can't, so I reckon there's no use to try." He was silent a moment, seeming lost in some far-off, obscure thought. "I can't get married," Mr. Lincoln said.

"Well—?" Mary heard the sound of her own voice, sharp and brittle. Feeling everything go out from under her—as though the room, the bright fire, the soft light from the table lamp had been blotted out by darkness—she clung to that one word, steadying herself against it. "*Well—?* Why should you tell me that, Mr. Lincoln?"

He lifted his hands, then let them drop again, helplessly, at his sides.

"Because I didn't know—I—" He paused, wretched and uncertain. "I couldn't help but think maybe you were—expecting me to marry you."

Mary sat motionless. Not all the thinking, not the despair, the doubts and questions in the long, bitter nights, had prepared her for this. She must say something, she thought. Tell him he was mistaken. Say something light—inconsequential. Anything to show she didn't care. To hide the awful, unbelievable bluntness of this moment. She groped for the words. But nothing came. Nothing, only a cold, sick numbness.

Mr. Lincoln went on. He was sorry—more deeply sorry than she could know—if he had said or done things that would lead her to think he intended, or could possibly intend, to marry anyone—

"*Anyone*, Mr. Lincoln?"

He seemed not to notice the irony of her tone. It

wasn't a question of his feeling for her, he said earnestly. He had always held her in the very highest esteem—but she must surely see for herself the reasons why marriage was utterly impossible. He had no money—no confidence of ever having any. He had debts . . .

Mary listened in stony silence, while he struggled on. It was as though, having once made the plunge, some dogged, painful honesty forced him to go on, deeper and deeper.

"I want to do what's right, Mary," he said. "If you think we ought to get married—if you honestly feel it would make you happy—then I . . ."

"*Happy?*" The word was bitter and strange on Mary's lips. It couldn't be, she thought suddenly, that this was real. It wasn't possible he was saying these things—meaning them. It must be some dream. Some hateful, unintelligible game . . .

"Your happiness would be worth anything in the world to me, Mary. You must believe that." There was no doubting the distress, the utter humility in his voice. "But I can't help but think it's fair to tell you the truth. If we were to get married, and you weren't happy—I'd never forgive myself. That's the thing that worries me so. It's seemed like, the last weeks, I haven't been able to think about anything else. I reckon Josh Speed would tell you that—"

"Thank you," Mary said. "I hardly think we need to call in any witnesses."

Mr. Lincoln sighed.

"I guess maybe it was wrong to tell you these things," he said, "but I've been nearly crazy, worrying. I tried to write you a letter—but I couldn't seem to get it right. And Josh said that wasn't the way to do it. He said I ought to talk to you—face to face. He said the only fair thing was to find out how you felt about it—" He broke off abruptly as Mary stood up.

"That was most gallant of Mr. Speed, I'm sure." A wave of icy mortification swept over Mary as she pictured what the scene must have been. The two men sitting together in the room they shared over Josh Speed's store—both of them in stocking feet, no doubt, with their coats off and their galluses comfortably let down—discussing between them the state of her heart.

"Another time, Mr. Lincoln, I might suggest that when you are in any doubt about a lady's feelings you would do better to consult her directly, however delicate Mr. Speed's perceptions may be."

Still frozen tight in anger and unbelief, she turned toward the door, but for a moment he made no move to follow. Looking back, she saw him watching her with eyes so full of misery and sorrow that her heart gave way.

"Mary—wait—"

She went to him swiftly, and he put out his arms.

"Oh—Mr. Lincoln—" She pressed her face against his shoulder, feeling the tears, hot and blinding, in her eyes. For the first time since the night on the hill, they were together again. Drawing back a little, she looked up, and saw that there were tears in his eyes too. For one instant more, the shining thread held them close. Then he shook his head.

With a sound like a low, choked moan, he took his arms away.

"Good-bye, Mary . . ."

She made no answer, and he did not look at her again. When she heard the sound of the outer door closing, she still stood where he had left her—motionless, waiting—in the silence of the firelit room.

Not until later, when Joseph came in to ask if they were ready for tea, did it occur to Mary that never once, in all he had said, had Mr. Lincoln said he loved her.

Next Sunday, Elizabeth came home from church with the news that Mr. Lincoln had left town. Josh Speed had put his store up for sale, and the two of them had simply started out, not saying where they intended to go, or for how long.

"Nobody seems to know what took Mr. Lincoln," Elizabeth said briskly, "but it's my opinion he's out of his mind."

Ninian pointed out, diplomatically, that there might be other possible explanations.

"Just because a man does something you didn't expect, Elizabeth, it doesn't necessarily indicate insanity."

Elizabeth was firm. She wasn't the only one who had noticed how queer Mr. Lincoln had been acting lately. Judge Logan said he hadn't done a scrap of work for the past month. Just mooned around the office and talked, when he spoke at all, about going out west somewhere and taking up farming.

"And Cousin Lizzie told me she saw him going down the street New Year's evening about suppertime, splashing along through puddles like something demented, and *carrying* his hat and coat, if you please—just as though it weren't the dead of winter. And when Lizzie spoke to him, he stopped in his tracks and stared at her for a minute, for all the world as though he'd never set eyes on her in his life, and then without so much as a word he put his head down and rushed on. It gives her the creeps, Lizzie says, every time she thinks of it."

No one could tell her, Elizabeth said, that any man in his right senses would act like that—rushing off, heaven only knew where, leaving a perfectly good law practice behind him.

It was all most regrettable, to be sure. But at the same time Elizabeth could hardly fail to be relieved at having the impasse between Mr. Lincoln and Mary so unexpectedly resolved—and in a manner that could not possibly be construed as any reflection on Mary. When Ann reported that she had heard a rumor that Mr. Lincoln had proposed to Mary, and been driven to despair by her refusal, Elizabeth was so struck by the appropriateness of the story that she virtually admitted to Ann that it was the truth.

"Did Mary tell you that?" Ann inquired sharply.

Well, not in so many words, Elizabeth admitted. But

then, Mary would scarcely be likely to speak of a matter so delicate and painful.

"We have to remember, Ann, that Mary has always been extremely sensitive, and a thing like this is bound to be a shock to her. It's no wonder she seems a trifle peaked and out of sorts. But she'll get over it, in time."

"I don't suppose it ever occurred to you," Ann said, "that everyone in the whole world isn't precisely like you."

Elizabeth looked startled for a moment, then she smiled.

"All young girls like to fancy themselves different," she said. "But in the end, I daresay Mary will discover she's quite like the rest of us."

So it hadn't been a dream after all, Mary thought. He had really meant those things he said, and now he was gone—far away, where she could never see him, never guess what he was thinking, never know anything at all. Unless, of course, he should write. It was a forlorn hope, but after a time he did write. He wrote from Kentucky, saying that he was well, that he and Josh Speed were just traveling around for the present, that the weather had been bad. He hoped Mary was well. Above all, he hoped she would be happy.

It was a strange letter, full of bad conscience and unhappiness, but giving no return address. Tearing it to bits, letting the pieces drop one by one into the fire, Mary felt the last slim strand of hope slip from her fingers.

7

IT WAS STRANGE, MARY SOMETIMES THOUGHT, HOW TWO people could live in the same town, walk the same streets and trade at the same stores—have friends in common and go pretty much to the same houses—and yet see each other so seldom. Strange, too, the way a situation that had once seemed so awkward, so agonizingly filled with mingled dread and expectation, could in the end become quite commonplace.

She remembered how she had felt that first day when she heard Mr. Lincoln was back in town. She and Elizabeth had been standing at the woolens counter, down at Smith's dry goods store, when someone in the next aisle spoke casually.

"By the way, I ran into Abe Lincoln this morning down at the bank—looking very well too. He tells me he's in Judge Logan's office again. I'd understood he might go to Washington on some government appointment, but I guess that fell through when President Harrison died . . ."

Even now, after nearly a year, Mary could still recall the exact pattern of sprigged blue challis she had been fingering, the way her throat had suddenly gone dry, and the sick, faint wave of excitement that swept through her. For the next few days she had lived in a misery of anticipation, searching the mail each morning for a letter, feeling her heart pound as though it would choke her every time there was a strange step at the front door—alternately resorting to panicky excuses to stay home lest she should encounter him somewhere and inventing needless errands downtown that would take her past his office.

But the weeks passed, and there was no word from him, no unexpected meeting; and things subsided gradually to normal. When at length she did see him, one frosty December morning, Mr. Lincoln was coming out of the post office. He had his collar turned up, against the cold, and his eyes looked grayer and more withdrawn than ever in his bronzed, lean face. He seemed glad to see Mary. They talked for a few minutes, pleasantly, and Mr. Lincoln told her she was looking well.

After that, there was no more waiting for the postman. Mary no longer started whenever someone knocked at the door. They met now and again, always by accident, but as Mr. Lincoln's work took more and more of his time, the occasions grew less frequent, and though there was plenty of company at the Edwards house, Mr. Lincoln never seemed to be included. In the family, it was thankfully observed that Mary had got over her nonsense at last, and when Judge Logan came to dinner, he seldom took occasion, any more, to tell amusing anecdotes about his partner.

During the summer Mary went home to Lexington for a while, and when she came back she struck up a sudden and rather unexpected friendship with Mrs. Simeon Francis, whose husband owned the Springfield newspaper. On the whole, Elizabeth was more relieved than otherwise when Mary took to spending long afternoons at the Francis house. It gave her an interest outside herself, and seemed in general to perk her up, and Elizabeth concluded that a youngish and sympathetic friend was precisely what Mary had needed.

There was one morning, in early October, when Polly Francis sent a note asking if Mary would come to tea that afternoon. She had a friend coming, whom she was specially anxious for Mary to meet. Elizabeth was pleased.

"Of course you'll go, Mary. I daresay it's some friend of Mr. Francis'. He meets a great many interesting gentlemen in his work. Why don't you wear your new blue merino? And if you like, I'll lend you my beaver jacket. It's becoming, and goes well with the frock . . ."

Polly Francis was waiting near the door when Mary came in. There were people in the parlor—Mary could hear the sound of their voices. But Polly Francis drew her aside. She opened the door into a small sitting room.

Standing before the fire was a tall man, in a long black coat.

"You two be friends again," Polly said, and closed the door.

Afterwards Mary could never quite decide whether that afternoon meeting had been by accident or by design. There had been hints, certainly, from Polly. Questions about Mr. Lincoln—small remarks, dropped casually, to the effect that all was not well with Mr. L. He was lonely, unhappy. He had been heard to say he wished the clock could be turned back—that he could have another chance to right certain mistakes he had made. Looking back, Mary found it difficult to account for the way her heart had pounded while she walked toward the Francis house that afternoon—for the sudden confusion, only half expected, that gripped her when Polly closed the door and left her face to face with Mr. Lincoln. She could remember how they looked at each other, solemn and questioning—the way he had started to say something polite, and had stopped, and simply held out his arms. It was in that moment, held close, that Mary knew the truth for the first time. She had thought once that Mr. Lincoln needed her. She could recall how she had planned for his future, thinking he only wanted someone to spur him on, to be tactful, to guide him with knowing steps toward the destiny that everyone seemed, rather strangely, to expect of him. But in that instant Mary knew that it was she who needed him. That she would go on needing him, so long as she lived, with an intensity that left her shivering and helpless.

One thing more she knew, without question, that afternoon and all the afternoons that followed. That this time no one should interfere. Not heaven or earth or Elizabeth would know anything that would let them break the shining thread again.

It was a November morning, raw and lowering, when Ninian saw Mr. Lincoln on the square in front of the State House. Mr. Lincoln was hurrying along, his head bent down, the upper part of him bent against the wind, as though anxious to get somewhere faster than his long legs would take him. At first he seemed about to pass without speaking, but suddenly he drew himself up. Speaking rapidly, with no trace of his usual roundabout drawl, Mr. Lincoln said, without preamble, that he and Mary were planning to be married.

Ninian took off his hat.

Mr. Lincoln, after a moment's hesitation, removed his also, and the two men stood facing each other soberly. Eight o'clock in the morning, beneath a slate-gray sky, with their fellow townsmen jostling past them on their way to business seemed a curious place for such an announcement, but Ninian did his best. He put out his hand.

"This is a surprise, Abe—"

Mr. Lincoln nodded. Having blurted out his tidings, he seemed incapable of further comment, and merely stood, gloomily inspecting the lining of his hat.

"Have you—" Ninian cleared his throat—"have you settled on a date yet?"

Mr. Lincoln nodded again.

"We're counting on doing it this evening, Ninian; that is, if it's convenient for you and Mrs. Edwards. Mary thought," he added a shade apologetically, "it might be a good idea not to say too much ahead of time."

"Well," Ninian said, "I should say she had accomplished her purpose, in that respect." He put out his hand once more, striving to inject the proper heartiness into the proceedings. "I wish you every happiness, Abe—now and in the future."

Mr. Lincoln shook hands.

"Thank you, Ninian," he said. "I'm sure you mean it."

That evening was impossible, since Elizabeth had already arranged to entertain the Dorcas sewing circle. But the following night they were married in the Edwards parlor.

"I never heard of such a thing," Elizabeth said helplessly. "No time to arrange anything—Mary hasn't even got a wedding dress. And if I'd known, for one minute, why Mary was sneaking off to visit Polly Francis—"

For once Ninian was firm.

"You'd better take the chance, Elizabeth, before Abe changes his mind again. I realize that certain aspects of this romance appear to have taken place without your supervision, but since it seems that we must acknowledge that some other force is at large in the universe—"

"Please don't be sacrilegious, Mr. Edwards."

"Indeed, I hadn't the slightest intention of being. We have to face competition, my dear—we must try to do it gracefully."

On the day of the wedding, toward candlelighting time, the wind pulled round to the east. The dusk came dismally filled with a gray rain that blew across the prairie, rustling on the dry corn shucks, and whining against the shutters like something forlorn and lonely, wanting in.

"It's a poor kind of time for a wedding," Ann said.

All day she and Frances and Cousin Lizzie Grimsley had worked: helping in the kitchen, tacking up greens around the improvised altar in the living room.

Stepping down from the ladder, after adjusting one last branch of laurel, Cousin Lizzie sighed so that her stout waist seemed about to burst its dove-colored satin bounds.

"Is Mary dressing now?"

"I expect so, Lizzie." Elizabeth's voice was vague. She was worrying about the punch. "Why?"

"Well, I don't know—" Lizzie clasped her hands uncertainly—"it seems as though someone ought to be with her. One of us . . ."

The sisters exchanged a glance.

"Mary's all right." Ann bent to straighten a chair. "No one can say, certainly, that she's going into this with her eyes closed. We've told her plainly enough she was making the mistake of her life. Abe Lincoln doesn't amount to a row of pins, and never will. But Mary won't listen. She's got some notion in her head she's going to make him over." A thin smile, curved and malicious, twisted Ann's lips. "Once she's married, I daresay Mary will discover it's not as easy as it looks to change a husband."

"Oh, but, Ann—" Cousin Lizzie's pale, rather prominent eyes filled with distress—"Mr. Lincoln adores Mary—I can see he does."

Ann sniffed. "If that's the case, I can only say that he conceals it remarkably well. I passed him in the street this afternoon, and if ever I saw a sorry-looking sight, he was it. Looked more as if he were headed for an execution than a wedding."

Lizzie clasped her hands nervously.

"Well, I only hope Mary is going to be happy."

"Precious few people," Ann said firmly, "are cut out to be happy, Lizzie. And unless I miss my guess, Mary's not one of them. If you're bound to be sorry for someone, it's Mr. Lincoln you'd better worry about."

Nevertheless, during the ceremony, Lizzie couldn't help feeling Ann must be mistaken. Mr. Lincoln didn't look a bit sadder than usual—just dignified and solemn, the way a man ought to look while he's getting married. And in his long black coat, with his hair combed so neatly, he was almost handsome. Ann was very clever, of course, Lizzie reflected. But then, so was Mary.

One thing, at any rate, Lizzie was thankful for. Elizabeth had got Mr. Dresser, the new Episcopal rector, to read the service, and the sight of him, in his impressive canonical robes, made Lizzie feel easier. As if the Lord, somehow, had lent his backing to the proceedings.

"*For better for worse . . .*" The sonorous accents of Mr. Dresser's words rose, rich and reassuring, above the dismal beat of the rain against the shuttered windows.

"*For richer for poorer . . .*"

(It must be richer, certainly, for Mr. Lincoln couldn't very well be any poorer than he was already.)

"*In sickness and in health . . .*"

(They didn't need to worry about that part—both of them were healthy enough.)

"*Till death us do part.*"

Lizzie sighed.

When the moment came for Mr. Lincoln to slip the ring on Mary's finger, his friend Judge Brown, who was standing up with him, took the gold band from his pocket.

"*With this Ring I thee wed . . .*"

Mr. Lincoln's voice, repeating the words, did have a mournful ring, Lizzie had to own. Perhaps, though, it was only the effect of the silent room and the wind that howled and shuddered until the candles on the mantel flickered and melted wax dripped down their sides.

As Mr. Lincoln's voice continued: " . . . I thee endow with all my worldly goods and chattels, all my lands and tenements . . ." Judge Brown stirred uneasily at his side, and a look of alarm came over his face.

"God Almighty, Abe—" his nervous whisper carried through the hush—"the statute fixes all of that."

It was the only time, during the ceremony, that anyone saw Mr. Lincoln smile.

After the bride and groom had left for the Globe Tavern, where they were planning to board (just temporarily of course, Elizabeth was careful to explain, until they had time to find a house), the others lingered over the supper table. It had been a very pretty little wedding after all, they agreed, and Mary had looked sweet.

Pouring toddies for the gentlemen, Ninian was suddenly struck by a melancholy thought.

"Now that we've finished with the sisters," he said to Elizabeth, "do we have to begin on the half sisters?"

Mr. Lincoln was a trifle apologetic about the accommodations he had engaged. The tavern, a square, somewhat dejected-looking structure of weather-beaten clapboard, was certainly not prepossessing from the outside. And the rooms, on the second floor front, Mr. Lincoln said he guessed were nothing extra when it came to style. But Ed Boliver, who owned the Globe, was a friend of his, and a good fellow, and had promised to do what he could to make things comfortable. And altogether, seeing that they were to have lodging and meals for four dollars a week, it had seemed about the best he could do on such short notice.

Mary smiled reassuringly. Since they were to stay only a short time, she said, she was quite certain it would do nicely. Besides, she couldn't imagine finding serious fault with any home Mr. Lincoln chose to bring her to. Climbing the dark and rickety stairs, his hand on her arm, she felt a surge of confidence, warm and sweet; as though everything in her life up to this moment had been a dream from which she wakened, now, to a world of peace and tenderness—and hope.

Not even the sight of the low-ceilinged rooms, with their dingy furnishings and the doleful, liver-colored paper that hung in blistered and peeling strips on the walls, could mar the spell of that enchantment. Not even the thought of what Elizabeth would say when she saw the worn carpeting and the grimy, dispirited curtains at the windows.

Over the iron bedstead hung a steel engraving of Washington crossing the Delaware. But when Mr. Lincoln, inspecting it, observed that it looked as though the general were determined to sink or swim, but probably expected the former, Mary seemed not to hear.

She had crossed to the window and stood looking out. It wasn't of the street below she was thinking. It was of a moment, two years before, when she had stood at the rail of an excursion steamer and watched a log bobbing and twisting, drawn by the swift, relentless pull of the ship's wake. She remembered how the stars had arched above. Stars—and the night wind—and the churning wake in a dark river. They were all part of a pattern that made the shabby, close room behind her fade into insignificance.

"You know, Mr. Lincoln, I was just thinking—" She turned, her eyes full of a shining eagerness.

"Yes?" His voice seemed to come from infinitely far away.

Mary shook her head, feeling the words escape her. As she looked at him, so tall that the top of his dark head was barely a few inches from the ceiling, she recalled an afternoon when she and Polly Francis had been talking about Mr. Lincoln. "I think he must be the loneliest person in the whole world," Polly had said.

But surely now, Mary thought, it was going to be different. Everything would be different—and there would be no loneliness any more—not ever again.

"I—was only going to say—" Mary smiled—"I think the rooms are very nice, Mr. Lincoln."

He smiled too then, in the way he rarely did—lighting up his whole face, so that the strangeness in his eyes was gone.

As she went to him quickly, Mary felt the last shred of doubt go out of her heart. It was a while before either of them spoke, and then, out of the silence, she heard him draw a long breath.

"I hope you're not going to be sorry, Mary," Mr. Lincoln said.

Part Two

8

ON A LATE JUNE MORNING, WHEN MACKEREL CLOUDS were scudding across a sky of brilliant blue, Mary sat by her window in the Globe Tavern sewing. She was finishing the last of a dozen linen shirts for Mr. Lincoln, and as she came to the end of a seam she stopped to rest her eyes from the fine stitches. Elizabeth said it was absurd to spend hours putting tucks in shirt bosoms that were only meant for every day. But then—there were so many things Elizabeth found absurd.

"I mean to have Mr. Lincoln the best-dressed lawyer on the circuit," Mary said complacently. She was careful not to add that when she laid out his things for a trip, she was often dismayed to discover, after he had gone, that the fresh pile of linens had been left behind on the bed, and his suitcase had been stuffed, instead, with the odd collection of books and old newspapers that Mr. Lincoln still insisted on taking with him.

As Ann frequently pointed out to Mary, there was no use looking for miracles. It could not be said, certainly, that marriage had wrought any miraculous changes in Mr. Lincoln thus far. After eight months of Mary's most diligent efforts, he still seemed surprisingly much as he had always been. Not that he put up any active resistance to improvements. Indeed, he was invariably agreeable to her suggestions. When Mary indicated that it was not always necessary, or even particularly desirable, to go about at home in stocking feet, Mr. Lincoln nodded. When she pointed out the custom of using the butter knife, instead of his own, to serve his plate, he said he hadn't a doubt it was a good idea. He merely continued, serenely and without argument, to do precisely as he had always done before.

Sometimes, really, Mr. Lincoln could be extremely puzzling.

In the first weeks after they were married, Mary had set about to reorganize a number of things. First of all, there were the rooms to be fixed up. Fresh white curtains to be made and hung. A new spread for the old iron bedstead, and a desk to be arranged for Mr. Lincoln, with rows of pigeonholes where his multitudinous assortment of papers could be neatly sorted and filed. And shelves for the books.

Dear heaven, the books. Mary remembered the days when she had struggled with the problem of disentangling Mr. Lincoln's belongings from the confusion of books. A pair of muddy boots wrapped up in his second-best broadcloth coat. An umbrella, ancient and rusty, crammed in with his clean shirts. His stovepipe hat stuffed with an assortment of socks—no two of them mates, and all in shocking condition. And scattered through everything, spilling out of the most unlikely corners, came books and more books. Geometry texts, spellers, grammars, arithmetics. Plato's dialogues, a dog-eared volume of Shakespeare. A copy of some Hindu religious writings, and a worn black Bible, bulging with newspaper clippings of a humorous and illiterate journalist. Books of philosophy, physics, poetry and jokes.

Books were all very well, Mary had said; but books belonged on shelves, and not mixed in with what properly went into bureau drawers. She had sorted them most carefully, but in spite of all her system they had a most alarming way of getting unsorted and appearing in weird places. One night Mr. Lincoln would be reading *Othello*. The next evening Mary was careful to lay the volume of Shakespeare, with a marker, beside Mr. Lincoln's chair. But when they came up after supper, his gaze would wander vaguely around the room. What had become of those papers he'd been reading? The ones with the pieces by J. Flannigan?

"I threw those out a week ago, Mr. Lincoln. I supposed, of course, you were finished with them—and they were only cluttering up the room, gathering dust—"

Mr. Lincoln would give no sign of being annoyed. He would simply descend to the woodshed and prowl around until he found the missing papers in the rubbish—and likely bring up a few discarded magazines for good measure.

The next night, when Mary had conscientiously stacked the papers on his table, Mr. Lincoln would scatter them all over the floor and ask where the Shakespeare had disappeared to.

"Why, I put it away on the closet shelf. There's no more room in the bookcase—and I thought you were through with it."

There were other, less tangible changes to be instituted, and in those early weeks Mary had attacked them energetically. For one thing, there was the matter of Mr. Lincoln's policy about money. He talked a great deal about being poor and saddled with debts—but it didn't take Mary long to discover that the reason they had no money was simply because Mr. Lincoln had a curious reticence in regard to charging his clients for services rendered. His fees were absurdly small to begin with—and he was so easygoing about collecting them that half the time they were never paid at all.

Mary was brisk, sensible, and firm.

"There's no earthly sense in not being paid for the work you do, Mr. Lincoln. Charity is well enough where it's deserved—but nine times out of ten your clients who tell you they can't afford to pay have more money than you have."

Mr. Lincoln rubbed his chin. He hadn't a doubt, he said, but that was true enough. The only trouble was, most of his clients were friends of his.

"Well, they won't be your friends for long, Mr. Lincoln, if you keep on this way. No one has much respect for a man who doesn't stand up for his rights. You must simply be firm with them."

"Yes," Mr. Lincoln said, "I suppose I must."

"I'll say one thing for Mary," Elizabeth observed to her husband. "She's certainly building fires under Mr. Lincoln."

"The only question is," Ninian said as he stirred his coffee reflectively, "whether Abe will turn out to be non-inflammable."

In the spring, when it was time for Mr. Lincoln to travel the circuit, Elizabeth had asked Mary to come and take her old room at the Edwards house.

"Mr. Lincoln certainly can't expect you to stay cooped up in those miserable rooms for two whole months, Mary. And besides, with the baby coming, you oughtn't to be alone."

Mary had replied, rather shortly, that she was all right where she was. Now that the rooms were fixed up with what Mr. Lincoln called her trimmings, she had grown quite fond of them. And she was hardly alone, with Ed Boliver and his wife right there in the house.

As a matter of fact, Mary had found the weeks while Mr. Lincoln was out on the circuit as pleasant as any she could remember. Even now, when the June heat had begun, and the dust blew thick from the prairies, she didn't mind staying indoors most of the time. Elizabeth made it a point to bring her sewing over several afternoons a week, although Mary troubled less and less about returning the visits.

"Why don't you come out for a drive, Mary? It would do you good. I declare, I don't know how you stand being stuffed up under this hot roof."

"I daresay I shall have plenty of time to go driving," Mary said, "when I have a carriage of my own."

"Oh, very well—if you want to be stubborn . . ."

It was easier when Cousin Lizzie or Polly Francis came to call.

"I don't care what anyone says," Lizzie confided one afternoon, "*I* think you're being perfectly wonderful, Mary. I said to Elizabeth just the other day—" She paused, squinting while she threaded a needle. "There's no sense in always worrying about Mary, I said. Mary knew when she married Mr. Lincoln that things weren't going to be so easy—just at first, anyway. But you'll never hear a word of complaint out of Mary, I said, no matter how it may turn out."

The best days were when no one came at all. When she didn't have to be explaining, guarding—forever on the watch for unspoken criticism of Mr. Lincoln. It was nice then, just to do as she pleased. To read, or sew, or write letters.

Somehow, writing to Mr. Lincoln, it was easy to overlook so many things. To forget the queer, uneasy moments when they discovered how extraordinarily different two people could be. The moments when Mary found her quick decisiveness blunted and sidetracked by the peculiar, maddening slowness of Mr. Lincoln. His odd silences, that left her puzzled and hurt; and the curious, roundabout unpredictability of his nature. They were both startled by those moments, and a little troubled.

But in her letters, long and gossipy and affectionate, Mary could picture everything just as she wanted it to be. The future seemed to stretch out then, lovely and exciting. There were no remarks from Elizabeth to spoil it, no patient sympathy from Frances, none of Ann's sharp sarcasms. Not even the presence of Mr. Lincoln, often so disturbingly solid and uncompromising. In the letters Mr. Lincoln could be all that she had dreamed.

There were times, in those early summer weeks, when Mary remembered the old days in Lexington. The way the family used to pack up for the annual pilgrimage to Orchard Springs. The pleasant, orderly commotion of departure. Piles of starched petticoats and fresh muslin dresses heaped on the beds, and the servants hurrying around under Miss Betsy's watchful eye, fixing the big hampers of picnic food for the journey. Carriages piled full of luggage, nurses for the babies, the jingle of harness as the horses pranced smartly in the driveway. And then the big, rambling, frame hotel up in the Kentucky hills. The candlelight in the dining room, and the large round table that was always reserved for the Todd family. New arrivals bowing. The darky fiddlers playing during dinner and later, in the ballroom, for dancing. The mountain nights cool and starlit. Picnics and horseback rides, beaux and young ladies, and flirtations, and tears. And the mammas sitting in the rows of rocking chairs on the verandas, exchanging gossip and symptoms in mysterious whispers.

Lying awake sometimes, in the hot bedroom over the tavern, Mary would twist about, trying to find some comfort for the nagging ache in her back. She remembered how it had been at home when her stepmother was expecting a new baby. The busy preparations in the nursery—and Mammy Jane, who had nursed all the Todd babies, waiting on Miss Betsy hand and foot. Rubbing her back, and gentling her forehead with cologne handkerchiefs. Mammy Jane ordering Mr. Todd to keep his segars away from Miss Betsy's room. All of them fussing over Betsy—treating her like something delicate and precious.

But, Mary reflected, the thing was—the thing that Elizabeth could never understand—that she wouldn't have traded places with Betsy for the whole world. Not for anything under shining heaven.

By the time Mr. Lincoln came home, they were saying in Springfield that nobody could recall when they'd had such a long dry spell of heat.

"It's not a bit of use hoping for a garden this year," Elizabeth said. "We might as well give up trying."

The evening Mr. Lincoln arrived, he and Mary walked

over to Elizabeth's for supper. Afterward, on the porch, the air was like a bake oven, motionless and stifling.

Elizabeth fanned herself.

"Well, Mr. Lincoln, did you have a good trip?"

He was sitting on the top step, and from where she sat, next to Elizabeth, Mary could see him raise his head.

"Oh—about the usual."

"You haven't told us any stories yet, Abe," Ninian said. "I've never known you to come home without a supply of new ones." He rose to offer his guest a segar, but Elizabeth pointed out sharply that the smoke might bother Mary. About time, she thought, that Mr. Lincoln was reminded of Mary's condition. For all the attention he paid, Mary might not be having a baby at all.

Mary shrugged impatiently.

"What nonsense, Elizabeth. Of course I don't mind if they smoke. There's no use acting as though I were an invalid."

But Mr. Lincoln shook his head, and Ninian put away the segars in silence.

They left early and on the way home Mr. Lincoln did not speak. Walking beside him, Mary was aware of an odd, perverse disappointment. It was as though, now that he was here, all the wonderful anticipation of seeing him had been lost, somehow. At a crossing she stopped suddenly, and Mr. Lincoln turned.

"What's the matter, Mary? You don't feel sick, do you?"

Mary bit her lip. "It wouldn't be strange if I did. The way you rush me along—"

"I'm sorry, Mary; you should have told me I was going too fast."

But the next minute she pulled her arm away.

"Heavens and earth, Mr. Lincoln. You don't have to creep."

He speeded up again, without comment.

The rooms were unbearably hot that night. Sitting on the edge of the bed, Mary saw that Mr. Lincoln kept glancing at her—as if wondering what to say. Very well then, let him wonder. Mary set her chin stubbornly, but in spite of anything she could do her lips began to tremble,

"Mary—won't you tell me what the trouble is?"

She blinked back the tears furiously.

"There isn't anything to tell. I just—don't feel well, that's all."

He stood looking down at her, his expression so helpless and puzzled that she turned away sharply and buried her face in the pillow.

"You don't want me to get the doctor, do you, Mary?"

She shook her head, pressing her face tighter. A wave of something curiously like homesickness swept over her, confused and miserable. Couldn't he see for himself what the trouble was? Couldn't he have said just one word, after all those weeks, about having missed her? Couldn't he have acted a little bit pleased about being home again—instead of sitting like a wooden Indian all evening? Mary could imagine what Elizabeth and Ninian had said after they left.

"I don't see why you had to be so rude and hateful tonight—" her words were muffled resentfully against the pillow—"when you've been gone all this time—and Ninian and Elizabeth were trying to be nice to you—"

There was a silence, then she heard him sigh.

"Well, I'm sorry." He sat down beside her on the bed. "I didn't mean anything—but to tell you the truth, I wasn't thinking much about Ninian and Elizabeth. I guess I'd been sort of looking forward to getting home—and seeing you again—" He broke off, startled by the suddenness with which Mary sat up and faced him.

"Oh, Mr. Lincoln—" Her voice sounded queer and shaky. "Why on earth—couldn't you have told me that before? When all the while I've been so miserable and lonesome—thinking you weren't glad to see me at all."

She flung her arms around him—clinging as though she never meant to let him ago.

"Well, I don't know, Mary—" he patted her shoulder,

sounding puzzled—"I reckon I thought you knew that—without my saying anything . . ."

In the last week of July, the dry spell broke at last. A series of thunderstorms swept over the prairie, and the rain poured down, freshening the dark earth and bringing the shriveled corn to life.

Once, coming home in the midst of a storm, Mr. Lincoln found Mary in the parlor downstairs, her face white and shaken with fear. She'd come down to look for Mrs. Boliver—and had been terrified to find herself alone in the house. After that, Mr. Lincoln was careful to leave the office at the first rumble of thunder, to hurry home and stay with Mary until the storm had passed.

One evening Ed Boliver was carving the roast at a side table in the tavern kitchen when the scullery maid came clattering down the back stairs. She had just been up to fetch some linen, Nellie said, and Mrs. Lincoln had called her and said she wanted to speak to Mr. Boliver.

"You'd best go quick!" Nellie rolled her eyes. "She's carrying on something awful. Something's happened to Mr. Lincoln, she says—I couldn't make out what—but she *is* in a state. And in her condition and all. I'm scared—"

Ed took the steps two at a time.

Mary was waiting at her door, her face white and streaked with tears. Talking rapidly, in a queer, feverish voice, Mary told Ed he must go to Mr. Lincoln's office at once. Something had happened to him, she said. She was certain of it. He'd never been late coming home like this without sending her word. It was two hours past his usual time . . .

Ed tried to reassure her. Abe must have been detained by business. There wasn't any reason to get upset. Why not let Nellie bring up her supper on a tray? After a nice hot cup of tea she was sure to feel better—

Mary wouldn't listen. "I tell you, I *know* something has happened to him." Her voice was shrill. "I *know* it. I've felt all afternoon something terrible was going to happen."

She clutched convulsively at Ed's arm. "You've got to find him for me. And hurry—oh, please hurry!"

Frightened by the look in her eyes, Ed promised hastily to go. He untied the apron he had worn up from the kitchen. "Now you just try and take it easy, Mrs. Lincoln. I'll fetch Abe back as quick as I can."

The moment Ed was out of the house, Mary rushed to the front window. She watched him down the street, saw him turn the corner into the square. Counting the minutes, she waited. Her eyes strained down the empty street, and with every minute that passed a thousand images of disaster tore at her heart. If something had happened—if Mr. Lincoln didn't come home—she couldn't bear it. She couldn't . . .

Two men came round the corner—and for one moment everything in Mary's mind seemed to stop. The men came nearer. She saw Mr. Lincoln's gray coat, and his easy, swinging stride. She saw that he was saying something to Ed, and then, just before they turned in at the tavern gate, she saw Mr. Lincoln stop and throw his head back. He was *laughing* . . .

Something blind and dark rushed at Mary. She turned from the window and ran through the hall, down the stairs—half stumbling, clutching at the banister. She threw open the front door, just as Mr. Lincoln came up the step, and flung herself straight into his arms. Sobbing and trembling, unaware of his dismayed astonishment, she clung to him.

"Why, now, Mary—there's nothing to get so riled up about—"

Nothing! He called it nothing that he'd kept her waiting more than two hours without one word. When he knew quite well she'd be beside herself with worry. She threw the words at him bitterly—heedless of Ed's embarrassed stare and the curious glances of the tavern guests who laid down their knives and forks to listen.

"How could you make me suffer so, Mr. Lincoln? And then *laugh* about it. How could you—"

He touched her arm, awkward and distressed. "I'm sorry, Mary. I hadn't any idea you'd be so upset. I just stopped at Diller's on the way home, and got into a game of checkers. That was all . . ."

That night, long after Mr. Lincoln was asleep, Mary lay stiff and wretched, staring into the darkness. It was true, she thought. Everything Elizabeth had said—all of Ann's mean little hints—they were all true, after all. He didn't care about her really. He didn't care any more than to forget her for a game of checkers. He didn't care—and he didn't understand—and he never would. Not in a million years, he never would.

She was alone, really. She'd given up everything in the world for him—believing in him—and now she was alone. He might as well be a thousand miles away as lying there beside her, never even hearing when at last she got up and went into the other room. Huddled in the old pine armchair, the night shadows bleak around her, she rocked slowly back and forth, locked in a misery of loneliness.

There were faint streaks of dawn in the windows when Mary leaned stiffly over the bed and touched Mr. Lincoln's shoulder.

"Mr. Lincoln—"

His eyes opened.

"*Mr. Lincoln—*" Her voice was sharper.

"What is it? What's the matter, Mary?" He sat up, seeing her face, strained and queer in the gray light. Her fingers on his arm were icy cold, and she was shivering so that her teeth chattered.

"You'll have to go—for the doctor, Mr. Lincoln. As quickly—as you can . . ."

For a long time after that everything was a blur. A blur of sleep that kept coming, confusingly, dropping like a dull, black curtain between the stretches of pain. And through it all, through the sleep, and the sound of her own moaning—through the doctor's voice, calmly reassuring, and Elizabeth's directions, brisk and experienced —at the bottom of everything there was the knowledge, cold and bitter, that she was alone.

It was evening when Mary opened her eyes. For a time everything seemed unreal, out of focus, as though she had wakened to a strange world. Then, gradually, the familiar outlines came back. The bed, the walnut dresser, and the windows beyond, squares of dull blue in the twilight.

Slowly, she began to remember. The doctor's voice speaking close to her ear.

"You've got a little boy, Mrs. Lincoln. A good, healthy boy."

Strange that the room should be so still. She turned her head a little, surprised at the effort it required. And then she saw Mr. Lincoln sitting by the bed, his hands resting on his knees, his head bent. In silence, Mary lay watching him. Watching the look in his deep-set eyes, strange and brooding—forever locked beyond her reach. Like an echo, weak and faint, the memory of the long night returned. And the loneliness . . .

"Mr. Lincoln—"

He turned, seeming to come back over a long distance.

"Mr. Lincoln, what were you thinking about just then?"

He didn't answer for a minute. Looking down at his hands, he drew a long breath.

"I was thinking about something I heard yesterday, down at Diller's," he said slowly. "They were saying Reverend Dresser wants to sell his house. The white frame one, over on Jackson Street. I don't know whether it's anything you'd want, Mary, but it's got a nice yard. I was thinking maybe we ought to buy it—"

"You mean—" Mary felt as though she could scarcely trust her voice—"you mean—right away, Mr. Lincoln?"

"Well—yes. If you like the place, that is." He looked at her doubtfully, as if she might not quite approve. "I reckon we want to have a real home now—for the little boy. He's a fine boy, Mary."

"Yes—I know." Mary smiled. She let her eyes drift shut, content with the utter sweetness of the moment.

After a while Mr. Lincoln sighed. "We've got one thing to be thankful for anyway," he said. "Elizabeth says the baby doesn't look like me a bit."

9

IT WAS THE TWELFTH OF FEBRUARY, AND MARY WAS planning a special dinner for Mr. Lincoln. Elizabeth and Ninian had been invited. It was the first real party Mary had given in the new house—and everything must be just right. Since early morning she'd been busy, dusting and polishing until the whole house shone like a new pin. She set the table herself, with the best silver and embroidered linen, and spent a good hour showing Aggie, the Irish girl who came three days a week now, exactly how the dinner must be served.

By five o'clock everything was ready, and Mary looked around with a sigh of satisfaction. Not even Elizabeth, she thought, could find a speck to mar the perfection. Bright fires burned in the grates, and in the warm light the horsehair and mahogany furniture gleamed. Starched curtains hung crisp and immaculate, framing the potted geraniums on the window-sills—and a smell of roasting turkey, rich and plummy, drifted in from the kitchen.

Mary went upstairs to feed the baby before she changed her dress. It had been well worth the trouble to have the house so pretty. Worth even the scolding that had been necessary to persuade Aggie that silver must be polished properly. Worth all of Aggie's crossness and impertinence, and her bitter groans that Mrs. Lincoln made her work so hard she could hear her poor bones crying out to the holy saints for mercy.

Drawing the bedroom blinds against the wintry dusk, Mary fixed the baby's gruel, and bent over the walnut-spindled cradle to take him up. Thank heavens, he seemed to be in one of his amiable moods. It would be too awful if he should decide to take a howling fit while Elizabeth was in the house. Elizabeth was very firm on the subject of howling babies. There was no excuse for it, she said, since babies, like husbands, only needed proper handling to keep them blissfully contented—or, at the very least, quiet. It was true, certainly, that neither Elizabeth's babies nor her husband had ever been known to give her any noticeable trouble. Trouble, Elizabeth pointed out frequently and with conviction, was something that came only to those who were fools enough to invite it.

Though she would have died rather than admit it to Elizabeth, there were times when Mary looked back with a sort of baffled wonder at the way Elizabeth's household could accommodate itself to a new baby without the slightest sign of undue stir. Elizabeth's babies slept when they should, waked when they should, allowed themselves to be gorged with food, and then subsided into silence until the time came for them to be stuffed again. There never seemed to be any screaming in the night—no demands for attention at awkward and improbable hours. And when exhibited to company, Elizabeth's babies went from lap to lap, cooing agreeably, and never dreamed of shrieking and turning dark red at the sight of strangers, as little Robert was so apt to do.

Nevertheless, Robert was behaving admirably tonight. He downed his gruel hungrily, in dribbling gulps, and gazed at Mary out of eyes that were beginning to turn hazel, like his father's.

It would have been nice, Mary thought, to have had the birthday dinner a surprise for Mr. Lincoln. But experience had already taught her that Mr. Lincoln just wasn't the surprising kind. As surely as she planned an unexpected party, he'd choose that night to be an hour late for supper —or worse still, he'd bring some crony or other home from the office. Why not come along for a bite? he'd say cordially. He guessed Mary'd be able to scare up enough for an extra—and she'd be tickled to have the company. Kind of perk her up after being by herself all day.

It wasn't that Mary objected to providing the extra food on these occasions. She was as ready as the next person to welcome a guest—particularly if it happened to be someone she thought Mr. Lincoln ought to know. But it was the *sort* of people Mr. Lincoln chose to bring with him.

"Where on earth do you *find* them, Mr. Lincoln?" she asked sometimes, despairingly. "Don't any decent people ever come into your office?"

"Well, I don't know, Mary—" Mr. Lincoln would rub his chin—"I thought he seemed like a nice sort of fellow . . ."

"He had a five days' growth of beard, Mr. Lincoln—and the most abominable table manners I've yet to see. Stuffing himself like a pig—and dropping segar ashes all over the floor."

"That shows he enjoyed the food anyway. He said it was the first real Kentucky meal he'd had in months. I should think that would please you."

"Kentucky meal, my foot. From the amount he ate, it was more likely the first food of any sort he'd sat down to in a week. And if he ever clapped eyes on Kentucky—which I doubt—you can be sure he never set foot inside any decent house. I declare, Mr. Lincoln, you're the most gullible man I ever saw. Anyone could flatter you out of house and home, if they'd a mind to."

"Well, I guess that's so, Mary. Maybe the trouble is I don't get enough exercise resisting flattery. If you want to try giving me a little practice at home . . ."

At least, Mary sighed, there was no danger of his turning up with any strays tonight. She had told him about the party, and reminded him again the last thing before he left for the office, and he had promised solemnly to be on time, and unencumbered—in a frame of mind suitably reverent to meet his Maker or the Edwards.

She wiped the rim of milk from Robert's mouth and laid him on the bed, winding his flannel band good and tight, to strengthen his spine, before she slipped on his nightgown. As an extra precaution, she left him a sugar-tit to suck until he went to sleep. Tiptoeing out, she paused a moment to listen. If he was going to roar, he'd start the instant the door was shut. But there was no sound. Mary drew a breath of relief.

Looking in the mirror, a few minutes later, she was thankful to see that her lilac moiré looked as smart and becoming as new. She fastened the waistband, and settled the full rustling skirt. It was a mercy, certainly, that she hadn't got fat after the baby. Not even Elizabeth could find fault with her figure. She parted her hair and brushed it smoothly, fluffing the curled ends behind her ears. There . . .

She was just starting down the stairs when the sound of voices made her draw back frowning sharply. Ninian and Elizabeth weren't due for at least another half hour—and these were strange voices. Cautiously, still frowning, she peeked over the banister. Two bonneted heads were visible in the hall light, and the top of a bald head, gleaming pinkly.

What on earth—?

It couldn't be—it simply *couldn't* be that Mr. Lincoln had forgotten. But there was his voice now—explaining cheerfully that Mary would be down in a minute.

"I reckon she's upstairs, getting her trotting harness on."

Mary felt the sharp prickles of anger on the back of her neck, as she heard them laugh. How *could* Mr. Lincoln speak like that? And bringing home people—after she'd reminded him so carefully. Well, she wouldn't go down. She'd simply wait until he came up to find her, and then tell him that he had to get rid of them, somehow, before the Edwards came . . .

But the next moment, having caught sight of her skirt through the banisters, Mr. Lincoln called her.

"Come along down, Mary. I've got a surprise for you."

Surprise, indeed. But there was no escaping now. The strangers had turned to follow Mr. Lincoln's glance, and the three of them stood gawping up at Mary while she gathered her skirts in one hand and started down, her lips set in a tight, straight line. Name of heaven, wouldn't you suppose the man might at least have enough sense to show them into the parlor, instead of lining them up in the hall and shouting at her, as though announcing a train?

These were old friends, Mr. Lincoln said, looking for all the world as though he had something to be pleased about. Mattie and Tom Renfrew, from New Salem, and this was their daughter Ella.

"I've been bragging to Mattie and Tom about what a fine wife I had," Mr. Lincoln said, "but I figured they'd never believe until they'd seen for themselves." He turned to the visitors, beaming proudly. "Well, isn't she just as good as I said?"

Mary could have wept. Being paraded like this before his bumpkin friends, as though she were something Mr. Lincoln had acquired at an auction. And of all the moments he could have chosen to put on such an absurd display . . . She nodded, as slightly as possible. "How do you do?"

The two women's smiles wavered uncertainly before the chill in Mary's voice.

"Very pleased, I'm sure." Mrs. Renfrew drew her Paisley shawl closer about the shoulders of her dark woolsey dress, obviously abashed by the spectacle of Mary's elegance.

The girl Ella said nothing. Her stare, beneath a country bonnet gaudily festooned with a row of nodding purple pansies, was hostilely appraising, and there was a look of touch-me-if-you-dare in her prominent black eyes.

Tom Renfrew, plainly not a party to the social qualms of his womenfolks, stepped up to grasp Mary's hand and wring it heartily. "It's a treat to meet you, ma'am. I'll own I thought Abe was stuffing us with all his talk about getting himself such a grand wife—but he didn't overshoot the mark a mite. No, sir—not a mite."

Mary allowed herself the faintest shadow of a smile as she extricated her fingers from the calloused grip. "It's always a pleasure to meet Mr. Lincoln's old friends," she said coolly. "I'm only sorry you couldn't have come earlier, in time for tea."

There was an awkward silence, while the Renfrews digested this. But Mr. Lincoln, bland and cordial, came to the rescue. With never so much as a by-your-leave, or a glance in Mary's direction, he said supper was better than tea anyway—and of course they would stay.

Mrs. Renfrew pulled at her shawl again, her glance hovering unhappily between Mary's frigid countenance and the dining room beyond, where the table, set for company, was plainly visible. "Well now, Abe—that's kind of you, but I don't know as we ought. If Mrs. Lincoln's expecting company, she don't want a lot of strangers horning in . . ."

For an instant, Mary took hope. It was on the tip of her tongue to suggest another evening for supper—but Mr. Lincoln gave her no chance.

Nonsense, he declared heartily; they needn't think they were going to get off as easy as all that. They were staying to supper and no more argument about it. "That's right, isn't it, Tom?" He clapped Mr. Renfrew soundly on the shoulder. "Now you just come right along in the parlor and make yourselves comfortable while I fetch out a little elderberry wine." Paying no more attention to Mary than as if she had been a wax dummy standing by in helpless dismay, Mr. Lincoln led his guests past her into the parlor.

The dinner, certainly, exceeded Mary's worst expectations. With the arrival of the Edwards, the three Renfrews lapsed into a frozen and dreadful silence, from which, to be sure, Elizabeth's air of astonished disapproval did nothing to retrieve them. Sitting on the edges of their chairs, they stared unhappily, seeming moved beyond all possibility of speech by the sight of Elizabeth, in her jet-embroidered silk, and Ninian, slim and elegant, with his satin waistcoat and patent-leather boots. It was the boots that appeared to impress the Renfrews most deeply. They eyed them with a kind of mournful fascination, from which nothing could rouse them until Mr. Lincoln appeared with glasses and wine.

Mrs. Renfrew, noticing that Mary and Elizabeth refused the wine, shook her head nervously. But Mr. Lincoln only laughed.

"Now, Mattie, don't you be put off by these women-folks." He filled her glass. "You'll never get me to believe you've gone and signed the pledge behind my back."

Mrs. Renfrew tittered slightly, glancing apologetically at Mary. "You be careful now, Abe. You know I never could stand much."

Miss Ella accepted her glass without argument, and after a few warming sips, she seemed quite suddenly restored to the power of speech. She looked coquettishly up at Mr. Lincoln. "Say, Abe, do you remember that story you used to tell in New Salem about the farmer that had to pull the pig out of the quicksand?" She turned to Mary. "Honest—it was funniest thing I ever saw the way he used to act the whole thing out. No matter how often we heard Abe tell that one—we'd laugh fit to bust every time."

For one excruciating moment, Mary caught the look on Elizabeth's face. From the dining room across the hall came sounds of rattling silver and the ominous clank of glassware. Gritting her teeth in despairing rage, Mary could picture Aggie's struggles with the problem of adding three extra places to the table.

Mr. Renfrew, wrenching his gaze with difficulty from the hypnotizing spectacle of Ninian's boots, set down his empty glass with a thud. "I'll tell you, Abe, this is a real tony place you've got here." He stood up, thrusting his hands deep into the pockets of his homespun trousers. "Of course, we'd heard you were doing well, but I reckon the folks back in New Salem are going to be mighty proud when we tell 'em how fine you're set up here. Isn't that right, Mattie?"

Mrs. Renfrew nodded. "We always were proud of Abe. We used to say he'd get on someday—when he got his mind set to it."

"Yes, *sir*—" Mr. Renfrew teetered on his heels. "We always knew we could count on Abe to do big things. Many's the time I've said that, Abe, back in the days when you used to bring your extra pair of pants around, to see could Mother squeeze one more patch onto 'em." He chuckled reminiscently. "I reckon your wife don't have to worry about patching your britches nowadays, do you, ma'am?"

The last remnants of Mary's smile congealed.

"Well, I guess not and that's a fact," Mr. Renfrew went on, undismayed. "I hear you're making quite a name in politics, Abe." He turned to Ninian, genial and expansive. "I suppose you're in politics too, Mr. Edwards?"

Ninian crossed his knees, letting one slender, gleaming boot swing lightly.

"Well, yes and no, Mr. Renfrew," he said. "I've lived with politics all my life, so to speak. But I can't say any fires of statesmanship burn in my breast, as they do in Abe's. Personally, I've always felt I'd rather just sit back and watch the show."

Mr. Lincoln smiled good-naturedly. "Guess you've got the right idea at that, Ninian."

"Maybe so. Maybe so," Mr. Renfrew pondered, frowning. "All the same—" he bent his eye sternly on Ninian—"it's a good thing for this country we've got young fellows like Abe here—that are willing to get right in the show and ain't afraid to get their elbows skinned."

Mary stood up.

"Dinner is waiting, Mr. Lincoln," she said. "We'll go in."

It was close on midnight when Mr. Lincoln came upstairs. Ninian and Elizabeth had mercifully departed as soon after dinner as was possible. Feeling that she could bear no more, Mary had presently excused herself, saying she had a headache. Her departure, however, had failed to cast the slightest blight on the Renfrews' evening.

Undressed and in bed, Mary lay listening to the laughter and voices from below. It was absurd, of course, to let that sound make her feel lonely. She ought to be feeling merely angry. And she was angry. But, oddly, it wasn't so much Mr. Lincoln she resented now, as Ninian and Elizabeth. Remembering their air of supercilious detachment, the way they had exchanged glances over Mr. Renfrew's pompous remarks and Mrs. Renfrew's cackling, country laugh, Mary felt a sudden surge of indignation.

The Renfrews had been quite impossible, of course—and it *was* infuriating of Mr. Lincoln to have dragged them in and spoiled her party. But all the same, there was no need for Elizabeth and Ninian to assume that she was ashamed of Mr. Lincoln's friends. She remembered the gleam of amusement in Ninian's eye as he watched the Renfrews go off into fits of admiring laughter over Mr. Lincoln's stories—and the way Elizabeth had raised her brows, ever so slightly, at Ella Renfrew's frequent giggling references to the old days when she had been on very intimate terms indeed with Mr. Lincoln.

Closing her eyes, Mary suddenly realized that her head did really ache. She had meant to punish Mr. Lincoln and snub the Renfrews by coming upstairs early—and now, most perversely, it seemed she was the only one who had been punished.

When, at last, she heard Mr. Lincoln's step in the hall, Mary turned her back on the room and lay very still. She could hear him moving about, getting ready for bed—winding his watch, fastening the blinds. She had expected him to speak—to try, somehow, to make amends—but the silence only grew longer. What on earth was he doing now—waiting there, not making a sound?

Mary turned abruptly and sat up.

He was over by the window, standing with his hand on the back of a chair, staring down at the floor, with a queer, half-closed expression in his eyes.

"Mr. Lincoln—"

"Well, what have I done wrong now, Mary?"

She hadn't meant to scold—but at the sound of his voice, cold and patient, all the anger rushed back, and into bitter words. He knew well enough what he had done. She'd worked all day, trying to have things nice for the dinner—and he'd deliberately, *purposely* ruined everything by dragging home those ridiculous people. And as though that weren't enough—he'd spent the whole evening flattering them, encouraging their stupid jokes, giving them too much wine. He had ignored her—been rude to her family. He was stupid, boorish, utterly inconsiderate of her feelings.

"For weeks, Mr. Lincoln, I've slaved over this house—trying to make it nice for you and your friends. But I get no thanks from you. You don't even notice what I've done. And when I try to have Elizabeth and Ninian here—instead of always going to their house, as though we were poor relations—what do you do? You insult them—and make a fool of me. I don't see how you expect me to go on trying . . ." her voice broke, miserably, on a sob.

For a long moment Mr. Lincoln did not speak. Then he came over to the bed.

"Well—" he said, "I'm sorry, Mary."

He leaned over to blow out the lamp, and in the blackness the dying wick left a tiny glow that shone for a minute and then winked out, leaving an odor of oil smoke, faint and acrid, in the room.

After a while, Mr. Lincoln spoke again.

"There were lots of times," he said, "when I'd have gone hungry, I guess, if Tom and Mattie hadn't been willing to give me supper. I reckon it wasn't always convenient for them to have me—but they'd never let on they weren't pleased to see me."

There was not the slightest trace of reproach in his tone. "Well—good night," he said.

In the darkness Mary could hear him turn over, feel him settling down to sleep. She was tired now—too utterly weary to think any more. Only she knew that everything had got confused and wrong, and that somehow she had been the one to blame. Only—it wasn't fair. It wasn't fair . . .

Not until long after Mr. Lincoln was asleep did it occur to Mary that no one had wished him a happy birthday. Unless, perhaps, the Renfrews had remembered.

10

THE YEAR ROBERT WAS THREE THERE WAS A NEW BABY, Edward, in the walnut-spindled cradle. And that summer Mr. Lincoln ran for Congress.

Down at Diller's drugstore they had a whole flock of new stories to tell about Abe and the campaign. The one they never got tired of repeating, though, was about the time he went to hear his opponent, old Peter Cartwright, make a speech in a big revival tent. For as long as anybody could remember, Cartwright had been an old-fashioned hell-fire and brimstone preacher, and the trouble was, folks said, he couldn't seem to keep his politics and his religion straight. He'd start out right enough, telling why he ought to be elected to Congress, but before he finished he'd be pounding on the table and asking how many wanted to come to Jesus and be saved.

The day Abe went to hear him, sure enough, old Cartwright puffed along on the tariff and states' rights for a while, and then he peeled off his coat and asked everybody in the audience who wanted to repent their sins and go to heaven to stand up. There was a scuffle in the big tent, and one by one people got to their feet—till they were all standing except Abe, down there in the front row.

Reverend Cartwright leaned down out of the pulpit and stared.

"Brother Lincoln," he bellowed out in that bull voice of his, "I see you don't care to be one of us."

Abe never so much as peeped.

Well, sir, old Cartwright straightened up then and said he was going to ask his honorable opponent, the Whig candidate, just one question. He pointed his finger straight at Abe's nose.

"Brother Lincoln, if you don't want to go to heaven, speak up and tell us—*where do you expect to go?*"

Abe didn't say a word for a minute, then he stood up, cool as you please, and picked up his umbrella.

"Why, I expect to go to Congress, Brother Cartwright," Abe said. And he put on his hat and walked out.

Two weeks later, when the votes were counted, Abe had beat the old preacher two to one.

You'd have to get up mighty early in the morning to get ahead of Abe, they said at Diller's. Good thing he was going to Congress too. Reckon they'd hear plenty from him once he got to Washington. Abe'd show them government money-wasters a thing or two.

During the campaign, however, Mr. Lincoln had his troubles. One thing was, he said, he never could think what to say when people brought their children up to shake hands with him after he'd made a speech.

Ninian said that was easy.

"If it's a girl," Ninian said, "just pat her on the head and say you hope she grows up to be as pretty as her mother. And when it's a boy, all you've got to do is tell him to grow up and vote the Whig ticket."

The next time Mr. Lincoln came home, they asked him how it had worked.

"Well, I'll tell you how it was," Mr. Lincoln said. "The first one I struck was a girl, but she had buck teeth and her eyes were crossed—so I figured I'd better not try it on her. Then a farmer came along with a real likely looking lad, and I did just what you said, Ninian. I patted him on the head, and told him I hoped he'd always be an honest citizen and grow up to vote for the Whigs."

"And was he pleased, Abe?"

Mr. Lincoln looked thoughtful.

"I guess he was pleased enough," he said, "but his father leaned over and shook a fist at me. 'Yes,' he says, 'and I'll break his damned neck if he ever does.'

"I don't know, Ninian—" Mr. Lincoln ended, "maybe we'd better think up something new."

Getting packed, and the house ready to leave, kept Mary busy. It seemed almost a pity to be breaking up when she'd hardly more than settled the place really nicely. But of course it was wonderful that Mr. Lincoln was elected —and life in Washington was surely something to look forward to.

You might think to hear Mary talk, her sisters agreed, that Mr. Lincoln was going to be an ambassador at least. From the airs she put on about his career—anyone would suppose no man had ever gone to Congress before.

"She's forever talking about society—and meeting interesting people in Washington," Ann said. "I guess it's plain to be seen she's never considered Springfield worth her while."

Elizabeth shrugged. "Ninian says he's afraid Mary's due for a shock when she finds out that a new congressman's wife isn't any more noticed in Washington than a new lamppost. But never fear. If Mary doesn't meet a single soul she'll give us to understand when she comes home she's had dinner at the White House every second Tuesday."

By the end of November they were ready to leave. Mr. Lincoln was turning over his law office to his new junior partner, Billy Herndon, and he and Mary and the two babies were planning to stop in Lexington for a month to visit the Todds.

"I notice," Ann said dryly, "that Mary took good care not to have Mr. Lincoln visit in Lexington until now—though they've been married five years, and I know for a fact Papa has written every summer to invite them. I daresay Mary thinks now Mr. L. is going to Congress, she can show him off better."

On the whole the visit was a success.

After some of the things they had heard, the Todds were a trifle apprehensive about meeting Mr. Lincoln. They expected some sort of cross between a homespun backwoodsman with an ax over his shoulder and a penchant for shoveling peas with his knife and a spellbinding orator who might overwhelm them at the slightest provocation with flights of political rhetoric. It was a surprise, really, to find him so normal.

The night the Lincolns arrived the Todds were lined up in the front hall, southern style, to welcome the visitors. Mr. Todd, whiskered and important, stood nearest the door, with his wife leaning on his arm. An assortment of aunts and cousins came next, then the Todd children, starched and pinafored, in descending stair-steps down to the red-haired baby Alex, who was the same age as little Robert Lincoln. In another group, at a respectful distance, the household servants stood together, waiting curiously to catch a glimpse of Miss Mary's husband.

Mammy Jane told Mary later she'd been surprised, at first, by Mr. Lincoln's size.

"The way Miss Elizabeth were always talkin' down 'bout him, we all pictured him kind of weazened like."

All the Todds agreed that Mr. Lincoln was considerably more prepossessing than they had been led to believe. Not handsome certainly but for all he looked so long and sort of rattle-boned, there was something about his eyes that kept him from being really homely. And the way he'd come in that first night, in a long black ulster and a fur cap fastened with a strap under his chin, and walked right down the line shaking hands with each one, white and black—you couldn't help but see he had a friendly knack with him. Later they discovered he knew a good horse when he saw one, and could argue politics in true Kentucky style.

As for Mary, the family was relieved to find that marriage to what Elizabeth had called a barbarian had certainly done her no harm. She seemed prettier than any of them remembered her being. Her face was as round and pert, her eyes as bright, and her curls as soft as they had ever been. And her tongue was just as sharp.

"I can't see that Mary's temper has improved noticeably," her stepmother said. "But at least she's kept her figure—that's something."

For all the Springfield talk about the Lincolns being poor, Mary was as well dressed as any of the Todd ladies. She talked a great deal about their house, and Mr. Lincoln's increasing law practice. His new partner, Mr. Herndon, she said proudly, was one of the most brilliant young lawyers in the state of Illinois—and yet he had jumped at the chance to come into Mr. Lincoln's office. There was no need to add, Mary felt, that she had more than once pointed out to Mr. Lincoln, with considerable emphasis, that he had undoubtedly ruined his career by associating with Billy Herndon, who was known to be wild and a hard drinker—and an atheist besides. And if Betsy didn't guess that Mary had sewed her stylish frocks herself, there was certainly no need to enlighten her.

Mr. Lincoln seemed mildly puzzled by hearing their affairs described so glowingly.

"I don't see why you want to make us out so fancy, Mary," he commented privately. "The way you tell it makes me sound like such an important fellow that being just a plain congressman seems like kind of a measly comedown."

Mary smiled. "There's no harm in putting your best foot forward, Mr. Lincoln. It's no worse to tell only the good things than only the bad ones—as you seem so fond of doing."

"No, I suppose not." Mr. Lincoln sighed. "Only people always seem to enjoy hearing the bad ones more."

Her smile vanished.

"Nonsense, Mr. Lincoln," she said sharply. "Unless you think well of yourself—how can you expect others to?"

"Well—I don't think that I do, necessarily. I guess you're probably right though. Only it seems kind of funny—" He paused thoughtfully. "If that's all there is to being a success—I should think your father would have been president long ago."

With the youngest members of the Todd household, Mr. Lincoln scored his most complete success. It took the children a few days to get used to the idea that young Robert was not the least bit awed by his parent. But after a period of uncertainty, during which they hung back, thumbs in mouths, they made full use of the lovely uncle in their midst. It was novel, and slightly confusing, to see a papa whom nobody seemed to be afraid of. A papa who seldom scolded, and never appeared to think about his dignity at all.

Following Robert's example, timidly at first, the little Todds were soon in raptures over Mr. Lincoln. No matter how incessantly they followed him about or how often they interrupted him, he didn't get cross. He didn't even mind having his hair mussed, and he seemed actually to enjoy going out to the woodshed and rolling up his sleeves to chop a pile of kindling. He told stories whenever he was asked, rode them piggy-back with endless fortitude, and was willing to get down on all fours and play bear in the parlor, even when there were visitors.

It was all most delightful—but baffling.

"I don't see how you can be a regular papa," Alex Todd observed. "You don't wear whiskers or a gold watch chain, or shout."

Mammy Jane confided beamingly to Mary that she never had seen a gentleman like Mr. Lincoln before.

"I declare to the Lord, Miss Mary, the way he takes to chillun just naturally does my heart good. Mr. Lincum don't seem a bit like white folks."

Mary was pleased, all the same, to notice a certain improvement in Robert's manners under Mammy Jane's training. Even the baby Edward seemed affected by the benevolent regime of the Todd nursery, and settled down in a most orderly way. There were no more tantrums, no evenings when supper became a nerve-racking ordeal of trying to ignore ear-splitting howls from overhead.

Of course it was lovely, as Mammy Jane said, that Mr. Lincoln was so devoted to the babies. But there were moments when Mary wondered whether a little less devotion and a little more discipline might not make things happier all around.

There was no doubt, however, in young Robert's mind.

"Alex says he likes my papa much better than his own papa," Robert announced proudly, at breakfast one morning before the assembled family. "And so do I."

It was Grandmother Humphreys who said the thing that pleased Mary most.

For as far back as she could remember, Mary had admired Grandmother Humphreys more than anyone she knew. For all she was such a grand lady, and lived in a house full of beautiful furniture, and poured tea every afternoon from a chased silver service, Grandmother Humphreys had a mind of her own. She could read Voltaire in French, and quote whole scenes from Shakespeare, and argue down Henry Clay in politics.

Grandmother Humphreys wore black silk gowns with real lace at wrists and throat. She'd had two duels fought because of her, and had once been known as the most beautiful woman in Kentucky. And she had decided, when she was eighty-two, that she was in favor of emancipation. She taught her slaves to read and write, and provided in her will that they were to have their freedom, along with sufficient money to take them north and establish them as freemen. And when her relatives howled, she smiled and gave them tea.

Mr. Lincoln was taken to call on Grandmother Humphreys one afternoon, and a few days later Mary went to tea alone.

"I expect you're dying to hear what I think of your Mr. Lincoln." Grandmother Humphreys stirred her tea. "After all, since you've always been my favorite granddaughter, I hoped you'd marry someone I liked—and I wasn't disappointed."

She put down her cup with a small, decisive click. It was a sound Mary could remember hearing when she was a little girl in pinafores—and it meant that Granny Humphreys had made up her mind about something.

"I liked him, Mary. He's got good eyes and good hands—and he made me laugh more than anyone has for twenty years."

She folded her slender, veined hands and looked at Mary steadily for a moment. Then she nodded.

"I don't wonder you're so proud of him," Grandmother Humphreys said. "Your Mr. Lincoln is a gentleman, Mary."

11

FROM WASHINGTON, MARY WROTE HOME TO ELIZABETH that they were comfortably settled in a boardinghouse on Capitol Hill.

> . . . Our rooms are *small*, but adequate, and afford a pleasant outlook toward the Capitol building. Mrs. Spriggs, who owns the house, caters to a most *select*

clientèle—mostly the families of Congressmen, officials, *etc.*, which makes the atmosphere at meals lively and stimulating.

Social life in the city is extremely active. The ladies, I notice, take a prominent part in all affairs, political and otherwise, and there is much of what Mr. Lincoln calls "flourishing about in carriages." Theaters, balls, receptions and formal visiting take a *great deal* of time—and everywhere we see the very latest in fashionable gowns and *coiffeurs*, the ladies apparently believe the success of their husbands' careers depends entirely upon the number of feathers and furbelows they can manage to crowd upon themselves.

The city, on the whole, is disappointing. There are a few fine homes, mostly around Lafayette Square and the President's House—but good and bad sections are for the most part quite mixed up—so that in order to reach one of the large establishments, we must frequently pass through the meanest, unpaved streets. Even the negro settlements, picturesquely known as *Crow Hill* and *Swampoodle*, are in plain view from many of the best houses.

The whole town is seething with talk of emancipation, *pro* and *con*. But for all the abolitionist talk that emanates from the Capitol, I have never seen slavery more in evidence or more abused than in Washington. Almost every day we see gangs of negroes, often chained together and in a miserable condition, led up Pennsylvania Avenue *en route* to the Slave Pen—a disgraceful shambles which occupies a block adjoining the Smithsonian Gardens.

Mr. Lincoln has taken no *public* stand on the slavery issue, in spite of *great pressure* on both sides. His recent speech, criticizing the President's action in prosecuting the Mexican War has, as you have no doubt read, attracted much attention. I have *heard*, in fact, that Mr. Daniel Webster called it the most impressive utterance by any member of the new Congress. (This is *confidential*, of course.)

I thank fortune we keep well, and the Washington climate appears to agree with us so far. I only pray my precious boys will not succumb to any of the dreadful fevers which are so prevalent—due, in my opinion, to the general lack of sanitation and proper drainage. The boys are lively as ever, and we all enjoy ourselves. . . .

"It sounds well enough, I must say," Elizabeth observed to Ninian. "But if I know Mary, there's plenty she hasn't written."

But what could one write about evenings spent alone in a boardinghouse parlor, sewing or reading—except to say that they were very dull?

And why trouble Elizabeth with the information that the problem of fitting two active and hitherto totally unrestrained children into the pattern of boardinghouse life had led, on a number of occasions, to decidedly caustic criticism from Mrs. Spriggs and some of her other guests?

It was true that Mr. Lincoln was making his mark in Washington. More and more frequently now he was invited out—and Mary couldn't help but be pleased when, every so often, he was pointed out and recognized on the street.

"See that man over there—the tall one in the plug hat? That's Abe Lincoln. Comes from out west somewheres. Kind of a solemn-looking duck—but I hear he's real comical when he starts telling stories. They say even Daniel Webster comes down to the Capitol post office at lunchtime to hear Abe Lincoln's yarns . . ."

One evening Mr. Lincoln came home with the news that he'd been asked to one of the Sunday breakfasts at Mr. Webster's house.

Mary looked up from her sewing.

"Why, Mr. Lincoln, that's wonderful. All the most important people in Washington go there." She pursed her lips thoughtfully. "Let me see now—I should think my green velours ought to be just about right. Or perhaps the ladies dress more formally. Maybe the black watered silk—" Mary stopped, aware that Mr. Lincoln was looking at her with a peculiar expression.

"To tell you the truth, Mary—" he shifted uneasily, digging his hands into his pockets—"I didn't hear anything about any ladies being invited."

Sometimes, having her supper upstairs alone when Mr. Lincoln was working late or had been invited to join a group of men at an evening bowling party, Mary was puzzled. It was a fact, as she never failed to mention in her letters home, that Mr. Lincoln's career was getting on. But somehow she couldn't help feeling that it wasn't so much her influence as the long apprenticeship in the back of Diller's drugstore that was bearing fruit.

"I'm sorry you don't like it better here, Mary," Mr. Lincoln said. "Maybe if you got out a little more—"

Mary shrugged impatiently.

"How am I to 'get out,' Mr. Lincoln—when there is no one for me to leave the children with? And where, pray, would I go? Without any carriage, or any husband to take me most of the time—I'd be a fine sight parading the streets and hopping over mud puddles."

"Well, I don't know—" Mr. Lincoln sighed. "I should think you might make friends here in the house. Mrs. Spriggs seems nice—and then there's that new Miss Tompkins. I was talking to her at lunch today."

"Yes—so I noticed." Mary gave a sharp twitch to the shirt she was mending. "Thank you, Mr. Lincoln, but I think I prefer to wait until the time comes when you see fit to introduce me to some of your friends you talk so much about."

"I don't meet anyone but men, Mary; and they never seem to ask me whether I'm married."

"I suppose you couldn't possibly mention it—without waiting to be asked."

Mr. Lincoln said nothing.

In June, when the hot weather began, Mary took the boys back to Springfield. It was only sensible, after all, to get them out of Washington during the months when the fever epidemics swept over the city and every second person succumbed to malaria or the typhoid.

They agreed that she was to return in the fall—but when October came, the trip was delayed for one reason and another. First Mr. Lincoln was away—speaking in New York, and attending to various political matters in New England. Then he wrote that Mrs. Spriggs was extremely sorry she had no rooms available for Mary and the boys just at present. With Washington so crowded, it wasn't likely they could find another place that would suit them . . . Perhaps later, after Christmas . . .

But with the winter half gone, it began to seem foolish to break up the Springfield house again, just for the few months that remained. Mr. Lincoln couldn't get away from Washington to come and travel east with them—and he didn't like to think of Mary making the long trip alone, with the two children to take care of.

If she was really anxious to come, Mr. Lincoln wrote, why not ask Elizabeth to come along?

It was that, as much as anything, that made Mary decide to stay in Springfield.

After all, she explained to Elizabeth, Mr. Lincoln's term in Congress would be over so soon—it was hardly worth while establishing themselves in Washington. Of course, she said, Mr. Lincoln was terribly disappointed. His letters spoke constantly of how much he missed them. But he had agreed that it was the best thing all around for him to stay on alone.

Elizabeth, taking neat, rapid stitches in the napkin she was hemming, made no reply.

12

LOOKING BACK SOMETIMES, MARY WAS STARTLED TO FIND how she could remember things without really feeling them. It was so queer the way days vanished into weeks, and weeks into years—and the long, soldierly line could disappear over the horizon, taking all reality with it—except for a few landmarks that rose like peaks, snow-capped, still visible but no longer very important except as a means of placing events.

"That was the spring Mr. Lincoln won the big case for the Illinois Central. I remember, because it was when we added the second story to the house . . ."

"It must have been the summer they paved the sidewalks around the square . . ."

"Don't you remember—it was the year Robert took the croup and was so awfully sick . . ."

There was the birth of Willie to remember, and only a few weeks later, the terrible night when they had watched little Edward die of fever.

Then there was a morning when Mr. Lincoln had leaned over the walnut-spindled cradle and looked at another baby boy. This one was named Thomas, for Mr. Lincoln's father—but Mr. Lincoln said he looked like a tadpole, with such a big head on a long, thin body—and they called him Taddie.

Taddie was his father's favorite, so Mary said.

"Funny thing," they used to say down at Diller's. "It looked for a while there as if Abe was set to do big things. Going off to Congress—and sassing the President, and hobnobbing with Daniel Webster and all. But nothing much seemed to come of it. Guess he decided Springfield was good enough for him, after all."

Mary was in the kitchen, delivering a lecture to Katie, the current Irish girl. It had rained all day, with no sign of clearing, and the boys had been noisy and troublesome. Mr. Lincoln was late for supper, the porch roof had developed a leak—and now Katie was in one of her unreasonable grouches.

It was past eight o'clock, and the younger boys ought to have been in bed and asleep—but they had wound up the long day by a furious quarrel, the repercussions of which still drummed in Mary's ears.

Willie, it seemed, had gone out to the woodshed to find that Tad, for want of better amusement, had hung his turtle. It was a pet turtle, and Willie was attached to it with the passionate devotion he lavished on all small creatures. He was still out in the shed now, brooding over the limp remains of the turtle—his usually mild and placid nature roused to a storm of indignant tears.

Taddie, banished to bed in disgrace for his barbarous deed, was by no means penitent. Mary could hear him banging the bars of his crib against the wall, while he shrieked with rage against the indignity of his punishment.

In the parlor, Robert was reading. Like his father, Robert had a maddening knack of burying his nose in a book and remaining completely oblivious to other people's difficulties. He was expected, during Mr. Lincoln's absence, to take care of the fires—but he had forgotten, as usual, and the house was damp and drafty.

How, demanded Katie, was she to do her work, when no one else did theirs? The fire in the range was half out, and not a stick of wood had Robert fetched for her.

"You should have got it yourself then—or else reminded Robert."

That, said Katie, tossing her head, was not her work. It wasn't as though she didn't have enough to do, cooking and scrubbing all day and picking up after the boys who ought to be taught to do for themselves, they were certainly old enough, and somebody at her heels every minute telling her do this do that, she tried hard to please, goodness knows, though there were some people the saints in heaven couldn't satisfy, but there was one thing she wouldn't do and that was break her back carrying wood, not for the blessed saints themselves, she wouldn't . . .

Mary put her hands over her ears suddenly.

"For God's sake, Katie, stop talking. I'll get the wood myself."

For one thunderstruck moment Katie glared after her mistress, rendered speechless by this final indignity. Then, with furious haste, she began untying her apron.

Never, Katie muttered, never in her life had she expected to see the day when she would be sworn at. And by a lady, too. It was more than decent flesh and blood could bear. Supper or no supper, Mr. Lincoln or no Mr. Lincoln, Katie McGonnigle would stay no longer under this roof. She was leaving.

Having struggled in from the drafty shed with an armload of wood, just in time to witness Katie's flouncing departure to pack her bag, Mary dumped the logs into the woodbox and came back to the shed where Willie, shivering and tearful, still hovered over his turtle. She had snagged her new lace cuff on a frayed end of bark, and driven a splinter into her finger.

"Willie, you must come to bed now. I won't stand for another moment of this nonsense. The turtle is dead—and your hanging over it isn't going to bring it back to life."

But Willie only clung to the bench tighter, his round face white and tragic.

"I'm going to wait for Papa," he said, between chattering teeth. "Papa can fix my turtle. I know he can."

Mary pushed back her hair, her lips trembling.

Dear heaven, why must they all, forever, wait for Papa? Even Katie had announced, darkly, that she wouldn't set foot out of the house until Mr. Lincoln came. As though, Mary thought bitterly, Mr. Lincoln or anyone else could solve the problem of managing with one servant to do the work of three.

And for that matter, whose fault was it that meals were

delayed until all hours and unannounced guests turned up at the last minute, expecting to be fed? It was Mr. Lincoln who went blandly on his way, forgetting his chores, and leaving Mary to cope with the hired girl's grumbling over unchopped wood and sidewalks piled with snow.

But they would never think, of course, of blaming *him*. In Mr. Lincoln's presence they were as mealy-mouthed as sucking doves. Mr. Lincoln was such a kind-spoken gentleman, God love him. And though they complained, loudly, that Mrs. Lincoln drove them past endurance and they were plagued beyond bearing by the boys' naughtiness, it never seemed to occur to them that Mr. Lincoln might occasionally lend a hand in disciplining his children.

"You'd better do what Mrs. Lincoln says . . ."

"I reckon your mother knows what's best . . ."

This was the most he could be counted on to offer in dealing with domestic problems.

"I should like to have the angel Gabriel change places with me for a week," Mary said once, "and see whether all the heavenly powers could make this house run properly."

Mr. Lincoln had looked up over the edge of his book.

"That might be a good scheme, mother," he said mildly. "And while you were in heaven, you'd probably be able to think up a few improvements in the management there."

Taddie's roars still issued, unabated, from upstairs when Mr. Lincoln came into the house. He walked straight through to the kitchen, to be confronted by Katie, bag packed, arms folded, and murder in her eye. Briefly, in highly explicit terms, Katie informed him of her reasons for leaving.

Mr. Lincoln put down his hat.

"Katie," he said, "I don't blame you."

He stood a minute, looking at the half-cooked supper on the cooling range with an eye so sad and hungry and altogether weary that Katie's heart misgave her. But she squared her shoulders.

Mr. Lincoln sighed. Then he reached in his pocket and drew out a silver dollar. "Katie," he said, and the voice of him would have pulled tears out of a stone, "if you were to have an extra dollar every week—just between you and me, and not a word to another soul, do you think you could see your way clear to stay?"

Katie stared at the dollar, her blue eyes suffused with a sudden tenderness.

It wasn't, she said, that she wanted to leave *him*. And to part with the boys, especially little Taddie, God love the innocence of him, would surely break her heart. But still and all—Katie shook her head—she couldn't live under the roof with any woman that treated her so. Just because a teacup had got broke—and cracked already it was, and just slipped out of her fingers—Mrs. Lincoln had said she'd take twenty-five cents out of her wages to pay for it. And it wasn't just the money she grudged, but the shame of it. And then calling her names, and swearing at her—when she couldn't carry in the wood fast enough, on account of her lumbago . . .

Mr. Lincoln reached in his pocket again.

"If you had twenty-five cents to pay for the cup, Katie, and another twenty-five not to mention this to Mrs. Lincoln, and an extra fifty cents—do you think you could tell her you were sorry?"

"Well, sir—" Katie set down her bag—"it wouldn't be for the money, if I did." She pocketed the silver firmly. "But I'd never hope to see the day when Katie McGonnigle would disoblige a Christian gentleman like yourself, sir. I'll stay."

Mr. Lincoln went up, two steps at a time, to Taddie's room.

"Now then, Tadpole, what seems to be the trouble?"

Sobbing and twisting against his father's shoulder, Taddie poured out a wildly grieved account of his injuries.

Mamma had hitted him—because he had just touched

Willie's stinky old turtle. And she had hurt him bad—and the turtle had been all deaded anyway . . .

Mr. Lincoln listened gravely, saying nothing. Hoisting the boy higher on his shoulder, he crossed the hall to his bedroom and opened the bureau drawer.

"Taddie," he said, pulling out a small brown sack, "do you think a peppermint drop would make you feel like going to sleep?"

Taddie made a grab for the bag. Then he choked back a last sob, doubtfully.

"Can I have them all, papa?"

"Well—I expect so."

Taddie rubbed his nose.

"Can I eat them now?" he demanded.

"Well—"

"If I don't tell Mamma?" Taddie's glance was sidelong. "Can I?"

Mr. Lincoln sighed.

"I guess so, Taddie; only mind, you mustn't cry any more or tease Willie about his pets."

On his way past the parlor door downstairs, Mr. Lincoln paused to remind Robert about the fires. Then he went out to the shed.

Hearing his step, Mary turned to see him in the doorway.

He came over and put his hand on Willie's shoulder.

"Is something wrong here, mother?"

The last remnant of Mary's patience snapped.

"Something wrong *here,* Mr. Lincoln?" she demanded bitterly. "Where isn't there something wrong in this house, I should like to know? Katie is leaving because Robert refused to mind the fires; Taddie had to be spanked and put to bed because he hung Willie's turtle; and now Taddie is crying himself sick and Willie insists on staying out here where we shall both catch our death of cold—and then you come in, two hours late for supper, and ask if something is wrong."

"Well, mother, it seemed the quickest way of finding out."

"Now you've found out—perhaps you can do something with this stubborn boy. He won't budge from his stupid turtle that was dead hours ago."

Willie's furious wail cut in.

"He's *not* dead, papa. He's *not*. I saw him move—just now. See, papa—look at him. You *see*—"

Mr. Lincoln bent down a moment, then he lifted the turtle's box and took Willie's hand.

"I'll tell you what we'll do, Willie," he said. "We'll just try moving Mohammed to the mountain—since the other way around doesn't seem to work. Let's take the turtle up to your room and fix him up there. Then he won't take cold—and neither will you."

"Mamma won't let me." Willie gulped, his blue eyes turned on Mary accusingly. "She doesn't like my turtle. She says he's dead—and he isn't—"

"Oh, I think Mamma will. Please, ma'am," he asked politely, "may we have safe-conduct into Willie's room for one turtle, guaranteed to be harmless, free from vicious habits?"

Seeing the small, wan smile that dawned on Willie's forlorn countenance, Mary turned on her heel.

"You can do anything you like," she said, and walked into the house.

In the kitchen, Katie looked up from the stove where she was tasting a kettle of stew. Very red of face, and not meeting Mary's eye, she mumbled something indistinct about having changed her mind and being sorry the old cracked teacup had broke itself.

Mary said nothing. Passing through the hall, she could hear the sounds of a briskly crackling fire, and she saw Robert on his knees before the grate.

She went upstairs.

Taddie was lying in his crib, his covers pulled up neatly, and as she bent over him he gave her an angelic smile—all the more touching because his subdued moments were so rare, and because of the way his puckered lip made the smile twist to one side.

Poor baby—he was all worn out. His cheeks were stained with tears, streaked and grimy. Taddie's tempers always vanished like this—as suddenly as they came—and Mary never failed to be disarmed by the way he could forgive his punishments. There was none of Robert's silent, passive stubbornness. None of Willie's shy, secretive ways that made his occcasional outbursts so frighteningly intense and mysterious. With Taddie everything was on the surface—good and bad alike.

Of all her babies, Mary thought, Taddie was the most truly her own.

It wasn't until she bent down, tenderly, to wipe his cheeks that she detected the unmistakable odor of peppermint drops that lingered on the guileless, rosy curve of Taddie's smile.

Standing in front of her mirror, smoothing her hair before going down to supper, Mary looked at her reflection. She could see the lines, faint, but no longer to be denied, around her eyes and the corners of her mouth. Lines that came from too often pressing her lips into the tight downward curve of exasperated weariness.

With a kind of vague wistfulness, she found herself wishing suddenly she could tell Mr. Lincoln she was sorry. Perhaps—if she could tell him, she could make him understand. Perhaps he might even comfort her—as he could comfort Katie, and give Taddie peppermints, and bring Willie's turtle back to life . . .

But it was no use. He would have forgotten already that there was anything for her to be sorry about—just as Katie had forgotten, and Taddie, and Willie.

And besides—Mary straightened her lace collar hastily—there was no time. Supper would be waiting, and unless she reminded Mr. Lincoln to hurry, there was no knowing how long he might stay with Willie, fussing over that wretched turtle.

And it would be a pity, certainly, to risk making Katie cross all over again.

13

IT WAS BEGINNING TO LOOK AS THOUGH THE SLAVERY issue would have to be decided, after all. The Whig party had held out as long as it could—trying to straddle the ticklish question—and had finally died, still straddling. The Democrats managed to keep themselves on the fence —but sooner or later they'd have to make the jump.

"The North won't let slavery alone," Mr. Lincoln said, "and the South can't afford to give it up. One way or another—it looks like we're headed for trouble."

He was back in politics now, helping to form the new Republican party that was made up of leftover Whigs and a few Democrats who were tired of their own party's quibbling. Still, in spite of the Republicans' firm stand against the extension of slavery, Mr. Lincoln hadn't altogether made up his mind.

More and more, people spoke of the possibility of war. Of secession, and a split country. But mostly they talked without really meaning it. In the prairie summer, while the sun rose and set just as it always had, and the corn grew tall in the fields, war seemed a far-off and impossible thing.

"If there should be fighting," Elizabeth asked one afternoon, "which side would Mr. Lincoln take?"

Mary was evasive. He hadn't decided. There were many factors to be considered. Moral rights were one thing, but property rights were quite another—and so long as the Constitution guaranteed both, how was a person to decide and be certain he was right?

Elizabeth bit off her thread.

It wasn't so much a question of being right, she observed sharply, as being anywhere at all. And if Mr. Lincoln didn't hurry up and decide—he'd find himself nowhere.

But when Mary said the same thing to Mr. Lincoln, he only sighed.

"I reckon it's like the story of the old Scotch elder that used to make the same prayer every Sunday: 'O Lord, point me right—for Thou knowest if I get started wrong Thou, Thyself, can't change me.'"

After a minute, he sighed again.

"I wish somebody'd point me right," he said.

That was the summer Stephen Douglas came back to Springfield. He was running for the Senate, on the Democratic ticket, and it was up to the Republicans to put up a man strong enough to give him a run for his money.

And money, they said, was something the Democrats had plenty of.

"Don't know as they'll get anybody fool enough to try to beat Douglas." They shook their heads down at Diller's. "Douglas is the best vote-getter in Illinois—and always was."

"Well, we've got plenty of fools around, I reckon. That's one crop never fails—specially in politics."

Mr. Douglas was married now, and there were those who hinted that his wife, who was younger than he and very handsome, already had her eye on something more important than the Senate. Adele Douglas was a smart one, all right, and she knew that if Mr. Douglas made good in this election, the Democrats were likely to put him up for president. And if money and good looks and influence could turn the trick, she meant to see to it that he won.

When the Republicans first began to talk of running Mr. Lincoln for the Senate, Mary was annoyed by the apathy with which he received the news. After all, this was his chance. The chance they had waited for, that had been so many years in coming. But when she tried to say this, Mr. Lincoln looked gloomier than ever.

"Yes," he said, "it's a chance to take a skinning. With all the money the Democrats are pouring into Illinois, Douglas can't possibly lose. And anyway, he's already the most popular man in the state."

Mary set her chin.

"And how did he get so popular, I should like to know? Not by magic, Mr. Lincoln. He went out and worked for it—and you can do the same thing, if you've a mind to."

Mr. Lincoln shrugged. There was only one stick big enough for Douglas to stub his toe on, he said, and that was slavery. And Douglas was too smart to risk committing himself there. He'd walk the fence, same as he always had, and get the vote on both sides.

"Unless," Mary said, "someone is smart enough to push him off that fence. Unless somebody asks him point-blank to state his mind."

It was some weeks after Mr. Lincoln was nominated for the Senate that he surprised everybody, most particularly his opponent, by challenging Mr. Douglas to a series of public debates that would put the slavery question fairly and squarely up to the voters.

"I'd like to know how Abe Lincoln expects to argue anybody down on something he hasn't made up his own mind about," Elizabeth said.

But it seemed that Mr. Lincoln had been doing more thinking than Elizabeth or anyone else, except maybe Billy Herndon, realized. He had read newspapers from the South and studied their arguments, not only supporting slavery for blacks—but for the lower class of white workers as well. In the so-called free society of the North, they said, there were thousands of servile laborers who were incapable of self-government and yet were given the power to vote. The time was coming when the North would rid itself of this burden of ignorance and incompetence. It was natural for some men to be masters and some slaves—as natural as for parents to take responsibility for their children—and, late or soon, all thinking people must come to see this. There were certain groups of powerful interests in the North that were beginning to listen to these arguments—and to believe in them.

So—that was the way the wind was blowing. And Mr. Lincoln, having felt its cold breath, was ready to answer.

If it was not possible to give freedom to every living creature, he said, at least they must do nothing to impose slavery upon any other creature.

Speaking one summer afternoon to a crowd that stood quiet and attentive under a broiling sun, Mr. Lincoln lifted his voice:

> "When you have succeeded in dehumanizing the Negro, when you have put him down, and extinguished his soul . . . are you sure that the demon you have roused will not turn and rend you? . . . Our reliance is in the love of liberty which God has planted in our bosoms. Our defence is in the preservation of the spirit which prizes liberty as the heritage of all men, in all lands everywhere. Destroy this spirit and you have planted the seeds of despotism around your own doors. Familiarize yourself with the chains of bondage, and you are preparing your own limbs to wear them . . ."

Mary listened that afternoon, standing in the crowd. Even from a distance, every line of Mr. Lincoln's face was familiar—each inflection of his voice she knew as well as though it were her own. He had taken off his coat—and the shirt he wore was one she had made. And yet the words were new. The words—and something more. A kind of spirit that came from him and from his listeners—like something that had slept a long time and was wakening. The crowd sensed it too—she could feel their response in the silence all around her—in the upturned faces.

The current, dammed over the slow years, was flowing now.

When Mr. Lincoln finished speaking, he pulled out a red cotton handkerchief and wiped his forehead. There was applause—and then the audience stirred, beginning to break up. A few went up to the platform, and she could see Mr. Lincoln reaching down to shake hands. But Mary stood quite still. And presently she was surprised to find that there were tears in her eyes.

That was one of the few times Mary heard Mr. Lincoln speak. Most of the summer, while he was away campaigning, she stayed in Springfield. For one thing, the current hired girl was as unreliable as her predecessors, and Mary had to take care of the boys and the house; for another thing, there wasn't enough money in the Republican chest to pay her traveling expenses.

While Mr. Douglas swept into one town after another in a private car, surrounded by his entourage, Mr. Lincoln was more likely to arrive carrying his own suitcase, after a long, dusty ride in a day coach.

"We've got to make up in elbow grease for what the Democrats put on in show," Mr. Lincoln said. And he worked hard, coming home between speeches so tired that Mary watched him anxiously.

For all the fanfare of the Douglas tour, Mr. Lincoln was holding his own.

"I've got a kind of sneaking hunch," he told Mary, "that folks would just as soon see a candidate act like a regular human being instead of landing in a town the way Douglas does—with a brass band and a torchlight parade, as if he'd been fighting the country, and had just succeeded in conquering it."

There were others who were skeptical.

"I don't see why you can't work up a little more show, Mr. Lincoln," Elizabeth said one night when he came to supper. "People like to be entertained—and there are bound to be plenty who vote for the party that makes the most noise. It makes them feel safer."

Writing to Billy Herndon from Chicago, where Mr. Douglas had just addressed the populace from the balcony of the Tremont House, Mr. Lincoln was still doubtful of his opponent's heroics. "Douglas likes to make it look as if he were having a triumphal march into the country," he said, "but it is about as bombastic and hollow as the bulletins Napoleon sent back from his campaign in Russia. I read in the paper the other day that Douglas carries his own brass cannon, nowadays, so he'll be sure of being saluted at every stop."

There were other papers that made equally uncomplimentary remarks about the homespun Republican candidate. Lincoln could split infinitives as well as rails, they noted, and it had been plain ever since the day he said that a house divided against itself cannot stand, that he was bent on splitting more than rails or the king's English. With his wild, half-baked notions on slavery, Lincoln was trying to set one half of the country against the other. He was preaching war—and making an alarmingly good job of it into the bargain.

Answering, Mr. Lincoln said merely that there was a difference between expecting a crisis—and wishing it. Kind of like the difference between a horse chestnut and a chestnut horse.

"I never aimed to make this a personal fight," Mr. Lincoln said to Mary when he came home from Peoria one day. "But when Douglas accused me of running a grocery store and selling whisky, I couldn't resist saying the difference seemed to be that while I was behind a bar—he was out in front."

Telling a crowd how the Democrats had used the old states' rights argument again and again to fool the voters, Mr. Lincoln said it put him in mind of a fisherman's wife whose husband was brought home drowned and full of eels. They asked her what she wanted done with him, and she said they'd better take out the eels and set him again.

After one of the debates, a lady said, "I felt *so* sorry for Mr. Lincoln while Mr. Douglas was speaking—and then I felt *so* sorry for Mr. Douglas when Mr. Lincoln replied."

All in all, it wasn't an easy summer for Mary. With Mr. Lincoln gone so much and the law office closed down entirely, what money they had on hand had to go into his campaign expenses. But for once, even though the bills stayed unpaid, Mary made no complaint.

It gave her an odd feeling sometimes, when she read about Addie Douglas in the papers, to remember that there had been a time when people had talked about her marrying Mr. Douglas. Not that she had any qualms about having made the wrong choice. But she couldn't help wishing the voters would see things more her way.

Even from the start of the campaign, no one seemed to have much doubt about the outcome. Lincoln had put up a good fight, they said. Starting from way behind, he'd made Douglas sweat for every vote he got—but still you could hardly say anyone was exactly surprised, in November, when the Democrats carried the state.

"I reckon nobody ever expected me to win," Mr. Lincoln said, "excepting maybe Mother."

He was wrong, though. Mary hadn't thought he would be elected any more than anyone else had. But when it was all over, and Mr. Lincoln was back home again, she knew one thing for sure. She had been right when she kept him from taking the appointment he could have had as governor of the Oregon Territory. At the time, he had thought they ought to go—seeing no possibilities for anything very promising where they were.

She had been firm—and they had stayed, and now she saw that she hadn't been mistaken.

Because, even though Mr. Douglas was going back for another term in the Senate, there had been a sudden end to the talk of putting him up for president the following year.

Mr. Lincoln had been defeated. But he had said some things that wouldn't be forgotten in a hurry.

With money so scarce that winter, Mary had to give up the hired girl altogether, but while she cooked and scrubbed and mended the boys' clothes, she was happier than she had been in a long while. Things worked out in queer, roundabout ways sometimes. Most of all, she remembered the afternoon she had heard Mr. Lincoln speak and the look on the faces of the people around her—listening.

On a December afternoon, Elizabeth entertained the ladies of the Literary Circle at tea, and Mary went over to help her receive. When Elizabeth first asked her, Mary said she didn't see how she could come. With no one to look after the boys, she couldn't leave the house. But when Elizabeth insisted, Mary had finally agreed.

"After all," Elizabeth said, "it will look queer if you're not here—being my own sister. Even if Mr. Lincoln wasn't elected—you don't want people to think you're *hiding* . . ."

So Mary had engaged the Underhills' daughter, from down the street, to come and mind the boys, for twenty-five cents, until Mr. Lincoln got home from the office.

Sitting in Elizabeth's parlor, Mary felt uncomfortably conscious of her plain black silk amongst the more elegant costumes of the literary ladies. But they were all most kind.

It wasn't often, Mrs. Gurney pointed out, that they had the pleasure of seeing Mary at one of their meetings these days.

"I must say, though," Mrs. Gurney added charitably, "I'm sure you set an example for us all in the way you devote yourself to your family, Mrs. Lincoln. Especially when you think of how Mrs. Douglas went everywhere with her husband while he was here campaigning. Why, they say she was on the platform every time Mr. Douglas made a speech—and always in a new gown, of course."

The other ladies took up the subject with enthusiasm.

"Personally," Mrs. Fox said, "I don't believe a real lady has any place in politics—no matter if she is as handsome as Mrs. Douglas. My husband said it was a question of which one was really running for the Senate—Mr. Douglas or his wife."

"I don't doubt Mr. D. felt it a great advantage to parade her around. But when all's said and done, I'm not so sure a man's well thought of for being tied as close as all that to his wife's apron strings."

"I daresay—" Ann glanced sharply at Mary's well-seasoned black gown—"Addie Douglas never wore anything that could be called *apron strings.* They say she has all her clothes made in New York—and I've heard for a fact she paid fifty dollars just for the lace trimming on one of her evening dresses."

"There's no doubt about it, Mrs. Lincoln," Mrs. Gurney said, nodding, "you can congratulate yourself on staying right here in Springfield and letting your husband do his own campaigning."

Mary smiled. "Nevertheless, we can't altogether overlook the fact that Mr. Douglas was elected."

There was a pause—before Mrs. Gurney hurried on.

"Well, of course—" her laugh was a trifle uncertain—"things are always so unpredictable in politics. In any case, I'm sure everyone feels Mr. Lincoln did his best."

Mary stood up, glancing at Elizabeth. "I'd better see about fresh tea," she said. "This has gotten quite cold."

When the others had gone, and Mary was helping tidy up the parlor, Elizabeth glanced at her sharply.

"Don't you feel well, Mary?"

Certainly, Mary said. She had never felt better.

"Well, I was just wondering. You were so quiet today. The ladies couldn't help but notice."

14

WITH MR. LINCOLN BACK AT THE LAW OFFICE, MONEY began to come in again, and the bills were paid. But Mary still had no help in the house. Robert was going to Exeter Academy in the fall, and she had to save for his tuition.

"I can't see any mortal sense in sending Robert halfway across the country when there are schools right here in Illinois," Elizabeth said.

But Mary was firm. "I mean to have the best of everything for the boys. I've always intended Robert to go to Harvard, and he needs a year at a good eastern school to prepare him."

"Well, I must say—" Elizabeth shrugged—"it seems like going a long way just to get an education. If Robert went to Transylvania he could live with the family, in Lexington—and you'd be spared all this expense."

"Yes," Mary said; "and he'd grow up just as we did, thinking there was nothing in the world outside of Kentucky. You don't understand, Elizabeth. I want my boys to be different. I want them to meet people—and have the right opportunities—"

Elizabeth looked at her curiously. "What does Mr. Lincoln say to all this?"

Mary smiled. "Mr. Lincoln leaves such things to me," she said complacently. "He's devoted to the boys, but he has no more ideas about planning for their future than a kitten. So long as they keep out of mischief and learn to read and write, I don't suppose he'd notice what they did. He doesn't realize that if the boys are ever going to amount to anything they must have their chance—but I do. And I mean to see that they have it."

A few weeks after Robert left for Exeter, Mary's younger sister Emilie came to visit. Mary was fond of

Emilie, and in a vague sort of way she hoped Emilie might marry and settle down in Springfield. But nothing came of it. Shortly after her return to Lexington, Emilie wrote that she was engaged to Ben Helm, and they would be going to live in Georgia as soon as they were married.

As Ann pointed out, Mary was altogether too wrapped up in herself to be any sort of matchmaker.

Reading Emilie's letter, full of happy plans for the future, Mary felt uneasy. Three of her sisters were already married to Southerners, and all her brothers were living in the South. And the dark prophecies of secession and war grew no less.

She wondered sometimes how much Mr. Lincoln regretted having lost the election to Mr. Douglas. He seemed completely taken up with his law work again, and though there were occasional visits from gentlemen who came to smoke their segars in the parlor and confer with Mr. Lincoln, he spoke little about politics.

"I'm glad for your sake, Mary," Elizabeth said, "that Mr. Lincoln has gotten over this nonsense of running for office and settled down to business. I daresay it was a disappointment to you when he lost the campaign—but I suppose we all have to learn sooner or later that our husbands aren't cut out to be great men. Taking things by and large, Mary, I don't mind saying Mr. Lincoln has turned out a good deal better than I ever thought he would."

One winter evening, after supper, Mr. Lincoln came into the sitting room where Mary was darning socks. Instead of picking up a book, he sat down on the sofa, his elbows on his knees. With Robert away, and Tad and Willie upstairs asleep, the house was very still.

Suddenly, out of the silence, Mr. Lincoln sighed.

"I was talking to Jesse Fell this afternoon," he said.

Mary nodded. She didn't know Jesse Fell, and she was wondering at the moment whether she had remembered to tell Robert in her last letter about the new shirts she was sending him. When Mr. Lincoln didn't go on, she looked up.

"Yes?"

Mr. Lincoln sighed again. "Fell's got a lot of notions about the elections next fall. Seems to have the idea that if the Republicans put up the right man—they might stand a chance to get in."

Mary snipped off her thread and rolled up a sock. She rubbed her eyes. Sewing by lamplight always made them ache, but she made an effort to seem interested.

"He said"—Mr. Lincoln rubbed his chin—"there'd been some talk that maybe they were thinking of putting me up to run. But I don't know . . ."

For a moment Mary continued to inspect one of Willie's socks. Then, as suddenly as though an explosion had rocked the familiar, firelit room, the meaning of Mr. Lincoln's words dawned on her. She leaned forward, gripping the sock so tightly that her knuckles showed white.

"What did you tell him, Mr. Lincoln?"

"Why—" he seemed surprised by the way Mary was staring at him—"I told him I didn't think much of the idea. I said if they were looking for someone that stands a chance of being elected—they were barking up the wrong tree. Seward, back in New York—or Chase, or Simon Cameron—any of those men are better known than I am."

"Mr. Lincoln—" Mary stood up, not noticing the lapful of socks that spilled at her feet. "Mr. Lincoln, you don't mean to sit there and tell me you refused."

"Well, no, not exactly, mother. I just told Fell they'd better think it over. After all, you've got to remember nobody outside of Illinois has ever heard of me."

"No," Mary said, "but they will, Mr. Lincoln. They will hear of you."

At the odd, fierce intensity in her voice, Mr. Lincoln glanced up again, uneasily. There wasn't any use, he said, taking this thing too seriously. It was nothing more than a conversation, between friends. Didn't mean a thing, most likely; he'd just thought to mention it.

Mary shook her head, brushing aside his words. From somewhere deep inside her a strength seemed to rise. As if all the hopes, all the efforts that she had squandered for so many years on a thousand things that never really mattered were suddenly concentrated. Quite calmly, she stooped and gathered up the scattered socks from the floor. She put the basket on the table.

"Mr. Lincoln, you must listen to me." Mary sat down facing him. This was the moment—she knew it now. The moment she had always known was coming, when the tide would run swift and full. "This is the time when you must decide what you are going to do, Mr. Lincoln. Now—before it's too late. Before the chance is gone—"

"Now, mother, there's no call to get all excited. You can't force a thing like this. And besides, there's no such luck for me."

Mary watched him steadily. "There's no luck about being president, Mr. Lincoln," she said. "And these things can be forced. They must."

He looked up, and for a minute, in the still room, he almost seemed to catch the intensity that burned in her eyes.

"Promise me you won't answer that way again, Mr. Lincoln. Promise me—"

For a moment more her glance held his. Then Mr. Lincoln smiled.

"Well," he said, "it seems kind of early to be making campaign promises—" His voice dropped back into the old, easy drawl. "But if it makes you feel any better, mother, I'll promise that when they come and knock at the front door and ask me to be president—I won't say no."

The snowball gathered slowly.

For more than a month after Mr. Lincoln spoke of his conversation with Mr. Fell, the days came and went much as usual. Mr. Lincoln was busy at the office. Willie fell off the porch and sprained his knee. Grandmother Humphreys died in Lexington and left Mary a legacy of a thousand dollars and her amethyst brooch.

During those weeks Mary was careful not to let Mr. Lincoln see that she was waiting. There was no need, she thought, to try to hurry things. The seed was planted. But for the first time in years she showed no irritation when Mr. Lincoln was late for meals or the boys tried her patience. It was as though a calm, deep and certain, had dropped over the house.

But the snowball was gathering.

By the time spring came, people in Springfield were beginning to say they'd heard talk of Mr. Lincoln being put up for the nomination. It seemed an unlikely kind of idea, they said. But still, they mentioned it.

When Elizabeth heard it from Ninian, she spoke to Mary. Mary only shrugged, and said it was far too early to listen to such rumors.

"It's a queer thing," Elizabeth said to Ann. "You might suppose Mary would take some interest in all this talk. She's always been ambitious for Mr. Lincoln."

Ann smiled. "I daresay Mary's had her fill of watching Mr. Lincoln run for office and get nowhere," she said. "I don't blame her for not encouraging him this time. So long as he's getting on in his work, he'd better have the sense to leave well enough alone."

Mr. Lincoln had to go to New York, to make a speech at Cooper Union, and before he got back to Springfield the news of his speech had spread all over the country. Newspapers everywhere had reprinted his words—along with editorials praising or condemning his stand.

"I can't figure out what they're driving at," Mr. Lincoln said. It was the first evening after his return, and he and Mary were alone after supper. "When they could have Seward for the asking, it doesn't make much sense to think they'd want a candidate no more fit than I am."

"Fit or not, Mr. Lincoln," Mary said, "you're in the field now—and you may as well make up your mind to it."

He looked at her curiously for a minute, but when he spoke again, it was about something else.

In the late spring there was a week of unseasonably raw weather, and both Tad and Willie came down with colds. It always frightened Mary to see the boys sick, and when Taddie's cold settled in his chest, she insisted on sitting with him at night until, worn out with nursing and anxiety, she came down with a chill herself.

Cousin Lizzie Grimsley was sent for, and for several days she took care of the house while Mary rested. When Cousin Lizzie went home, she was puzzled.

"I just can't make Mary out," she said. "You know how particular she is about her house—and yet the whole time I was there she hardly seemed to notice what was going on. She'd just lie in bed and look at the ceiling, and when I'd ask her a question about anything, she'd tell me to do whatever I thought best. Half the time I don't believe she even heard what anyone said until Mr. Lincoln would come home. Then she'd want to sit up and fix her hair—and start to fuss at me if his supper wasn't ready the minute he wanted it. You might think from the way she treated him they'd been married a week—instead of nearly eighteen years."

One morning after Mary and the boys were well again, another letter came from Emilie. She was married now, and very happy. But she couldn't help being troubled by all the talk of secession. Did Mary suppose there was really going to be a war? And from Lexington came more letters. Was it true, as they kept hearing, that if Mr. Lincoln ran for president he would try to abolish slavery?

Mary answered at length. There was talk of his being nominated, but as for slavery, Mr. Lincoln stood precisely where he had always stood, she said. He was opposed to slavery as an institution, but as for being an abolitionist, he was not, and never would be. Such an idea was absurd.

She didn't bother to consult Mr. Lincoln about these reassurances she offered. It never occurred to her that it might be necessary.

The weather grew milder, and it was time to fetch down the summer clothes from the boxes in the attic, to mend and clean them, and let down the boys' trousers.

As the days lengthened, and the sun blazed in the bright skies, there was no sign of lessening in the tension that hung over the country. Storm signals were raised everywhere now, in plain view for all who wished to read them. North and South were being drawn more and more inexorably apart. Violent words were hurled back and forth —by the hotheads on both sides. The founding fathers and Holy Writ were quoted liberally, and with high feeling.

The most plentiful commodity on the market, Mr. Lincoln said, seemed to be hot air.

No one, in either the North or the South, took too much stock, for all the shouting, in the idea of an actual war. It was only a little group of radicals, mostly in New England, that went so far as to say they wanted to fight— and New England was very far away. War was a thing people didn't like to think about. But the little group had lighted the fires. And the fires kept on burning— popular or not.

They were trying to pin Mr. Lincoln down now. He had spoken against slavery. If it came to slavery or war— which would he choose?

"You'll have to tell them something, Mr. Lincoln," Mary said. "If you don't, you'll wind up like Mr. Douglas, with neither side trusting you."

"Well, I don't know why they should," Mr. Lincoln sighed. "When I don't trust either side."

"It doesn't settle anything just to keep on saying there's wrong on both sides, Mr. Lincoln. There must be right on both sides too."

"Yes," he said. "That's just the trouble."

The snowball was rolling too fast to be stopped. No one seemed to know just how it had happened, but people everywhere were getting the idea that maybe this man Lincoln could do something to straighten out the mess. He wasn't one of your name-callers anyway. And if Lincoln thought there was a chance of bringing both sides around and stopping this thing short of ruining the whole country—well, maybe he was the man to do it.

On a rainy morning in May, the Republican National Convention met in Chicago.

Mary was up early, helping Miranda with breakfast, and the boys were already at the table when Mr. Lincoln came into the dining room. Mary turned, a pot of coffee in one hand and a plate of hot biscuits in the other. For a moment she and Mr. Lincoln looked at each other, then Mary smiled.

"Sit down, Mr. Lincoln. You look as though you needed some breakfast."

She poured his coffee, and put a helping of his favorite strawberry preserve before him, but he only sat staring at the food, seeming lost in thought.

"I was just thinking, mother," he said finally, "I'd better bring in some wood before I go down to the office. It's kind of chilly—maybe you'd like a fire."

Mary looked up quickly. It was the first time she could ever remember his offering to do anything around the house without being reminded.

"That's all right, Mr. Lincoln," she said. "Miranda or I can fetch the wood just as well as not. It's not a bit of trouble."

By midmorning the rain had stopped. Willie had gone to school and Taddie was out playing in the yard. The house was tidy for the day, and Miranda had started getting dinner. Mary went to the front window and stood looking out on the familiar street. There wasn't any use, of course, expecting news. It would be several days before the convention got around to actually deciding . . . And in the meantime she might as well find something to keep her busy.

She was upstairs sorting sheets to be mended when the front door banged and Taddie came pounding up the stairs shouting breathlessly that Papa was coming down the street.

"Is he the Presten*dent* yet, mamma?"

"No, no; of course not, Taddie." Mary hurried past him, not pausing to notice the mud he had tracked in on the clean stairs. She met Mr. Lincoln at the front door.

"Mr. Lincoln, what is it? Has something happened?"

He turned to hang up his hat.

No, nothing had happened; only there was no hope of getting anything done at the office. The place was full of people, all with nothing in particular to say and wanting to say it fast.

"If it's all right with you, mother, I guess I'll just stay home today."

That was Wednesday. All day Thursday and half of Friday they waited. Mr. Lincoln walked down to the office every few hours, but before long he'd be back again, with a fresh batch of telegrams. And between times there were streams of visitors, arriving at the most unlikely hours of the day and night—and letters, messages, and more telegrams.

The house was in a constant turmoil. Meals were interrupted a dozen times, there were segar ashes all over the furniture, the polished floors were tracked with footprints, and the boys were in such a stew of excitement that Mary had all she could do to keep them in any sort of order.

Reports and rumors came thick and fast from the convention. Billy Herndon had gone up to Chicago, and he telegraphed long bulletins of how things were going. Mr. Lincoln's name was given an ovation—but Seward got an even bigger demonstration when his name was put up. Everyone seemed to think Lincoln's chances looked good—

but it was still anybody's guess how the convention would vote.

By Friday morning, there were dark shadows around Mr. Lincoln's eyes.

"I'll be glad when it's over," he said gloomily. "There never was much of a chance anyhow."

"Nonsense, Mr. Lincoln. Nothing's over yet—and you'll feel differently when you've tasted Miranda's pancakes. She's the first girl I've ever had that knew how to make them properly." Mary handed him his plate and passed the syrup jug.

It was barely eight o'clock, but Mary had been up for two hours, straightening the house, planning the meals, and giving Miranda directions for the day. It was the only time she had the house to herself.

"I should think you'd be all fagged out," Mr. Lincoln said. "But you look more as if you were fixed up for a party."

Mary smiled. She had gone up just before breakfast to change into her blue sprigged muslin—just in case there should be early callers—and her hair was brushed and shining.

"Heavens and earth, Mr. Lincoln," she said, "one of us has got to keep cheerful."

While Mary got Willie off to school and helped Miranda clear away the breakfast things, Mr. Lincoln followed her about, his hands in his pockets. She couldn't help but be touched by the way he had seemed to turn to her in these days—as though there were some reassurance in her that he needed. It was strange, she thought, after all the years—after all the bitter, rebellious hours when she had felt so utterly shut out of his life—that he should come so close now, suddenly, at the very time when there was so much to pull him away from her.

By nine o'clock another telegram had come from Billy Herndon. Balloting would begin this morning, he said, and everyone was sure of a quick decision. By afternoon, at the latest, there should be news.

Mr. Lincoln read the message and handed it to Mary. "I wish it weren't Friday," he said. "It always was an unlucky day."

"I daresay it's just as likely to be unlucky for Mr. Seward," Mary put down the telegram and handed him a list. "If you're planning to go downtown before noon, Mr. Lincoln, I'd be obliged if you'd stop at the grocery on the way and bring me these things. We're out of vanilla and eggs—and Miranda wants to bake a cake."

It was a little past twelve when Mr. Lincoln came home and walked straight through to the kitchen to put down the packages.

"Here are your things, mother."

There was a note in his voice that made Mary turn quickly.

"While I was getting the vanilla," he said, "Ed Boliver came across from Diller's to tell me they'd got the news that I'd been nominated." He looked at Mary a minute, with a queer mixture of surprise and sheepishness. "I guess they really meant it, after all, mother."

Miranda was outside, hanging up wash, and Taddie had gone across the street to play. In that moment, they were alone in the house, facing each other across the packages Mr. Lincoln had brought home. Mary came around the table.

It was true, she thought. It was really true. The moment she had believed in and waited for, And now that it had come, surely all the weary background of impatience and misunderstanding and failure would be washed away. Fate had come knocking at last, and Mary stood ready to welcome her, like a long-expected friend.

She put out her hand.

"I knew this would come, Mr. Lincoln," she said. "I've always known it."

Mr. Lincoln took her hand, looking down at her. "Well—I'm glad you weren't disappointed, mother," he said.

The rest of the day was like being in a confused dream, where people appeared from nowhere, popping up in every corner of the house, shaking hands, shouting the same congratulations over and over. A band, hastily assembled, marched down Jackson Street and blared out a noisy serenade, half off key, and a dozen times during the afternoon Mr. Lincoln went out on the front porch to shake hands some more.

Telegrams came faster than ever. Every few minutes Tad or Willie came rushing in with new ones. There was no restraining the boys' excitement now—it seemed to Mary they were everywhere at once, stumbling over visitors' feet, hanging on Mr. Lincoln's coattails, their cheeks and pockets stuffed with candy which they received from the visiting strangers with shrieks of delight.

Elizabeth and Ninian were there, and Ann and Frances and the John Stuarts. And Cousin Lizzie, of course, bursting with pride and telling anyone who would listen how she had a feeling the day Mary married Mr. Lincoln that he would turn out to be a great man someday.

On all sides Mary heard them talking about Mr. Lincoln. How they'd always said Abe had something about him that was different.

"Seemed like he was almighty slow getting started—but I always figured Abe'd be heard from someday. Yes, sir . . ."

Even her sisters seemed awed by the news—and when they offered to stay and help Mary serve doughnuts and hot coffee, she accepted gratefully. Her cup was too full to leave room for bitterness.

By eleven o'clock that night, the house was still milling with people, and there were outraged howls from Tad and Willie when Mary finally marched them upstairs. Worn out herself, she managed somehow to get them undressed and into bed at last. But at the very moment when she was tucking Taddie in, a fresh burst of music blared from the street below, and Taddie was up again, like a bolt, dancing on the bed and demanding to *see the noise.*

With a sigh of resignation, Mary gathered him up and carried him to the window.

"Look, mamma—look at all the sticks on fire—" Taddie strained against her shoulder, wriggling with excitement.

It was a torchlight parade, and in the flaring lights the street and yard looked like some strange and unfamiliar place. People were crowded about the front step, shouting ragged scraps of campaign songs above the raucous brass of the band.

"Hurray for Lincoln!"

"Three cheers for Honest Abe!"

Taddie drooped suddenly against Mary's arm, overcome with sleep at last, but for a minute more Mary stood holding him. Feeling his head heavy on her shoulder, she looked up at the sky, arched and clear above the hullabaloo beneath. There—in the domed silence of the stars—hung the pattern, the shape of the future, bright and unreadable.

A breath of wind from the mild night stirred the ruffled curtains. Mary carried Taddie back to bed, and watched him settle down with one last long sigh. She crossed to her room, pausing at the mirror to smooth her hair, and she was conscious of the aching weariness in her back.

But when she went downstairs a few minutes later, to help gather up and wash the empty coffee cups, Mary was smiling.

15

IT WAS A QUIET SUMMER FOR MARY. MR. LINCOLN WENT to the office every day, preferring to stay in Springfield and leave the campaign speaking to Sumner, Chase and the others. Robert came home from Exeter, and in August the word came that he would be accepted for the freshman class at Harvard in the fall. Except for the great bundles of mail the postman brought each day, and the number of gentlemen who came to call, it might have been any other summer.

"I must say," Elizabeth admitted, "Mary is taking this a good deal better than I'd have expected. She hardly mentions the election—and I haven't heard her speak a cross word to Mr. Lincoln in weeks."

On election morning, Mary woke before daylight to find Mr. Lincoln already dressed, standing by the window.

"I couldn't seem to sleep any more." He came over and sat down on the bed, staring at his hands.

Mary watched him, thinking how tired he looked. Suddenly she wondered how he really felt about being president. It hadn't occurred to her to wonder before—she had been so sure he felt just as she did—but now she realized that not once, in all the months, had he ever said what he wanted. When she asked him, a little hesitantly, he didn't answer for a long time. Then he sighed.

"I don't know," he said slowly. "I guess there must be something wrong with me. I never have known what I really wanted—I never can feel sure . . ." He was silent a moment, twisting his fingers. "It doesn't matter much, I suppose. What's going to happen will happen—whether we want it or not."

"Well, I expect you'll feel differently, once we've heard the news." Mary made an effort to speak cheerfully, but she was aware of a twinge of disappointment.

While she dressed, Mary glanced out at the gray morning. The sky looked cold and disgruntled, and a sharp wind rattled the windows and made her shiver. It was like the morning of her wedding day had been. From across the hall, she could hear the boys arguing about something —Willie's voice low and persistent, Taddie's growing shrill and high, as it always did when he was on the verge of tears. Dear heaven, why did they have to start quarreling so early—and on this day of all days.

When she went in, Willie was sitting cross-legged on the floor.

"Taddie won't put on his clothes, mamma. He won't even start, and I'm all dressed. He won't be ready in time to see Papa be president, will he, mamma?"

Taddie, still in his nightgown, glowered from the bed.

"I want to put on my Sunday suit," he said, his lip quivering. "And Willie won't let me. He says I can't put it on—but I *want* to for Papa to be prestendent."

"He's silly," Willie said flatly. "He can't wear his Sunday suit when it isn't Sunday, can he, mamma? And anyway, he's a cry-baby."

"I'm *not*—" Taddie's face darkened furiously as the tears started down his round cheeks. "I'm not crying—are I, mamma?"

"Yes he is too. Look at him, mamma—"

Mary bit her lip with sudden impatience. If only everything needn't put her so on edge. She pulled Willie to his feet and ordered him downstairs, then she took Tad into her lap and began to dress him, pulling on his clothes with angry jerks.

Abashed by her set face, Taddie stopped crying and watched her warily. When he didn't hold his leg straight for her to draw on his stocking, she slapped him, and his lip began to tremble again.

"Are you cross because Papa is going to be prestendent, mamma?"

Mary stopped, the stocking half on, and drew him quickly toward her. "Oh, Taddie—I'm sorry. I—didn't mean to be cross, only I—I'm tired this morning."

He smiled, instantly forgiving. "That's all right. It didn't hurt anyway." He glanced up again, artfully.

"I *can* put on my Sunday suit, can't I, mamma?"

"Of course, dear—if you want to."

As she got up to fetch it, Taddie beamed with satisfaction.

"Willie will be mad," he said complacently.

At breakfast there was more trouble. Taddie, swollen with triumph, refused to touch his porridge, and when Mary ordered him to eat it or go back to bed, he shook his head.

"I don't have to," he announced blandly. "I don't have to do anything I don't want to—because my papa is going to be prestendent." With a defiant gesture, Taddie pushed the plate away, upsetting it on the tablecloth. A dribble of milk splashed down on the lap of his Sunday trousers.

Willie was ecstatic. "Taddie's spoiled his Sunday suit. Look, mamma—"

Mary put down her napkin, but before she could move or speak, Mr. Lincoln, without a word, rose and carried Taddie upstairs. When he came down, his face was grave.

"I've put him to bed, mother. It's where he belongs, poor little chap—he's all worn out." He sat down. "Please God, this will be over today," he said, sighing, "and we can settle down to being a regular family again."

Hearing Mr. Lincoln's words, and the weariness in his voice, Mary felt a sharp pang. Would they ever go back to being a regular family, she wondered. But the tide was running full—there was no looking back. It was too late . . .

Down at the State House they had reserved a room for Mr. Lincoln, where the returns would be posted as they were telegraphed in. When he was ready to go, Mary went to the door with him, and they stood a minute in silence. Mr. Lincoln took his hat down from the peg.

"I'll be back as soon as I can, mother."

Mary nodded. "The returns can't be coming in much before evening," she said. "I'll send Willie down at noon with something hot for you to eat."

He waited a moment longer, looking at his hat.

"Well—good-bye, Mary."

She stood at the door, watching him down the street. It was still early—no one much was out yet—and he walked alone, rapidly, in the sharp November wind.

At noon Mary sat down with the boys to dinner. Taddie unchastened by a morning in bed, was full of conversation.

"Isn't Papa prestendent yet, mamma?"

"Of course not *yet*," Willie said. "It takes a long time, doesn't it, mother?"

Taddie shook his head, unconvinced. "We have to go on the train tonight," he insisted. "Miranda said we did. And Willie has to leave his turtle here—and his pussy. And this is how the train goes—*whooooo . . .*"

Willie's face puckered in quick distress. "I *don't*. I don't have to leave them. If I have to leave them, I won't *go* to Washington. I'll stay here . . ."

Mary's head was aching. Her eyes burned—dear God, how long was it since she'd slept a whole night through?

After lunch Willie went back to school, and Mary sent Taddie out to play while she went upstairs. Three o'clock —four. She lay down on the bed, trying to sleep—but when she closed her eyes, the house seemed filled with a strange whispering . . . *When would he come home? When would he come? When . . .*

It was dusk when Mary got up. She told Miranda to light the lamps, and went out to call Taddie just as Elizabeth and Frances came up the front walk. They had come to ask if there was any news.

After a while, when they were gone, Mary was alone. At eight o'clock she went up to put the boys to bed, and when she came down, a message was waiting from Mr. Lincoln. The early returns were showing him ahead—but it was still too early to tell. They ought to know for sure by midnight. The boy who had brought the message said, grinning, he guessed Mr. Lincoln was the calmest man in town. Everybody else had gone clean crazy.

Mary went into the sitting room and got out her basket of mending. But it lay in her lap, unopened, while she sat staring into the fire, waiting . . .

It was one o'clock when she heard footsteps outside, and she rose, stiffly, to go to the door. It must be another messenger—but no—there was a sound of voices, and singing. Then she heard Mr. Lincoln.

"All right, boys; go home and get some rest now."

Mary opened the door, and he stepped inside.

"Well, mother," he said, "I've been elected."

Mary looked at him. At his face, his hat, at his eyes, deep-set, remote, and strange. Suddenly, without will, she burst into tears, pressing her face against his coat, while she felt Mr. Lincoln pat her shoulder soothingly.

His voice was patient, full of mild surprise, as he waited for her to stop.

"But, mother," he said, "I thought you wanted me to be president."

16

THE MORNING AFTER ELECTION MARY SLEPT LATE. SHE woke with a start, finding Mr. Lincoln already gone, and no sound from the boys' room across the hall. Her first thought was of something wrong—then she remembered. Sinking back, she lay for a moment, hearing sounds from below, smelling coffee and bacon.

There was a creaking on the stairs, and Taddie called her, but he was quickly hushed by Mr. Lincoln.

"Sh-sh, Taddie—Mother's sleeping."

A minute later Mary was up and dressing. There was so much to be done. So many plans—a letter to Robert—food to be ordered—things to be arranged.

Downstairs she found Mr. Lincoln and the boys in the dining room. Mr. Lincoln was opening a stack of mail, and as Mary took her place, he handed her a letter.

> Dear Mr. Lincoln, you have been elected. What are you going to do now?

Mary looked up to find Mr. Lincoln smiling at her ruefully. "I wish I knew," he said.

It was raining again, and after breakfast Taddie settled down with an illustrated paper on the parlor floor. There was a strange quiet over the house—a sense of letdown that hung heavy. Instead of going to the office, Mr. Lincoln went into the sitting room and stretched out on the couch.

Coming in, dressed to go downtown, Mary found him asleep. She stood a moment, looking down at his face. Then she tucked an afghan over him and tiptoed out, pausing at the parlor door to warn Tad to be quiet and not disturb Papa. Taddie glanced up at her thoughtfully, one hand resting on his stomach.

"I think, mamma, I ate too much porridge. I think I am going to be sick."

Mary felt his forehead. It was feverish. His face was white, his eyes ringed with shadows and too bright with excitement.

"I think," he said, more urgently, "I am going to be sick *now!*"

Mary put down her things, and took Taddie hastily upstairs. Leaving him safely in bed, some minutes later, she came down again to find Miranda sitting by the kitchen table, her head in her hands. She was full of rheumatism, Miranda said. And she felt as though she might be coming down with a cold. Mary sent her to her room to rest. Then she carried wood upstairs to make a fire in Taddie's room, and went back to the kitchen to see what she could find for lunch. When a kettle of soup was on the stove, and the downstairs rooms were swept and dusted, Mary sat down at the desk, remembering the letter to Robert. He would have heard the election news of course, but he'd be anxious for more details. And there was so much to tell.

She drew a sheet of paper toward her. The only sound in the still house was the slash of rain against the windows and the rattling of the wind. There was no sound from Taddie's room upstairs. Across the hall, Mr. Lincoln still slept. Mary shut her eyes for a moment, trying to ease the dull ache in them. Presently, dipping her pen, she bent with a sigh, and began to write.

My dearest Robert,

I fancy you can imagine, without my telling you, what excitement and rejoicing there is in the house this morning over the glorious news. If only you could be with us today, I believe your dear father's happiness would be complete. But we shall be together again soon—*in Washington*—where I am sure so much that is new and wonderful awaits us all. Your father is too busy to write to you himself just now, but I need hardly say he sends you dearest love. The little boys are well, and quite bursting with pride and joy—as, indeed, are we all . . .

Toward the end of November, Mr. Lincoln was to go to Chicago, where he would meet Mr. Hamlin, the vice-president-elect. There was to be a reception in honor of Mr. Lincoln at the Tremont House, and Mary was going too. At the last moment, in spite of Elizabeth's protest that it was quite impossible, Mary decided to take the boys with them.

The evening before they left, when she and Mr. Lincoln went over to the Edwards house for supper, Elizabeth lost no time in telling Mr. Lincoln she had offered to take care of the boys while they were away.

"I told Mary it was perfect nonsense to drag the children to Chicago. Goodness knows they've had enough excitement and spoiling already—without traipsing them into trains and hotels and what not. But it seems Mary doesn't trust me."

Mr. Lincoln looked up, obviously surprised.

"I don't see why that wouldn't be a good idea, mother. If Elizabeth is willing to keep them—"

Mary bit her lip. She hadn't the faintest intention of leaving Tad and Willie with Elizabeth—she could imagine well enough what Elizabeth would have to say on the subject of their behavior, with her notions of how children ought to conduct themselves. When Elizabeth had first suggested the plan, Mary had explained that Mr. Lincoln quite insisted on having the boys with them in Chicago. Now, of course, she was trapped.

"The plans have been made, Mr. Lincoln," she said, sharply. "I should think you might have the kindness not to upset everything at the last moment."

Mr. Lincoln seemed puzzled. "I only thought it might make the trip easier for you, mother."

"So far as I know, I haven't made any complaint about its difficulty, Mr. Lincoln. Of course, if you don't want your own sons with you—"

Elizabeth broke in, smiling blandly. "It doesn't make any difference, I suppose—so long as Mary is suited. I'm sure she knows what's best. Though I must say—I was only trying to help."

They were careful, for the rest of the meal, to talk of other things, but Mary sat silent, her cheeks flushed and hot. She knew they had thought her rude and unreasonable. She knew they were humoring her now—trying to pretend there was nothing wrong. It had been unfair of Elizabeth to trap her—unfair of Mr. Lincoln not to understand. She had been unfair to suggest that Mr. Lincoln didn't want to take the boys—when he was always so generous with them, never grudging them time no matter how busy and tired he was. It was all unfair. Unfair. Unfair . . .

Next day on the train the boys behaved like angels. They looked very smart in their new worsted suits, with peaked caps and square-toed, buttoned black boots. They were enchanted with everything on the trip, most of all by the brass band that met them in the Chicago station, and the delegation of welcoming gentlemen who were decked out so splendidly in badges and cockades. Taddie's hand tightened in Mary's and he looked up at her to whisper.

"Are they *all* generals, mamma?"

Smiling at Taddie, Mary thought suddenly she wouldn't have missed the boys' pleasure in the trip for anything. A moment later, when Mr. Lincoln turned to introduce his family to the committee, Mary heard the way he said, "These are my boys . . ."

She smiled again, confidently.

Elizabeth seemed a thousand miles away.

The days in Chicago were a complete success. At the hotel, Mary engaged a woman to stay with the children while she and Mr. Lincoln had to be out, and it was obvious that Mrs. Porter, a plump, friendly creature, was pleased and flattered to be employed by the new president's family. She treated Mr. Lincoln with beaming awe, and plainly regarded Mary as the most perfect of women. As for Tad and Willie, Mrs. Porter took them at once to her motherly heart, and told Mary again and again that they were the sweetest lambs and the best-behaved little gentlemen she had ever seen.

Accustomed to the lean and frugal diet of Springfield, Mary relaxed gratefully under the steady stream of Mrs. Porter's flattery. Indeed, everywhere in Chicago they seemed to meet with such kindness and approval that even Mr. Lincoln was impressed.

"I guess they like us, mother," he said, with a sort of wondering surprise.

On the night of the big reception, Mrs. Porter helped Mary dress. The new rose satin gown looked very well—and not the least bit homemade, which was a credit to the efforts of Mary and Cousin Lizzie. When Mr. Lincoln came in, dressed in his evening clothes, and Mary took his arm, Mrs. Porter stepped back and clasped her hands. Sure, she said, and they were a handsome couple. They were to enjoy themselves now, and never give a thought to the boys, who would be quite safe and sound, the lambs.

Elizabeth seemed two thousand miles away.

At the reception, surrounded by admiring and friendly guests, Mary realized that almost for the first time in her life she was being accepted at face value. These people thought her handsome and agreeable—and so she was. It was so easy, she thought, to be what was expected. It was all so very different from Springfield, where she felt tied by a thousand invisible strings to the past. Old failures, old mistakes and trials and shortcomings could never quite be forgotten. They were always bobbing up—making it impossible to change without seeming to be affected or queer. But here there was no past—no one to remember anything. It was wonderful, really, how comforting strangers could be. Surely, Mary thought, it would always be like this—once they were in Washington . . .

The morning they left for home Mrs. Porter came to the station with them, and parted affectionately from the boys.

"I'll never forget you," she said warmly, shaking hands with Mary and Mr. Lincoln, "nor all your kindness. God keep you both."

Seeing tears in Mrs. Porter's eyes, Mary was strangely moved. She couldn't remember when anyone had wept to see her leave.

On the train Mr. Lincoln was busy conferring with several gentlemen traveling with the party. Coming back to find Mary looking out the window, he sat down facing her.

"Well, mother," he said, "we managed to enjoy ourselves pretty well, didn't we?"

She looked up quickly.

"I was just thinking, Mr. Lincoln—I wish we didn't have to go back to Springfield. Since we've been away, everything has been so different—" She hesitated. It was difficult, trying to put the feeling into words. Her eyes searched Mr. Lincoln's face—hoping for some sign of response. "If only we could just go on—as we are now—"

Mr. Lincoln smiled kindly, a trifle absently.

"Well," he said, "I guess it does seem kind of humdrum going back to housekeeping after all the fuss and feathers we've had. But you'll feel better—once you're back home with Elizabeth and the others."

17

TWO WEEKS BEFORE CHRISTMAS MARY DECIDED SUDDENLY to make a trip to New York. There were a great many things she must buy before she would be ready for Washington. Clothes for herself and the boys—and new decorations to be ordered for the White House. Then, too, it would give her a chance to go up to Cambridge and visit Robert. He wasn't planning to make the long trip back to Springfield for the holidays—and he would need cheering up before his first Christmas away from home. Cousin Lizzie, hastily consulted, agreed to come and stay with the boys while Mary was gone.

Mr. Lincoln and Cousin Lizzie both felt Mary ought to have company on the trip. Why not ask Elizabeth or Ann to go along?

But Mary insisted she preferred to be alone—and once she was in New York, she was glad of her decision. New York was like Chicago—only more exciting—and having Ann or Elizabeth there would only have spoiled everything. She could imagine, for instance, what they would have said to the columns of flattering comment about the new First Lady that appeared in the newspapers. Shops and hotels vied with each other for the privilege of her presence. At first a little hesitant and uncertain about appearing alone, Mary found herself blossoming in the warming glow of limelight.

It was lovely to be deferred to—to find herself recognized and catered to wherever she went. And everywhere she was agreeably conscious of making a good impression. People were curious about her—and she took their curiosity for kindness and hugged it gratefuly. They were eager for her trade, and she saw friendliness in their eagerness, and accepted it with warmth.

After the first day or two, she went everywhere with assurance and a new sense of graciousness and ease. She read about herself in the society reports, saw herself described as handsome and stylish, witty and poised—and though she smiled over an occasional florid paragraph, she took the praise to her heart.

True—she spent a good deal more money than she intended. By the time she took the train to Boston for a few days' visit with Robert, she had quite lost track of her accounts. But surely it couldn't have been an unreasonable amount, she reflected comfortably, since the people in the shops had seemed to expect it. And they had all been so tactful and pleasant about the matter of credit. There was surely no need to worry. Nothing, they had assured her, need be paid for until it was *quite* convenient. Indeed, they had often seemed so reluctant to discuss prices at all that it seemed almost as though they were making her gifts of the things she selected.

Sitting back in the train, Mary drew on her black glacé gloves. It was a good hour before they were due in Boston, but she was ready to step off the train, comfortably assured of her elegant appearance in the new traveling suit of gray velours from Stewart's, and the stylish bonnet the clerk had exclaimed over so admiringly in the shop where she selected it. Robert would be pleased, she thought, to see her looking so smart.

She smoothed the fingers of the gloves, thinking with pleasure of the many more pairs, just like them, in her trunk. She had felt a little guilty, buying so many—especially all the white ones for evening. But the nice young lady at the glove counter had assured her that six dozen pairs was not a whit more than she would need.

Miss Harriet Lane, who had been the White House hostess for her uncle, President Buchanan, thought nothing of ordering *her* gloves by the dozen dozen, the girl had told Mary. A single evening of handshaking at a reception would wear out two or three pairs, Miss Lane said. At five dollars a pair, Mary thought this sounded a trifle staggering—but she could hardly doubt the clerk's word.

The girl had said such very flattering things about Mary's hands. Not much like *Miss Lane's* hands, she confided. Miss Lane was a handsome woman—but the look of her hands, if Mrs. Lincoln took her meaning, was better suited to hoeing potatoes than wearing a dainty white kid. Mrs. Lincoln now, took a whole two sizes smaller—and just see how pretty they looked. To fit a hand like that was a pleasure and a satisfaction.

Mary smiled, remembering the girl—and all the others who had been so kind. At the Metropolitan House, where she had stayed, it had been the same way. Mrs. Lincoln was to have the finest suite of rooms—the choice table in the dining room. And at Stewart and Company, Mr. Stewart himself had given orders that the entire store was at Mrs. Lincoln's disposal.

"Mr. Stewart says this lace is not to be shown to *anyone* until Mrs. Lincoln decides whether she will choose it for her inaugural gown . . ."

"Mr. Stewart wanted most particularly for you to see this sable cape, Mrs. Lincoln . . ."

"Here is a frock I should hesitate to show to most ladies. It's the very latest fashion—direct from Paris—but it takes a figure of your distinction to carry it off . . ."

"Miss Nelson, do come and see how this bonnet suits

Mrs. Lincoln. She's ordering two in Paisley colors, and one in blue, trimmed with velvet bands . . ."

Mary sighed, still smiling.

Then there had been Mr. Montrose, the delightful young gentleman in the interior decorator's shop who had had such excellent ideas about the new furnishings that would be necessary in the White House. Mr. Montrose talked a great deal, very rapidly, with a good many gestures. He assured Mary that he knew the White House *intimately*, and that it was, confidentially in a most shocking state of disrepair. Too many administrations had come and gone, leaving remnants of barbaric taste behind them—and Mrs. Lincoln would truly be doing a service to the nation in renovating the public rooms.

Put that way, Mary could hardly fail to listen. It was really wonderful the way Mr. Montrose's selections seemed to coincide with her own. Time and again, while they talked of repainting, upholstering and color schemes, some idea of Mary's would strike a kindred response in Mr. Montrose, and he would groan with pleasure over the prospect of a First Lady with truly distinguished taste. Together they fingered brocades and tapestries, and studied the effects of carpets and draperies. Whenever the subject of price was mentioned, Mr. Montrose waved it aside. Economy, said Mr. Montrose, was scarcely the object when it came to decorating the President's house. Indeed, any reference to the matter of money seemed to offend his artistic sense. He would grow vague and frown slightly, as though in obscure pain, and speak of "all that being taken care of in due time." Rather, Mary thought, as if at the proper moment a miracle would occur and the necessary funds would come down on a beam from heaven —and as if Mr. Montrose felt it indelicate to anticipate the miracle by speaking of it beforehand.

Best of all the new things she and Mr. Montrose had decided on, Mary loved the crimson draperies they had chosen for the East Room. The very feel of the material was rich and luscious, like the color. She remembered how

Mr. Montrose had described the room to her. White and gold and crimson—with crystal chandeliers. Even now, on the train, she could close her eyes and see the picture. Herself in white—with white flowers, standing beside Mr. Lincoln. Candlelight and music, and the murmur of voices . . . "Mrs. Lincoln, I have the honor to present . . ."

The train jerked, drawing into the station. A kerosene lamp was lit in the coach now—and by its light Mary could see her reflection in the dark window. She set her bonnet straight, and drew the new sable cape about her shoulders. She had worn the cape especially to surprise Robert. And besides—he might have some of his friends with him to meet her . . .

Mary saw Robert at once, standing alone a little back from the crowd around the train. She saw him catch sight of her—saw his glance, sober and reserved, taking in her new costume as he came forward, hat in hand.

"Well, mother—" He stooped, with a grave smile, to kiss her cheek.

It was always a surprise to find how serious Robert looked. Mary let him guide her through the crowd, finding her luggage—and she saw the slight lift of his dark brows as she pointed to the pile of bags and cases.

"All these, mother?"

"Why, yes—" She added rather hurriedly that the trunks had been sent directly on to Springfield—so at least they hadn't those to bother with.

Robert said nothing.

On the way to the carriage, he explained that he had engaged a hotel room for her. "I'm not sure you'll find it big enough though—" His eye was on the porters who struggled under the mounds of baggage.

His hand was on her arm, urging her along through the station at such a pace that Mary drew back a little, laughing. "Do wait a moment, dear—I've hardly had time to look at you. Must you rush me so?"

He paused dutifully. But there was a strained, embarrassed look about his mouth.

"Yes, of course, mother—but don't you think we'd better—"

She saw then, suddenly, what the trouble was. Someone had recognized her and pointed her out. And people in the station were turning to stare. Mary smiled back at them unperturbed, but Robert kept his head lowered, and he was frowning.

Mary lowered her voice kindly.

"You mustn't mind, dear, if people seem to be curious. They're bound to be—but it's only because they're friendly and interested. Oh, Robert, there's so much to tell you. Father sent his love of course, and he's very well. The boys are well too—though Willie had a cold when I left. But Cousin Lizzie writes that he's quite over it now—" She stopped suddenly, aware that Robert was hardly listening. But that was only natural. The dear boy wasn't accustomed yet to being stared at. Once they were alone, it would be easier.

But in the carriage, Robert sat stiff and straight at her side. It was almost like having a stranger with her, Mary thought, answering his perfunctory questions about the journey—the weather in New York. Mary heard herself replying quite formally. Then there was a moment's silence—awkward and self-conscious.

"How are your studies, dear?"

"Well enough, thanks."

Another silence. Mary turned to look out the window—at the glimmer of twilight in the winter streets. Boston looked so cramped and crooked after the broad avenues of New York, she thought. Turning to mention this, she caught Robert's glance resting on her cape. He looked quickly away, but she touched the fur apologetically.

"I expect you think I'm rather grandly gotten up for traveling, Robert—but I didn't know—I thought perhaps we might be dining with some of your friends—"

No, Robert said quickly, he hadn't planned anything

special for the evening. He'd rather expected she might be tired. "I thought just a quiet dinner at the hotel—in your room—"

Well, of course, Mary said quickly, that would be nice. And it was thoughtful of dear Robert—though she didn't feel at all tired actually.

At the hotel there was a great deal of confusion. The management had, it seemed, thought best to put Mrs. Lincoln in a somewhat larger suite than had been engaged. It seemed more suitable. It was Mrs. Lincoln this and Mrs. Lincoln that—quite the sort of attention Mary had found so delightful in New York. But here she hurried through the formalities as rapidly as possible, with one eye anxiously on Robert all the while. Settled at last, and the door closed behind the last lingering attendant, Mary breathed a sigh of relief.

"Now we can have some peace," she said, "and really talk."

But somehow, in the dark and formal sitting room with its massive furniture and hangings of a dark and bilious green, the things she had planned to tell Robert seemed trivial and foolish. It was a relief, on the whole, to have Robert ring for the porter and ask for a fire, and then occupy himself with the business of ordering their dinner.

The next afternoon, when Robert came to take her driving after his classes, Mary felt the odd discomfort in him again. Just as they were stepping into the carriage, a woman in a bedraggled cloak and outlandish hat, rushed up suddenly and seized Mary's hand. She wanted, the woman said, to wish God's blessing on Mr. Lincoln—a noble man if ever there lived one. Mary shook the woman's hand kindly, smiling after her as she bobbed a curtsy and hobbled away down the street, but Robert's face was flushed as he climbed into the carriage after Mary.

"How on earth do you stand things like that, mother?"

"Like what, dear?" Mary was tucking the robe over her knees. "Oh—you mean that woman just now? She meant no harm, poor old soul—there was nothing I could do but be polite—"

"But it makes such an absurd show of you." Robert frowned. "Curtsying to you—as though you were a queen or something. I can't see how you endure such fussing—but you seem to, well—almost enjoy it."

Mary was silent for a moment.

"The fussing, as you call it, Robert, isn't for me," she said. "It's for your father. I think you must realize that."

When Robert made no reply, Mary tried again, more gently. It had never done to be sharp with Robert. He was so unlike the other boys, who might be abashed for a few minutes and then, judging by the severity of her scolding, either went on as before or else tried to win her back with penitent sweetness. With Robert, she knew, the least hint of criticism was enough to send him into one of his queer stubborn silences.

"I know it seems odd to you, dear, to have strangers speak so. But you must get used to it. We all must. After all, I'm sure you are as proud of your father as I am—"

"Well, naturally—" Robert shifted uneasily. "But that's hardly the point. I don't see why just because Father is going to be president it needs to change everything. Even you, mother—you don't seem the same. Your clothes—and the way you fix your hair. And you always seem to be watching people, as though you were waiting for them to recognize you."

For one blank instant Mary struggled with the angry hurt that rose in her. It was intolerable, suddenly impossible, to feel her child grown up like this. Standing off from her, completely apart, judging her. It didn't matter that Robert wasn't pleased with her appearance. That he disapproved of the clothes she had thought he would admire. It didn't matter that he should seem more embarrassed and unhappy than pleased by his father's success. It only mattered that he shouldn't escape her so entirely. She must reach him some way—bring him back.

"Robert—" Mary put her hand out, touching his sleeve.

"Please, Robert, you mustn't feel so. It's not true. I haven't changed. I—" The next moment she breathed more easily. Robert was looking down at her hand, and the little-boy expression had come back into his face.

"Well—I'm sorry—" His voice was shamefaced, reluctant. "I didn't mean anything, I guess."

"Of course not, dear." Mary drew her hand away quickly. She remembered how Robert had always hated to be touched.

After that, things were quite easy. But when Mary asked whether he would care to ask one or two of his classmates to dinner with them, Robert was evasive. It was a bad time, he said. With midterms coming on next week all the boys were up to their ears studying.

"And besides, mother—there's no use parading."

Mary drew back, bewildered.

"I should hardly call it that, Robert—asking your friends to meet your mother."

"But you don't understand." Robert shook his head patiently. "They'd all think they had to be polite—about Father, I mean."

"And why shouldn't they be?"

"Well, it's just that I can't help knowing how they really feel—most of them anyway. You think just because people stare at you they're friendly—but Boston isn't like New York—or the West, where they really know Father. People here think he's nothing but a backwoodsman. One of the Boston papers called us a family of clodhoppers—"

"Yes," Mary said, "I saw that article. It said we'd track mud into the White House and keep pigs on the front lawn—didn't it?"

Robert was silent.

Mary sighed. It wasn't that she blamed Robert exactly. Somewhere, dimly, she had a troubled sense that Robert might be feeling a little as she did. It had never occurred to Mary before that Robert might have been unhappy at home, but now she wondered whether he too had been glad to escape from Springfield—from the people who had known him too well, who had pigeonholed him, catalogued him—decided about him far too long ago ever to allow for the possibility of surprise . . .

Mary drew herself up sharply. It was absurd to suppose that a child should think such things. And Robert was only a child, after all, for all his grown-up ways. She smiled forgivingly.

"I know it hurts you, dear, seeing such things written about your own family. But we haven't long to wait now, until your father is in office—and then, I'm sure, all this stupid criticism will be forgotten."

On the train going home, Mary fell into conversation with a woman who was on her way to visit her married son in Chicago, and they passed a number of pleasant hours discussing their children. Before long Mary found herself confiding other things as well. About her stay in New York, and the new clothes she had ordered—and the little chambermaid in the hotel who had wept with pleasure over the box of handkerchiefs Mary had given her when she left. She even described the crimson curtains she and Mr. Montrose planned for the White House.

The woman listened sympathetically to everything. "I can imagine how delighted your son must have been to have you visit him," she said. "The first year away from home is always so difficult—especially for a boy."

Mary agreed, smiling. She told how considerate Robert had been—how he had taken care of everything for her at the hotel, even to ordering their dinner.

While they talked, and the miles between Boston and Chicago stretched out behind them, Mary found the little edges of disappointment in her visit fading. The strained moments, the awkward silences, and the hurt at Robert's seeming disapproval were lost in a warm sense of her own good fortune in the eyes of this friendly stranger.

"Truly, Mrs. Lincoln—" the woman sighed, a trifle enviously—"from all you've told me, I should think you must be the happiest woman in the world."

Mary stroked the soft fur of the sable cape that lay across her knees. "Yes," she said. "Yes—I suppose I am."

18

THE NEW YEAR, THAT DAWNED IN SPRINGFIELD ON A clear frosty night, brought little sign of hope for the country. The southern states were seceding one by one. And with each new secession the lines grew sharper about Mr. Lincoln's mouth—and the troubled sadness deepened in his eyes.

After the brief calm that had followed the election, the storm was rolling round again. Violence was open now—in both North and South—and between them, like a gaunt shadow of hope stood the man in Springfield.

From everywhere came fresh demands that Mr. Lincoln do something. He must act, somehow, to save them from ruin. Promise the South security—promise to compromise—promise anything that would save the country. But the weeks passed, and he did nothing. Watching him, from day to day, Mary began to wonder.

She had long letters from her family. From Lexington, from her brothers in New Orleans, from her sister in Alabama, from Emilie Helm. From her uncles, cousins, friends. And in all the letters there was a new note of bitterness. The South had made up its mind. The South did not mean to give an inch—and it was time the North, and Mr. Lincoln, learned that. They were seizing arsenals all over the South, arming themselves—organizing to fight for their life as an independent nation.

Mary showed the letters to Mr. Lincoln.

Meanwhile, in Washington, old Buchanan waited. He was like a poultice, someone said, sitting on the festering head of rebellion. He was tired and confused—waiting to finish being president. Just as Mr. Lincoln waited in Springfield, through the cold weeks of January. And the North and the South waited. And Mary waited.

Since the first week after she came home from New York, Mary had been reading newspapers. She read dozens of them, sending Tad or Willie down to the office to get them from Billy Herndon. Newspapers from all over the country—Democratic, Republican, abolitionist, independent. Mary pored over them, pulling out her eyes over columns of close print, smudged with ink and filled with clamoring bitterness.

Coming in one evening, Mr. Lincoln found Mary beside a cold fire in the sitting room. The boys were in bed, and Mary looked up from the strewn heap of papers scattered about her chair. Her eyes were strained and dull.

"Well, mother—what news have you found today?"

Mary pushed the papers away with a sigh, and stood up.

"The same as always, Mr. Lincoln. Nothing but hatred. Hatred and blame and bitterness. All of them saying you must choose a side—" She stood looking at him, her hands pressed together. "If only it would end—" she said suddenly, as though the words were forced out of her. "If only the fourth of March would come—"

Every morning now the postman left a stack of letters at the Lincoln house. Letters with advice, questions, ugly threats. Letters demanding favors, asking for appointments, for offices, for money. Letters from friends—from enemies and from foolish, rambling crackpots. Every morning Mary read these and sorted them, slitting the envelopes, turning the pages feverishly, as though she must seek out each word of criticism, taste every bitter drop. Sometimes the howling tide seemed to rise about her, as though it would engulf the room where she sat—the desk—the very pen with which she labeled the sorted envelopes and laid them neatly to wait for Mr. Lincoln.

These were the days when the fears began to come. Only occasionally at first—then more and more often. Gradually the trembling and the sudden flashes of panic disappeared—and fear moved in, familiarly, like an old friend come to stay. Fear made itself at home with Mary—dined with her, and went to market. Sat with her while she mended, and watched in the evenings while she read stories aloud to the boys. No longer a stranger, to make her start and turn pale, fear came and went at ease, followed her to bed, whispering troubled warnings in her sleep until it waked her with an icy finger to the stillness of the house, and the sound of a train whistle over the prairie, and Mr. Lincoln's breathing, deep and slow.

A cry from Taddie's room in the night—and Mary would find herself standing by the bed, cold and shaken, staring into the darkness with dread of she knew not what. A silent, nameless terror that held her fast, long after she had found the boys safely sleeping and had crept back, shivering and sleepless, to bed.

The weeks of waiting dragged into February at last. They were to leave Springfield on the tenth, and Mary plunged with relief into packing and arranging—thankful for anything that kept her days busy and sent her to bed at night too tired to listen for the ominous tread of fear.

One afternoon Willie came home from school to find his turtle dead. It lay in its box, a small, lifeless shell, and no amount of gentle prodding or coaxing would move it. Willie carried the box in and laid it on the table where Mary was sorting the contents of an old trunk brought down from the attic. His round blue eyes were full of tears.

"He's dead, mother," Willie said. "I can't make him alive again this time."

Mary stared at the turtle a moment, then she sank down and drew Willie into her lap. Holding him there, her cheek against his, she wept over the dead turtle. All the strain, the long locked hours of fear seemed to burst her heart while she clung to Willie, rocking back and forth, shaken by helpless, choking sobs.

When Mr. Lincoln came in, Mary pointed to the turtle.

"Death is all around us, Mr. Lincoln," she said brokenly. "All around us."

It was Mr. Lincoln who took Willie upstairs to bed, sitting beside him in the dark until he fell asleep.

When he came down, Mary was quiet. The storm of weeping had passed, and she sat still, her hands in her lap.

"Mr. Lincoln—"

He turned, and in the lamplight Mary saw the look in his eyes, drawn away, guarded.

"Mr. Lincoln—what are you going to do?"

He shook his head. "I don't know . . ."

Mary bent toward him.

"But you must, Mr. Lincoln. You must know. The whole country is waiting for you to decide—to speak."

She paused. There was no answer. Mr. Lincoln sat motionless, his eyes half closed.

Mary stood up. She felt her knees uncertain beneath her. Dear God—what made him act this way—as though he was paralyzed, unable to speak? He had spoken often enough in the past. He had spoken for the Union—and said he believed slavery must end. What held him now at the moment when everything depended on his words? Why must he talk—when he talked at all—of being patient, of seeing the justice of both sides, of letting events take their course? Mary looked at him helplessly, powerless to guess what thoughts lay back of that veiled, impenetrable gaze.

She turned to a fresh batch of newspapers that lay on the table.

"If you won't listen to me, Mr. Lincoln, at least you must hear these. Listen to what even your friends are beginning to say—" She turned the papers, hunting for the places she had marked, but when she thrust them at him, Mr. Lincoln put his arm up suddenly, covering his eyes.

"Not now, Mary. For God's sake—let me rest."

Mary drew back. The papers fell from her hands, and for a moment she stood stunned, as though the utter weariness in his voice had been a blow. Slowly she stooped to gather up the papers, and threw them in the fire. Then she took the box with Willie's turtle, and started for the kitchen.

Waiting for the coffee to boil for Mr. Lincoln's supper, Mary glanced again at the turtle. Strange—that such a little thing could have made her weep. Willie had felt badly, of course—but it wasn't for Willie she had wept. She had forgotten now why it was . . .

While Mr. Lincoln had his supper, Mary took out her sewing. She tried to think of things to talk about that would sound cheerful. Robert's last letter—and the news that Emilie and Ben Helm were expecting a baby. Mrs. Reuther's husband, who lived at the end of the block and had been so ill with lung fever, was getting better she had heard . . .

Mr. Lincoln listened, answering now and then. But the deep melancholy did not leave his eyes, and when he went to lock up for the night, he stopped by Mary's chair and touched her shoulder.

"I suppose it will be easier when this part is over," he said.

She reached up and took his hand, resting it against her cheek. He seemed so lonely standing there.

"I'm sure it will, Mr. Lincoln." She felt his hand, motionless and heavy. Suddenly the brightness went out of her voice. "Only—I didn't know it would be like this," she said. "I didn't know—"

For three days they had a bonfire in the side yard, and burned up the accumulation of old papers, letters, broken furniture and worn-out toys that the attic had brought forth. Mary watched the strange collection disappear in the flames. The little yellow sled Robert had learned to coast on, the winter when he ran into a tree and cut his forehead. A tuft of faded strawflowers that had stood on the mantel in the parlor when the house was new. A velvet bonnet, dusty and streaked, that Mary had always meant, each winter, to have recovered, because Mr. Lincoln had liked her in it. The dog-eared, broken-backed grammar text that Mr. Lincoln had carried in his suitcase when he rode the circuit—and the saber belt he had brought home from the Black Hawk War—long before Mary had even known him . . . A rusty black umbrella, and a gray wool shawl the moths had got into . . .

Tad and Willie stood by watching too—alternately fascinated seeing the odd fragments smolder and wither in the crackling blaze and dismayed to see the last remnants of their once treasured playthings go onto the heap.

The morning his red express wagon was brought out to be burned, Taddie wept so loudly that Mr. Lincoln rescued it, and promised it could go to Washington. But when Mary sent him to the woodshed to nail up the crates and boxes already packed and ready to go, Mr. Lincoln looked at the piled-up collection doubtfully.

"Maybe we shouldn't take so many trappings, mother. They might not ask us to stay."

As fast as the old things were sorted and cleared out, it seemed, there were new ones arriving. Every mail brought its quota of gifts. Peculiar parcels of ungainly shapes and sizes were stacked in the front hall. Unpacked, these disgorged a weird assortment of articles without which, apparently, Mr. Lincoln's admirers were convinced he could not assume office. Hats of every size and pattern to fit the presidential head. An Indian chief's war bonnet, and a ceremonial squaw robe for Mary, complete with beaded moccasins to match. Western boots, elaborately tooled and studded with silver. A Pennsylvania spinster sent a china cake plate she had decorated for the White House pantry. There was a gaudy assortment of sofa cushions, some with embroidered mottoes: "God Bless our Noble President" or, less formally, "Hurrah for Old Abe." Handkerchiefs, jewelry, pipes, segars—and a hundred copies of a pamphlet published by an antitobacco crusader. There were neckties, shaving mugs, fancy waistcoats of every known material, Bibles—and always more hats.

Mary was in despair, and the boys pounced on each new bundle in fits of delight.

"If nothing else comes of all this," Mr. Lincoln said, "we'll at least have some new clothes out of it, mother."

One morning a crate was brought to the door with a pair of gray doves, huddled sadly in the corner. These were fallen upon at once by Willie, who revived them tenderly, and immediately inquired of his father whether he might take them to Washington.

Mr. Lincoln glanced over the top of his book. There was no reason, he supposed absently, why not.

Emboldened by success, Willie seized the moment to bring up the subject of Pussy. If Papa didn't mind the doves—could they also take Pussy with them when they went?

Mr. Lincoln was doubtful. He wasn't just sure what Mamma would think of that. "She's planning on having things kind of fancy when we get to Washington," Mr. Lincoln said. "I don't know as she'll want a lot of animals mussing the place up."

Oh, said Willie quickly, Pussy wouldn't muss anything. She was ever so good and quiet—and Willie could keep her just in his own room, couldn't he? And maybe let her out the kitchen door to play?

"*Please* say I can, papa." Willie hung on his father's chair. "Please say so."

Mr. Lincoln sighed.

"Well, as far as I'm concerned, Willie, I don't see any great objection. But you'll have to ask Mamma. She's the boss."

A few minutes later, Mr. Lincoln looked up from his book again. Mary, her sleeves rolled up to the elbow, her hands floury from the pastry board, stood in the doorway.

"Mr. Lincoln—"

Mr. Lincoln looked down quickly, engrossed in his reading.

"Mr. Lincoln, what's this about your giving Willie

permission to take that cat to Washington? He *says* you promised him—"

"Now, mother, I did no such thing. I told Willie he must ask you."

"And why, pray, should he ask me?"

"Well, I didn't know how you'd feel about it."

Mary set her lips angrily. "You know perfectly well how I feel about it. Of all the absurd notions—to traipse into the White House with a cat that's about to have kittens—"

"Is she, mother? I hadn't noticed."

"Yes, Mr. Lincoln, she is. And what's more, you needn't pretend to be so innocent about it. You have eyes in your head, I hope. And besides, Willie has talked of nothing else for the past three weeks."

"Well, I suppose I must have forgotten. And anyway—all I said was, it didn't make any particular difference to me."

"But you said I *could*, papa—you *promised*—"

Mary glanced at Willie, hopping on one foot in an agony of uncertainty. She saw the tears gathering in his blue eyes.

"Truly, Mr. Lincoln," Mary said, "I can't understand you. How you could deliberately raise the child's hopes—when you knew all along it was absolutely out of the question to let him take the cat. I don't see—"

At these ominous words, Willie's tears spilled over and he set up a howl that quite drowned out the sound of knocking at the front door. A moment later Miranda appeared, ushering in three frock-coated gentlemen who had arrived to pay their respects to the future president just in time to see Mary march past them, her sleeves rolled up, her eyes blazing, towing Willie, kicking and protesting, behind her.

Upstairs, while she tried vainly to silence Willie, Mary kept one ear cocked for the sound of voices below. Dear heaven—they'd surely think she was murdering the child to hear him scream so. And nothing she could say—no promises of a new pet in Washington, or the good home

Pussy would have at Cousin Lizzie's house—would quiet Willie.

He didn't *want* a new pet, Willie insisted loudly. He wanted Pussy. And Pussy didn't *want* a nice home with Cousin Lizzie—Pussy wanted to stay with him. And Papa had said—he had *promised* . . .

Mary saw the resentment in Willie's eyes. *She* was the one Willie would blame for losing Pussy—and it wasn't fair. It wasn't fair that she should forever take the blame—simply because Mr. Lincoln could never bear to say no. Willie looked up, still unconsoled, his lower lip pushed out accusingly.

"Papa *said* I could take Pussy," he repeated sadly, "and Papa is going to be the president. I thought presidents could do anything they wanted to."

Mary was silent for a moment, feeling curiously helpless.

"I used to think that too, Willie," she said, in a different voice, "but—I was wrong."

19

THE LAST WEEK IN SPRINGFIELD MOVED TOO SWIFTLY, with too many things to be done, to leave room for doubts. Caught solidly in the present, Mary could leave the future to a hazy, nebulous vista of receptions, servants, clothes, and a carriage of her own. And visions of endless, delightful conferences over the White House furnishings with Mr. Montrose, who would come down especially from New York. And crimson draperies, against the white and gold and crystal of the East Room . . .

Each morning Mary made new lists and memorandums to be checked off. She arranged with Elizabeth and Frances and Ann for them and their husbands to come to Washington for the inaugural. She found time for long letters to her family, filled with rashly generous promises of future favors and appointments for themselves and their friends, as soon as Mr. Lincoln should be in office.

To Ninian Edwards, Mr. Lincoln commented privately that if Mary and her sisters had their way, the new administration was likely to go down in history as the reign of the Todds.

"The only thing that kind of worries me," he said, "is whether I can manage to scare up enough post offices to go round."

Ninian was sympathetic. There was no occasion for worry, he said. If there weren't enough towns, Mary and Elizabeth would see to it that a few new ones were created.

Mr. Artemus Ward came to call, on one of the last days in Springfield, with an eye to writing one of his humorous pieces about the new president. He was at some pains, Mr. Ward reported later in print, to obtain entrance to Mr. Lincoln's presence, so filled was the house by various and sundry gentlemen all of whom had come to express their lifelong devotion to the new leader—and at the same time make perfectly sure that Mr. Lincoln would not overlook the matter of providing each of them with an appointment, with "*magnifisint and sootable emmolimint.*" One of these well-wishers appeared to have about seven inches of corn whisky in him, and approached Mr. Lincoln with "*tears of riverince in hiz eyes—addressing him as the Pra-hayrie Flower of the West, reeling slightly.*"

"'*If they wuz to look for a beootiful man, they'd hardly be likely to sculp you, Mr. Linkun,*'" Mr. Ward said. "'*But ef you do the fair thing by your country you'll make as purty a angel as any of us.*' . . . *He shook me cordyully by the hand, and we exchanged picturs, so we could gaze upon each other's liniments when far away from one another—he at the hellum of the Ship of State, and I at the hellum of the nonsinse byzniss . . .*"

Robert came home from Cambridge to make the trip to Washington, and the two days he was in Springfield, he spent at the Edwards house.

"Poor boy," Elizabeth said, "I daresay he feels quite lost, coming home to such confusion. At the first meal he took with us, he said he was relieved to find that some of his family could still sit down to a meal without being interrupted."

At the last moment Cousin Lizzie had been invited to join the party traveling to Washington, and she was in a quiver of gratitude and delight.

"You might think Lizzie had been given a ticket straight to heaven," Ann said. "Personally, I'm willing enough to go—for Mary's sake. But between us, I'll be thankful when all this fuss is over, and we can settle down again."

Ann was exceedingly generous, however, in lending her advice. She and Elizabeth were filled with suggestions concerning plans for the trip, all of which they offered freely to Mary. Listening to the talk of clothes, receptions, stopovers, and general arrangements, Mr. Lincoln shook his head in wonder.

"I wish I had half as many ideas what to do when I get to Washington as you seem to have, mother," he said. "From the sound of it, folks'll probably think we're a traveling circus coming to town."

Mary smiled indulgently. "Someone has to make plans," she said. "I daresay if it were left to you, Mr. Lincoln, you'd just pack up a clean shirt and a change of underwear and go."

The night before they closed the house, the Lincolns held a farewell reception. Seven o'clock to midnight—and the whole town invited.

Mary wore one of the gowns she had ordered in New York. White moiré, with a low round neckline that showed off her new pearl necklace, and white flowers in her hair. It was a pity, in a way, to put on one of the new frocks before she even left home—but then, as Cousin

Lizzie said, Springfield ought to have one chance to see Mary as she would look in Washington.

"There are times, I'll own, when I have to admire Mary," Elizabeth said to Frances that night. She glanced toward the parlor door, where Mary stood beside Mr. Lincoln, receiving the guests. "I know for a fact she's been up since before six this morning, working like an Indian ever since—and yet to look at her, you might think she'd had nothing to do all day but dress for the party."

Frances nodded, without enthusiasm. For her own part, she was exhausted, though it was barely eight o'clock and the real crowd had just begun to arrive. From the look of things, Frances reflected, shifting her weight to ease the pinch of her new satin slippers, half of Springfield had already come, not to mention innumerable strange creatures who had popped up from nowhere—all parched with thirst and famished, to judge from their frantic onslaughts at the refreshment table.

"Beg pardon, ma'am—"

Frances turned to make way for a stout gentleman who was attempting to squeeze his way past her out of the dining room. At the crucial moment someone jogged his elbow, and a trickle of punch splashed onto Frances' sleeve. The stranger whipped out a grimy handkerchief and mopped energetically at the stain.

"I didn't aim to do that, ma'am—" The man's face, looking quite throttled by his collar, flushed several shades deeper. "I was just going through to say howdy to Old Abe in there, when the feller pushed me—"

Still muttering apologies, the stout gentleman lumbered off, and Frances looked ruefully at her sleeve.

"Impossible creature," Elizabeth said indignantly. "Where in the name of mercy do you suppose Mr. Lincoln picked *him* up? Sometimes, really, I'm just as thankful Ninian wasn't a success at politics—when I see the sort of thing Mary has to put up with. On my word, though, I believe Mary actually enjoys it."

"Well, after all—she could hardly complain, could she?"

Frances smiled thinly. "When she was the one who nagged Mr. Lincoln into this whole thing. Though if you ask me, I should certainly hate to see my husband in Mr. Lincoln's position. Mr. Smith says he's heard there are people all over the country who are so opposed to Mr. Lincoln being president that they've even signed papers taking an oath to keep him from reaching Washington alive." Frances sighed. "You'd think Mary might be worried—but when I tried to tell her what Mr. Smith said, she was furious. She said it was only stupid jealousy that made people listen to such rumors and repeat them. You might suppose *I* was the one that threatened him."

Elizabeth shook her head. "Poor Mary—I don't suppose she'll ever get over thinking we're all consumed with envy of her precious Mr. Lincoln. All the same, though, I expect we oughtn't to be too hard on her. I daresay she'll find out soon enough her bed isn't all roses."

The next morning they closed the house, and took their luggage to the Chenery House, where they would sleep the last night, before taking the train. Mary and Mr. Lincoln went to the Simeon Francis' for supper, and walking back to the hotel afterward, they passed the corner of Eighth and Jackson.

Mary looked across at the house. She couldn't remember ever having seen it completely dark before. The windows, curtainless and blank, stared forlornly into the night, and under the big elm in the side yard she could see the last remnants of their bonfire. She stood still a minute, her hand on Mr. Lincoln's arm.

"It's strange," Mary said. "I thought I'd be glad when this moment came. There isn't anything in Springfield I really mind leaving behind—and yet, right now, I almost feel as though I couldn't go at all."

"I know, mother—" Mr. Lincoln spoke slowly, his voice sounding hollow in the raw night wind. "We've had some bad times in that house. More bad than good, I guess. But it seems as if even the troubles got to be old friends."

They stood a little longer. Then, not speaking again, they walked on together down the dark and empty street.

20

ON THE SECOND NIGHT OF THE JOURNEY, AFTER A STOP-over for a reception in Cincinnati, the Lincoln party came on board the special train late. So far, at least, the trip had gone smoothly. There were stops every few hours—for Mr. Lincoln to greet the crowds that gathered in the stations. Standing beside him, with Tad and Willie, Mary watched the faces turned up toward them. They were friendly for the most part, eager and ready to cheer the new president.

"Stick by the Constitution, Abe—and we'll stick by you."

The Cincinnati reception had been huge and confusing, but a distinct success, as even Elizabeth admitted. There had been toasts for Mr. Lincoln and a huge armful of red roses for Mary. Halfway through the evening, Mary suddenly remembered the date—and she lifted her glass, smiling at Mr. Lincoln.

"We must drink to Mr. Lincoln's birthday," Mary said, "and many more to come."

The guests were charmed. Through the applause and cheers, Mary saw Mr. Lincoln's eyes light up as he looked at her. He seemed more nearly happy, she thought, than in a long time, and for a moment, meeting his smile, Mary felt her heart lift. The wings of uncertainty, hovering and dark, were gone. The tide was running full.

Back on the train, the gaiety of the party held. In the special parlor car, the ladies laid off their wraps and gathered about the stove to warm their hands. Cousin Lizzie took the roses Mary handed her.

"They're *so* beautiful. It's a pity we have no vase to put them in—" Lizzie glanced about for a place to lay them. "Mr. Lamon, would you move that bag from the vacant chair there?"

Mr. Lamon had come along from Springfield as bodyguard for Mr. Lincoln. It seemed kind of a foolish notion, Mr. Lincoln said, but so long as everyone was kicking up such a fuss over his having a guard—he reckoned Ward Lamon better be it, since he was the only man anybody could think of who was taller than Mr. Lincoln.

Mr. Lamon picked up the bag Lizzie pointed to and glanced at it curiously. He wondered who it might belong to.

"Why, I don't know—" Cousin Lizzie was busy propping up the roses. "Someone just left it there, I expect. There—" She straightened up. "Don't they look lovely, Mr. Lamon?"

She turned, beaming, but Mr. Lamon made no reply. He was still holding the small, neatly strapped carpetbag, frowning slightly. Rather gingerly, he shook it. Something rattled. Mr. Lamon unfastened the straps, peered inside, and then, without so much as a glance at Lizzie, he marched rapidly to the end of the car and disappeared onto the open observation platform outside.

It was very odd, Lizzie thought, looking after him vaguely. Not to have answered her at all—and Mr. Lamon was ordinarily so polite.

A few minutes later Lizzie saw Mr. Lamon step inside again, and draw Mr. Lincoln aside, saying something in his ear. Mr. Lincoln had been in the middle of telling a story that was amusing the ladies. Lizzie saw the laugh die out of his face, as he heard what Mr. Lamon said. He stood quiet a minute, then he nodded once, gravely. The ladies were all looking at Mr. Lincoln, waiting for him to finish the story. Suddenly Mary stood up.

"What is it, Mr. Lamon?" Mary's voice rose sharply above the rumble of the moving train. The color was gone from her cheeks, and her eyes, wide and strained, were on Mr. Lamon's face. "You said something to Mr. Lincoln just now. Tell me what it was, Mr. Lamon—I insist—"

Lizzie heard Mr. Lincoln answering, trying to soothe Mary.

"Now, mother, there's no use getting all upset. It's nothing at all—"

All at once everyone was talking, and out of the babble, Lizzie caught the word *bomb*. There was a muffled scream from one of the ladies.

No, no—it wasn't a bomb at all. A grenade. There had been a grenade. Someone must have come into the car while they were all at the reception and left it on a chair. In a carpetbag. The fuse had been lighted, Mr. Lamon said. In another fifteen minutes . . . It was too horrible to think of . . . If Mr. Lamon hadn't discovered it in time . . .

Rather oddly, it was Mary who seemed the most composed of anyone. After the first moment of shock, she went back to her chair. "I think," she said, "we'd better not talk about this any more. After all, the danger is past—there's no use worrying over what might have happened. Suppose we order in some hot coffee . . ."

Truly, Lizzie thought, feeling her knees go limp, Cousin Mary was wonderful. They all said so, even Ann.

Only Mr. Lincoln, staring thoughtfully at the blazing fire through the chinks in the stove door, said nothing.

There were more stopovers, more welcoming committees, more speeches and dinners and receptions. Columbus one night, then on to Pittsburgh, where Mr. Lincoln addressed a huge crowd in the Municipal Hall. More bunting, more flags and cheers. More flowers for Mary.

After the one incident of the grenade, there were no further alarms, no threats or signs of anything but good will. Mary felt easier again, reassured by the friendly enthusiasm they met everywhere. Perhaps, after all, there hadn't been any real danger that night in Cincinnati. Mr. Lamon might have been mistaken . . .

The evening before they reached New York, Mary left the others and went into the sleeping car where the boys had been put to bed. They had stood the long trip remarkably well, but at supper she noticed Willie hadn't eaten much. He'd stared out the train window, hardly seeming to listen, while Mr. Lincoln told a story about a kitten that couldn't go out in the rain because it was made of striped peppermint candy, that had sent Taddie into fits of amusement. Moving cautiously toward the darkened end of the sleeping car, Mary hoped that Willie wasn't going to be sick.

She glanced at Taddie, sprawled in the berth spread-eagle fashion, already sleeping soundly. Across the aisle, Willie lay very still, his head hidden against the pillow in a queer way. Mary bent down, touching his shoulder, and felt its tenseness. She sat down beside him.

"Willie—"

There was no answer.

"Willie—tell me what's the matter, dear. Are you sick?"

There was a sudden motion. Willie dug his face closer into the pillow. Mary coaxed him, trying to turn him over, but when he pulled away, holding himself stiff, she was alarmed. He must be really ill, to hide this way. If he didn't answer, Mary said, she would have to call Papa—

There was a silence, then Willie's voice, very small and muffled.

"I'm not sick . . . I'm feeling sad about my pussy."

While Mary explained softly, not to wake Taddie, that Pussy was surely quite at home by now at Cousin Lizzie's house, Willie lay motionless, still turned away. Pussy wouldn't have liked the train at all, Mary said. She would have had to be in a box, nailed up, all these days. And it might have made her sick. The kittens might have died. She had been thinking, Mary went on, that when they got to Washington, where they would have a big stable of their own, they might be able to have a pony for the boys.

"Of course, Taddie is still pretty young to have such

a responsibility. But if you could help look after the pony —I think we might manage—"

Still no answer, but the shoulder under Mary's hand relaxed a little.

"Well—" Mary stood up. "You think about it, Willie. And in the morning, we'll see what Papa says."

She looked down a minute, feeling a pang at the sight of him, so straight and still beneath the covers.

"Mamma—" The voice was small against the clack of the train wheels.

"Yes?"

A pause.

"Do you think Papa could find a black pony? An all-black one?"

"I think so, Willie."

There was a sigh. "Good night, mamma."

Walking back through the swaying car, Mary heard the train whistle, clear and sharp, as it wailed and died away. She had heard the whistles sound like that often, in the night, back in Springfield. Always, then, she had been left behind, while the train shrieked on into the darkness. But now it was different. Now they were moving forward, boldly, surely—past sleeping towns, where the whistle would be heard for a moment, lingering and mournful, and then forgotten in the stillness.

The last stopover, next morning, was in Albany, where they were entertained by the mayor at a large breakfast.

"It's a mercy they didn't build any more cities along the line," Mr. Lincoln said, "or Mother would have run out of new dresses."

They parted, that evening, in New York. Mr. Lincoln and Ward Lamon and the other gentlemen were to go directly to Washington, while Mary stayed at the Metropolitan House with Robert and the little boys until the day before inauguration.

Tired from the long trip, Mary went to bed early. It was sometime toward morning that she wakened suddenly, sitting bolt upright. There had been a scream . . . She felt the lurch of panic, sickening and black, and then, a moment later, she realized it had only been Willie, calling out in his sleep. She went to him. Willie had had a bad dream. He had dreamed that Pussy was dead. A man with a black face had killed Pussy—and run away.

When Willie was comforted, Mary came back to bed. But her legs felt icy and numb, and she lay shivering, in the slow dawn that crept over the unfamiliar room, and she knew the fears had come again. It was the same queer terror she had felt the night Willie's turtle died. Now the dream had made it real again. A man with a black face, Willie had said, who had run away . . . She remembered the things Frances and Elizabeth had told her—rumors of assassins who had sworn that Mr. Lincoln would never reach Washington alive. And a carpetbag, left in a train seat . . . Mary clenched her hands, feeling them wet and cold. How could she have let Mr. Lincoln go on to Washington without her? If only she could send him word somehow—to warn him . . .

It was noon that day when the telegram came. All morning Mary had been in an agony of fear, and when the porter handed her the envelope her fingers were trembling so that Robert had to open it and read it to her.

Mr. Lincoln was safe in Washington.

Mr. Seward was at the station the evening Mary and Robert and the boys got off the train in Washington. It was pouring rain, and the air in the gloomy, vaulted station was damp and raw. Mary saw the drops of moisture on Mr. Seward's coat as he came through the crowd to meet them.

Mr. Lincoln couldn't get away from the hotel to come down himself, Mr. Seward explained. He was sorry—but some people had come in at the last minute and he had to stay and see them. He would be waiting at the hotel, where everything was ready for them. Mr. Seward was polite, inquiring about the journey and speaking kindly to the little boys. In answer to Mary's question, he said Mr. Lincoln seemed well, though naturally he had been very busy.

The red plush lobby at Willard's was thronged with people. Walking quickly through, her hand on Robert's arm, Mary was aware of a buzz of comment as they passed. People turned to stare—one or two smiled, and she smiled back, trying not to show the mounting agitation that pounded in her heart. But when they reached the second-floor suite and Mr. Seward opened the door, Mary saw Mr. Lincoln actually standing there, alive and safe—and such a flood of relief rushed over her that she could scarcely breathe. He stood with his back to the door, holding a sheaf of papers in one hand. There were a number of strangers in the room, and Mr. Lincoln was speaking to one of them—not noticing for a moment that the door had opened. Then Mary saw him turn, and the smile of welcome that came over his dark face.

"Oh, Mr. Lincoln—Mr. Lincoln—" Mary was clinging to his arm, hearing her own voice, trembling and broken.

"Well now, mother," Mr. Lincoln said, "I wouldn't cry. You see they haven't shot me yet."

21

THERE WERE GUARDS STATIONED IN THE HALL OUTSIDE Mr. Lincoln's room, and a special detachment of soldiers on duty in the lobby downstairs. The city was teeming with people, coming and going all night long, roaming the streets as though it were broad daylight. And everywhere there was talk of the rumors that were going around. Ugly rumors—threats of violence and death. There were five hundred men, some said, all armed, all at large in the city. They had sworn a pact that the new president would not live to sleep in the White House. Five hundred men, somewhere in the crowds that milled and shouted in the streets, waiting for morning.

Mary sat with Robert and the boys and the others of their party in the diplomatic gallery, watching the inaugural ceremony. Everything was going smoothly. Old Chief Justice Taney, looking small and shriveled in his black robes, had administered the oath while Mr. Lincoln towered above him. Now Mr. Lincoln was speaking.

". . . we are not enemies, but friends . . ."

It was strange to hear those words from him, when he had always been so slow to recognize either enemies or friends. It was all strange, Mary thought—as though being here was some part of a familiar dream. Long ago she had dreamed it—fancied herself in this moment, fancied the pride and the happiness of fulfillment she would feel. And the pride was here, filling her heart. But where, she wondered, was the happiness?

She watched Mr. Lincoln's face, and the faces of the men who sat near him, listening, and wondered what they were thinking. She wondered if they could hear, beneath the sure, even flow of his voice, the deeps of melancholy and doubt that she knew were in him. The present, with its triumph, was real—but the price of the triumph was real also. The endless weeks of waiting, the bitterness, the discouragements and loneliness—the dark horizon of the future. These things had been no part of the vision she had dreamed.

Stephen Douglas sat directly behind Mr. Lincoln. Mary could see the outline of his heavy and stocky shoulders. He sat quiet, his face impassive, as he listened. On his knee he held Mr. Lincoln's top hat. What was he thinking now? That he might have been standing where Mr. Lincoln stood? Was he sorry, disappointed, bitter? Or was he half thankful, perhaps, that he need only wait, holding Mr. Lincoln's hat?

Taddie, in the seat beside her, squirmed restlessly, and

started to whisper something. Mary shook her head, her finger on her lips. She could see Robert next to Taddie, then Willie, and Elizabeth.

Mr. Lincoln finished speaking. There was an instant's silence while he stood looking out over the crowd, his shoulders stooped slightly, his face solemn and intent. Then he stepped back—and there was a general stir. Applause—cheers—rang from the audience. Mary saw Mr. Lincoln turn and glance at her, and she met his eyes, smiling.

Cousin Lizzie was clapping her hands, pausing to wipe away her tears. Robert was applauding. Mr. Douglas rose, and handed Mr. Lincoln his hat. They were shaking hands now—Mr. Seward, Mr. Chase, Mr. Cameron . . .

Mary drew a long breath. She saw Elizabeth leaning across to nod approvingly.

"I must say, Mary—I think Mr. Lincoln did very well indeed."

They drove up Pennsylvania Avenue in the new carriage that had been sent for Mr. Lincoln from New York. A dress coach, of dark maroon, with scarlet brocatel upholstery. Beside them, in the thin March sunlight, rode a special guard of honor. Marshals with their bright scarfs and rosettes of orange and blue. In the seat next to Mr. Lincoln was General Scott, commander of the army, looking out at the cheering crowds that lined the broad street. The old general's eyes, beneath his cockaded hat, were pale and wary—watching.

At the White House, Mr. Lincoln took Mary's arm and they went in together. Edwards, the attendant who sat by the door with a bunch of large brass keys dangling from a chain on his belt, climbed down from his high stool and came forward. He shook hands with Mr. Lincoln and bowed to Mary, eying her narrowly out of sharp blue eyes.

Close behind Mary, pushing ahead of the rest of the party with shouts of excitement, came Tad and Willie. Their copper-toed boots clattered noisily as they slid across the bare parquet floor, and they made a dive for the wide staircase that curved upward from the reception hall.

"I'll race you down the banisters, Willie!"

Mary caught Taddie just in time, pulling him back as she saw the dour and disapproving frown on old Edwards's face. She kept the boy's hand firmly in hers while they walked through the downstairs rooms. But when they looked in the East Room, at the end of the corridor, Taddie broke away again, and he and Willie rushed about the long room, poking and prying and chattering like squirrels.

"*Look,* mamma—the piano's made of gold—" Willie went closer to inspect. "Only—the gold is all coming off in peelings."

Taddie stopped suddenly, his face puckered with dismay.

"Mamma—is *this* the President's house?"

Mary said nothing. She stood in the doorway, looking at the room she had pictured so many times. The room she and Mr. Montrose had discussed. White and gold and crystal, Mr. Montrose had said. But the white walls were streaked and grimy. The gilt on the frescoes was chipped, and the crystal chandeliers were filmed with dust. The long windows, where the crimson draperies would hang, were bare, and the cold March sunlight shone through them, on the dingy, ill-assorted furniture and the faded carpeting.

Mary turned to Mr. Lincoln. He was standing beside her, his eyes narrowed, lost in some thought of his own.

"We'd better get back to the others," Mary said.

They were gathering in the broad reception hall. Mary saw Elizabeth's expression as she and Ninian came in—the quick, appraising look, the slightly lifted brows. There was to be a luncheon for the new Cabinet members in half an hour, and the ladies, Mary realized, would expect to be shown upstairs to their rooms.

Taddie pulled at Mary's sleeve.

"Mamma, can I go see my room now? How soon can I unpack my red wagon?"

"Mamma—" Willie was on her other side, hopping excitedly. "Please, can Tad and I go out and look at the barn? I want to see where my pony will stay."

She sent them along, and then turned to her guests, but before the last carriage had drawn up at the front door the boys were back again. Willie's lip was trembling indignantly. There was a man out in the barn, Willie said. A very cross man, who had told them to go away and not bother him, and they weren't to come fooling around the stables.

"Isn't this our house now, mother?" Willie's round face was troubled. "Don't we *live* here?"

There was an abrupt wail from Taddie. Overcome by the strangeness of this new and hostile world, he buried his face against Mary's skirt and burst into tears.

"I don't want to live here, mamma. I don't like this house."

Mary looked about distractedly. What on earth was she going to do with the boys while they got ready for the luncheon? There seemed to be no servants in sight as yet. She glanced at old Edwards, but one look at his glum, wizened countenance and she turned away. She had a sudden, mortifying image of the way their arrival must look—with all of them standing about as though they were in a railroad station, and Taddie, refusing to be quieted, howling to high heaven and demanding to go home. Suddenly her eye lit on a pleasant-looking young officer, assigned for the day as an aide to the President, and Mary smiled hopefully. Would he, she asked the young man, be so very kind as to walk out with the little boys for half an hour or so, and show them the grounds?

Instantly, sensing the looks the others exchanged, and the slight, frozen pause before the young officer answered, Mary realized her mistake. Mr. Lincoln stepped forward.

"Never mind," he said quietly. "The boys can go out with me." He offered them each a hand. "Come along—

we'll see if the cross man can be persuaded to let me into the barn."

Mary bit her lip, feeling embarrassment sweep hotly over her. Mr. Lincoln meant to be kind, of course—but he had only put her more hopelessly in the wrong than ever. To think the new president must spend his first half hour in office minding the children—and before he had had so much as a chance to lay aside his hat. Mary turned quickly, to avoid meeting Elizabeth's eye.

"Let's go upstairs," she said.

In the room that was to be hers, Mary stood looking about. It was pleasant enough, large and square, with long windows that faced south across the sloping grounds down toward the river, and beyond to the hills of Virginia that showed the first pale yellow-green of spring. But the furnishings on the second floor were, if anything, more dreary and unprepossessing than those downstairs. She looked at the limp blue curtains, and thought of the crisp starched ruffles at the bedroom windows in Springfield. The bed was carved walnut, large and gloomy, covered with a counterpane of faded rose print. Mary laid her bonnet on the bare dresser. It was hard to think that until a few hours ago someone had actually been living in this room. She had a sudden, uneasy sense of being an unwelcome guest in someone else's house.

From across the hall, Mary could hear Elizabeth speaking.

"I must say, I should think the country could do better than this for the President's house. Did you ever see such furniture? It might have come out of the ark. And as for the carpets, if you please, half of them are worn clear through . . ."

Then Ann, chiming in sharply. "If I were in Mary's place, the first thing I should do would be to hire some decent servants. The only ones that have taken the trouble to show themselves so far are an incompetent-looking lot.

And the way they treated us—as though we were sight-seers or something. I call it disgraceful."

"Well, I daresay Mary will have everything running smoothly in no time—" That was Cousin Lizzie speaking—"with all the lovely things she ordered from New York. And Mary's always so clever about managing—"

Mary closed her door sharply and crossed to the window. She ought to be fixing her hair—getting ready for the luncheon. She looked down on the lawn, such as it was. Here and there, on the ragged expanse, were a few crocuses. She hoped, vaguely, the ground wasn't as damp as it looked. If Tad got his feet wet and came down with one of his colds . . .

This was it, Mary thought. This was the thing she had waited for, planned and dreamed. Now it was real. And when she woke up tomorrow morning it would still be real. *Tomorrow and tomorrow* . . . Those were words Mr. Lincoln used to read aloud sometimes by the fire in Springfield. It was a long time now, she realized, since Mr. Lincoln had read to her . . .

Mary went over and sat down on the bed. All of a sudden she knew what it was that made her feel like this. She was homesick. Homesick, like Taddie. Homesick for a house she knew and a familiar room—and one cross Irish hired girl instead of a staff of strange servants most of whom she hadn't even seen. She put her hands over her eyes. This was only a bad moment, she knew. It would pass—and everything would be right again, the way she had always planned it. But she did wish, wearily, that things needn't forever keep turning out so differently from what one expected . . .

There was a knock at the door, and Mary looked up, bracing herself quickly. That would be Elizabeth, no doubt, telling her she must hurry and get ready for lunch.

But instead of Elizabeth, a tall, light-skinned Negro woman stepped into the room. Her name was Lizzie Keckley, she said, and she had come recommended by Mrs. Breckinridge, who thought perhaps there might be work for her at the White House. She could sew, or press dresses, or help with the unpacking . . .

Mary considered a moment. Mrs. Keckley's manner was deferential. She spoke carefully, in a low voice, and Mary noticed her neat dark dress, and the way she carried herself with poise and dignity. There was some last-minute fitting to be done on her gown for the ball that evening. How soon could Mrs. Keckley start to work?

"As soon as you wish, madam. I can stay now if you like."

"Then do, by all means."

Mary stood up. The strangeness of a moment ago had vanished. There would be so much to do these first few days, she said to Mrs. Keckley, briskly. A good deal of entertaining, no doubt, and callers to be received. If Mrs. Keckley was experienced with children, she might help with the boys. They were restless, after the change and the long journey, and needed someone to keep an eye on them.

Mrs. Keckley nodded. She was very fond of children. "I have a son of my own, madam, going on eighteen."

"My oldest boy is just the same age—" Mary's tone warmed.

"Yes, I know. I've heard what fine children you have, Mrs. Lincoln. I'd be very pleased if you'd care to trust the younger ones to me."

Mary turned from the dresser where she was smoothing her hair, and saw that Mrs. Keckley, without being asked, had picked up Mary's bonnet and cloak and was laying them away carefully in the wardrobe. Mary smiled.

"I think," she said, "we shall get on very well together, Mrs. Keckley."

22

MR. LINCOLN ACCEPTED THE PRESENCE OF MRS. KECKLEY as unquestioningly as he did most things that appeared to please Mary. By evening, when it was time to dress for the ball, Mrs. Keckley had established herself as quite indispensable. She had taken the boys in hand, coaxed them to eat supper and read to them until they fell asleep. Mary's new gown had been adjusted expertly, her hair was dressed, and her gloves and flowers were waiting on the bed. When Mary was ready, Mrs. Keckley went to help the other ladies dress, and later Ann drew Mary aside.

"Mark my word, Mary—you have a real treasure in Mrs. K. Mind you don't let her slip through your fingers, though. If Mr. Lincoln talks and jokes with her, as he always does with servants, it will certainly spoil her—and that would be a pity. If I were you, I should speak to him about it."

"If you were me, Ann, everything would be managed quite perfectly, I haven't a doubt. And if you were God, I daresay the universe would be a great deal better off. But as it is, I expect God and I will have to struggle along as best we can." Mary's voice was sharp, but she smiled as she spoke. She was too happy to let Ann or anyone else spoil things for her tonight. She looked affectionately at Cousin Lizzie Grimsley and complimented her new coffee-colored silk gown until Lizzie's cheeks flushed with gratitude.

"Oh, Cousin Mary—" Lizzie scrubbed the tip of her nose vigorously—"who but you would think to notice my dress on a night like this?" She sighed, pushing back a stray wisp of hair that had escaped Mrs. Keckley's careful brushing and *would* keep falling over one ear. "You've been so thoughtful and wonderful—bringing us all here with you. But, then, I've always said you were the most unselfish woman in the world."

The Inaugural Ball was to be held at the Union Building, a few blocks from the White House. Stepping out of the carriage, Mary held her head high. Her hand was on Mr. Lincoln's arm. He was smiling at her, looking more rested and cheerful than he had for weeks. And he had said her new gown was most becoming. Mary smiled graciously as they walked into the muslin-draped ballroom together.

War—and the servant problem—could wait until tomorrow.

All of Washington, they said, was at the ball that night. All of Washington, however, seemed to include some unexpected elements. The fashionable southern set were there, having come, apparently, for the purpose of inspecting and commenting on the appearance of the new president and his wife. For weeks now, their Democratic dinner tables had seethed with stories of the Republican interlopers, and now, having seen for themselves, the inner circle found their worst fears confirmed. It was plain to be seen, they said, that the Lincolns were rustics. Westerners, to begin with, and definitely antislavery, which was shocking. Abolitionists were bad enough, in all conscience, but at least a New England abolitionist was a gentleman if scratched deeply enough. Whereas Mr. Lincoln, they agreed, was not only politically beyond the pale but socially as well.

"Quite, quite impossible . . . They say he'd never owned a pair of boots until he was elected—and having to wear them now is what makes him look so sad . . ."

"One can't help rather pitying *him*—after all, what can one expect of a backwoodsman who's been shoved into the limelight by an ambitious wife? But *she*, my dear —quite too awful. I'm told she made the most absurd spectacle of herself in New York. Rushing about to the shops and demanding all sorts of attention in the most overbearing way. She's going to do over the whole White House, it seems—and expect the country to foot the bill for her bad taste, I haven't a doubt . . ."

"She sides with Mr. L. in politics, they say—even though she comes from a quite acceptable southern family. It shows what a woman will stoop to when she's set on pushing her husband ahead . . ."

"You've heard, of course, about the dreadful thing she did to Lieutenant Page, poor dear? Actually asking him, in front of her luncheon guests, to mind her two brats this afternoon. She even expected him to bathe them. Oh—but it *is* a fact. Absolute gospel. I had it straight from my aunt's stepson and he heard it from Kate Chase who was there with her father for the Cabinet luncheon. Miss Kate vows she saw the whole thing with her own eyes. Just fancy—ordering an officer about as though he were a body servant. Miss Kate says she thinks poor Lieutenant Page would have sunk through the floor with mortification if Mr. Lincoln hadn't interfered. It just goes to show that even *he* has more sense of things than *she*—though I've heard that he lives in mortal terror of Mrs. L.'s temper . . ."

Miss Kate and her father, the new secretary of the treasury, were late arriving. When they came in, there was already a crush, but Mary was aware nevertheless of a stir of interest. From all over the crowded hall, people turned to look, to watch Mr. Chase shake hands with the President, to see what Miss Kate was wearing, and how she greeted the President's wife.

Miss Kate was very pleasant. If her manner was somewhat languid, Mary had already gathered that this was the badge of social distinction in Washington. Unlike the West, where people were eager, even effusive, it was evidently considered proper here to be offhand. Mary felt Miss Kate's fingers, slim and boneless, rest a moment in hers. They had rested a shade longer, Mary had observed, in Mr. Lincoln's—though she had looked up at him from under long dark lashes quite as casually as she did at Mary.

"How too awful—such a crush—" Miss Kate's glance swept over the room. "Doesn't it make you feel quite dreadful having all of us come just to stare at you, Mrs. Lincoln? Though I must say—" a smile of unexpected sweetness lighted Miss Kate's delicate oval face—"you look as though you were quite enjoying it. Doesn't she, Mr. Lincoln?"

"Being stared at is something one gets used to, I expect," Mary said.

Miss Kate made a little shrug, lifting her slim shoulders prettily. "I daresay you're right, Mrs. Lincoln. Personally, I find it very trying—but then, of course—" again the smile, candid and disarming—"you've had so many more years of experience than I."

As Miss Kate drifted away in the crowd, her white-gloved finger tips resting lightly on her father's arm, Mary stared after her. She saw the slender lines of Miss Kate's figure, and the elegant poise of her small head. She must be very young, Mary thought. She looked barely more than twenty. Yet Mary noticed how she greeted the older guests, particularly the gentlemen, with an air of easy, slightly bored familiarity. Miss Kate was wearing white too, but her gown was cut simply, without trimming, and she wore no jewels. Her shining red hair was parted in the center and drawn smoothly into a low knot at the back of her neck.

Mary looked down, suddenly conscious of the elaborateness of her own gown. And of the wreath of flowers in her hair. She felt short and tightly laced and middle-aged. But the next moment she remembered something she had heard a woman say about Miss Kate in New York. "Kate Chase is bound and determined her father will be president someday," the woman had said. "She's twice as ambitious for him as he is for himself—and that's saying a great deal. If she doesn't get her wish, it will be a bitter disappointment—and Kate's not used to being disappointed."

A smile, not unlike Miss Kate's own, lingered on Mary's lips. Beauty or no, middle-aged or no—she had a sudden conviction that between herself and Kate Chase she held the trump card.

The evening wore on and Mary became increasingly aware that there were a great many people at the ball who had nothing whatever to do with society. Mingled with the more fashionable element, rubbing elbows with the cave dwellers and diplomats, was a large and motley assortment of guests who appeared to have wandered in simply for the show—and were bent on improving the occasion by seeing how much they could eat and drink. They roamed about, gawking and commenting on all they saw, pocketing souvenirs, and making such forays on the refreshments that the supper tables were turned into a shambles.

Alarmed to discover that the food had vanished, along with virtually all the silverware and napkins before the evening was half over, Mary appealed to Mr. Lincoln.

"What are we to do, Mr. Lincoln? The tables are quite bare. They've even carried off most of the centerpieces—and there are still dozens of guests who haven't been served."

Mr. Lincoln shook his head. "I don't know what we can do, mother, unless we send out for some loaves and fishes."

It was also apparent, however, that no one besides Mary was seriously perturbed by the situation. Washington partygoers seemed to accept the presence of the barbarous horde as a matter of course.

"You mustn't let it worry you," Mrs. Breckinridge said cheerfully to Mary. "These sightseers turn up everywhere nowadays. We're quite accustomed to them."

Elizabeth remained scandalized. "Pigs are pigs," she said firmly, "whether Washington is accustomed to them or not. And I must say I don't see that the manners of the decent-looking people are much of an improvement. Of all the insolent, overbearing rudeness I ever saw—"

Only Cousin Lizzie seemed to approve of the party. Shortly after midnight she came up to Mary, beaming ecstatically.

"Isn't it simply wonderful?" Lizzie fumbled with the drooping lock over her ear. When Lizzie raised her arm, Mary noticed with irritation several gaping hooks at her stout and straining waistline. "I never *saw* so many people, Mary. And just to think they all came just to meet *you* and Mr. Lincoln. I should think you'd be flattered to death. Everyone seems to be having *such* a good time. You know that Miss Chase, Mary—the one that was at lunch today? Well, I never dreamed she'd remember *me*, but she came right up the minute she saw me and was ever so friendly. Not a bit standoffish. And you know, when she smiles she's quite pretty, in spite of being a redhead. I could see she's tremendously taken with you, Mary. She asked me all sorts of questions about you. All about your house in Springfield and the boys—"

"I've no doubt you answered them—fully."

"Well, after all—why shouldn't I?" Lizzie's round eyes were puzzled. "When she was so interested. And I know she admires you, Mary. I heard her talking to Mr. Lincoln later—and she told him she thought you looked just like a fashion plate. She said she never expected to see one come to life—right out of *Godey's*. So, you see—"

Mary's patience snapped suddenly.

"Oh, Lizzie, for mercy's sake don't be such an eternal fool. Can't you see Kate Chase was only making fun of me—of all of us?"

"Why, Mary—I didn't—I'm sure she didn't mean—"

Unable to bear the sight of Lizzie's stammering bewilderment another instant, Mary turned away. She couldn't bear anything more. Not tonight. She looked up to see Mr. Lincoln coming toward them.

"Well, Cousin Lizzie, it seems to me you've been quite a belle this evening. Every time I caught sight of you you had a new gentleman in tow—" Mr. Lincoln paused, looking from Lizzie to Mary for a moment while the smile died slowly out of his eyes. He put his hand on Mary's arm. "I guess maybe it's time we were getting home, mother," he said. "The party seems to be about over. And it's been kind of a long day."

Part Three

23

IT WAS EARLY IN THE MORNING WHEN MARY WOKE. SHE opened her eyes to discover Tad and Willie hanging on either side of her bed, arguing noisily about something.

Seeing her eyes open, the boys left off their discussion and began talking to her, both at once, in such agitation that for a moment she couldn't make out what they were saying. There were lots of people in the hall, Taddie said. He was bouncing on the edge of the bed excitedly. All sorts of people, right outside the door there—simply hundreds of them. Queer-looking men, mostly, and some ladies too, and they were all talking about getting in to see the President. One of them, Willie said, had given him a silver dollar just to tell which was the door of Old Abe's office. And another had offered Tad a pinch of snuff.

"See the dollar, mamma? It's a real one. See?"

"The people are all over the stairs, mamma. Just come and see. They're all *over*—"

Mary sat up. She couldn't think what the boys were prattling about, but when she opened her door a little and looked out, there, sure enough, were a number of odd-looking individuals, lined up, leaning against the wall, helping themselves to snuff and generally making themselves at home. Several of them turned to gape at her through the partly open door.

"Hello—who's she?" one man inquired. He hadn't troubled to remove his hat.

Mary slammed the door. She dressed hastily, sent the boys off to Mrs. Keckley, and marched down the corridor to Mr. Lincoln's office. A few of the bystanders, seeming to recognize her, fell back grudgingly to let her pass. She went in without knocking.

"Mr. Lincoln—"

He was alone at his desk, writing something.

"Mr. Lincoln, have you seen those people out there?"

"Not yet—but I expect I will." He looked up mildly. "That's what they came here for."

"But who on earth are they, Mr. Lincoln? Coming in like this—before we've even had breakfast—"

"Office seekers, mother." Mr. Lincoln put down his pen. "That's one commodity I reckon we'll never be short of."

"How did they get in?"

"By the front door, I suppose."

Mary folded her arms.

"They'll have to wait downstairs then," she said shortly. "I won't have the creatures cluttering up the halls—staring at us as though we were waxworks. One of them actually tried to give Taddie snuff. You'll have to speak to someone, Mr. Lincoln—at once."

"All right, mother, I'll see what I can do." Mr. Lincoln took up his pen again and stared at it for a moment, thoughtfully. "The trouble is, there doesn't seem to be anyone to speak to around here except me." He sighed. "But I'll do the best I can."

That day, however, and the next day and the next passed, and nothing had been done. The house swarmed with the favor seekers, crowding the staircase, pushing their way to the front of the line, clutching their credentials and arguing loudly over the relative merits of their claims. Now and then one of the visitors would wander out of his orbit and appear unexpectedly in one of the private rooms, where he would generally stand, gawking and unabashed, until requested to leave.

By the fourth day Mary was unnerved. Quite as she might have expected, Mr. Lincoln had done nothing whatever.

"After all, mother," he said, "I can't very well turn them out. These are the people who voted for me."

"And since when, I should like to know, does voting for a man include the privilege of walking into his family's bedrooms at all hours of the day and night?"

Plainly, if anything was to be done, Mary saw that she would have to do it. She spoke to Mr. Nicolay, Mr. Lincoln's secretary, and Mr. Nicolay, looking harried but patient, said he would speak to Mr. Hay, the other secretary, who would consult Mr. Stoddard, and they would see what could be arranged. But without definite orders . . .

The orders, said Mary, were quite definite. And what was more, she would be obliged if Mr. Nicolay would act on them promptly, since Mr. Montrose was expected from New York that afternoon to confer with her in the matter of redecorating the house.

Mr. Nicolay, looking noticeably more harried and less patient, agreed to do what he could.

Most unfortunately, an hour before Mr. Montrose's arrival, a large body of young gentlemen called at the White House with the patriotic purpose of offering themselves to the President as a volunteer company to defend Washington in the event that Rebels should invade the city. Old Edwards, at the door, ushered the gentlemen into the East Room, for want of other space, and there Mary discovered them when she came in with Mr. Montrose. The zealots, unable to restrain their feelings while waiting for an audience with Mr. Lincoln, were milling about the room, leaping onto chairs and vowing heroically that if they were only given guns they would bivouac where they were.

Mr. Montrose, already exhausted by his journey, seemed totally undone by the spectacle of so much virility, and it was with the greatest difficulty that Mary was able to extract any coherent opinions from him in regard to upholstery, carpeting and color schemes.

Eventually the stream of volunteer recruits, including

a large number of fashionable and unmilitary-looking gentlemen who were suddenly fired with a desire to be commissioned as brigadiers, was deflected to the War Department. And as the weeks went by, the influx of office seekers dwindled to a steady but manageable trickle. Mary was learning that in Washington problems were often best settled by the simple device of allowing them to settle themselves.

In household matters, however, she declined to be passive. The White House staff, when consulted, proved to be curiously immune to suggestions. Pride, custom, and precedent were their tenets, and the greatest of these was precedent. In the memory of the oldest usher, who dated back to the Van Buren administration, things in the White House had always been done a certain way. And no new president's wife was expected to give orders. She was merely to be tolerated, so long as she was willing to live and learn.

"It's absurd, Mr. Lincoln," Mary said. "This house is being run as though we were still in the Dark Ages. When I try to give an order in the kitchens, I'm told it can't be done that way because Mrs. Madison said fifty years ago it was to be done some other way. Who's running this house, I should like to know? Dolly Madison or me?"

Mr. Lincoln looked at her thoughtfully.

"Neither one, so far as I can see, mother," he said.

Cousin Lizzie was more sympathetic. "If you ask me," she said, "half these servants ought to be discharged. They've been here so long they think they own the house. They're positively insolent to you, Mary; and the things they say behind your back are disgraceful. They grumble over the least thing that makes a little extra work for them, and then they say you're stingy and unreasonable just because you object to their wasteful ways. One of the kitchenmaids told me she'd been here through four administrations, and you were the first mistress that ever came down to the kitchens every day. Spying, she called it—" Lizzie's nose grew pink with indignation. "She said it was plain to see that you weren't used to having servants—since you weren't willing to trust them. I took pains to tell her, you may be sure, that you'd been brought up to expect good service—and they needn't think they could fool you with their slovenly ways."

It was a relief all around when Mary discovered that a trip to New York would be necessary before she and Mr. Montrose could settle on the final details of the new furnishings.

For his part, Mr. Lincoln said, he thought the house looked well enough as it was. A lot better than any they'd had before. But if Mary was set on adding a few frills, he couldn't see any objection.

"You and Lizzie run along," he said. "Enjoy yourselves. Stay as long as you like."

Once in New York, Mary found herself soothed by the flattering attention of Mr. Montrose. They had long, engrossing discussions of designs and fabrics, during which each deferred to the other's opinion. They were always charmed, in the end, to discover how perfectly their tastes agreed. In the matter of lace curtains they were particularly harmonious, with the result that Mary found she had ordered, without quite knowing how, a double set for every window in the house. It was a trifle disconcerting to contemplate the probable cost of these, but Mr. Montrose, as usual, slid so delicately over the matters of price and credit that Mary hesitated to mention actual figures.

While they were there, of course, it seemed a pity not to look at a few of the new styles in spring clothes. And the clerks at Stewart's were as eager as ever to be of service. Encouraged by their friendliness and Lizzie's raptures over the gowns and bonnets, Mary ended by ordering a good many more than she had intended. But there was bound to be a great deal of entertaining in Washington, and, as Mr. Stewart himself said, it would never do for the First Lady to be outshone. Miss Kate Chase, he added thoughtfully, had been up only last week to buy her spring wardrobe.

Mr. Lincoln brought the boys to the station to meet them the night they got home. He looked tired, but he seemed pleased to have Mary home again, and listened amiably while she told about the new plans for the house, neglecting obligingly to inquire the cost of anything.

When Lizzie commented later on this singular omission, Mary smiled.

"Mr. Lincoln has no notion of such things," she said indulgently. "He likes to have the house in proper style, and he's always pleased to see me in what he calls 'fine feathers'—but he has no more idea than a kitten what it will mean to live up to our position here. I daresay he fancies a few yards of bonnet trimming and a new pair of slippers are all any woman needs to produce a whole new wardrobe."

By the end of the week Mr. Montrose had sent down his corps of drapers and upholsterers, and there was frantic activity in the house. Mary was busy all day, supervising and directing, but even in the midst of the hammering and confusion, Mr. Lincoln remained oblivious to the violent upheavals going on around him. When, one morning, he tripped over a man with a mouthful of tacks who was busily laying the new stair carpet, Mr. Lincoln only murmured a vague apology and went on his way, frowning and abstracted.

"You'll see, though," Mary said confidently to Cousin Lizzie, "how delighted Mr. Lincoln will be when everything is done."

Lizzie sighed. "I do think you're wonderful, Mary. Mr. Lincoln is a lucky man to have a wife who does so much for him."

It was on a Friday morning, in April, that the last new curtain and the final strip of carpeting were in place. Mary made a last round of inspection before the decorators were sent back to New York. And she found the results of their work all that Mr. Montrose and she had dreamed and planned. The old house had come to life again. Rooms that had been bare and dreary glowed with new color. Fresh damasks, rich and gleaming, covered the old furniture. There were new carpets underfoot. The windows were hung with lace curtains, and the fringed overdrapes pulled back with plump silken ropes and anchored by large rosettes.

After the workmen had gone, Mary went back for one more look at the East Room. It was perfection. The gold and white walls, restored to pristine freshness, gleamed in the morning sun. Hundreds of tiny rainbows spangled the ceilings in the light reflected from the shining prisms of the crystal chandeliers. And the crimson draperies, echoing the darker red of the deep-piled carpet, gave the crowning touch of color from their rich, full folds.

Mary sighed. She walked down the long room, moving softly, touching a chair here, a sofa there—standing a moment by the keyboard of the huge, newly gilded pianoforte. Let Washington come and see her house now, she thought, and they would find something to stir them out of their haughty indifference. They were so fond of talking—this would give them something to talk about.

It was lunchtime—Mr. Lincoln would be coming down from the office any moment—and then she would show him everything. He'd worked so hard these weeks, been so preoccupied and worried by all the new demands they were pressing on him, he'd scarcely had time to look up from his desk. But now, surely, the worst rush was over, and he could rest a little. She thought, smiling, how astonished he'd be to discover all she had done.

Out in the hall, Mary was surprised to see Mr. Seward just coming in the front door. It was an odd time for the secretary of state to call, surely. She started to speak, but he brushed past with barely a nod, and hurried toward the stairs, just as Mr. Lincoln appeared at the top landing.

The two men met midway, looking very grave, and Mary saw that Mr. Lincoln held a telegraph blank in his hand.

"You've seen this news?" Mr. Lincoln handed the message to Mr. Seward, who glanced at it and nodded.

"That's why I came," Mr. Seward said. "If it's really true that they've fired on Fort Sumter—it means we're in for war."

Mary saw the shadow that crossed Mr. Lincoln's face.

"It's true," she heard him say slowly, out of a long silence. "It's true."

The two men turned and came down the stairs into the hall together.

"We'd better go over to the War Office," Mr. Lincoln said, "and find out what Cameron knows."

They went out the door, Edwards watching from his perch on his high stool, his old face gnarled and impassive.

Neither of them had noticed Mary, where she stood waiting.

In a single hour the city was in a turmoil. No one had expected war. They had talked of it without really believing in it, and now that it had come, everyone was angry. Congress, having stewed and frittered for months without getting anywhere, boiled over in a fury of oratory and invective. Everybody wanted to blame somebody, and the President was the likeliest target.

"The North doesn't stand a show. We're caught unprepared—and it's Lincoln that's responsible. With all this prattle of peace, to get himself elected, he's left us a fair target—and now we're done for."

Other factions, equally bitter, shouted that it was the President who had deliberately shoved them into war.

"If he'd been man enough to own the South was right," they said, "we'd never have had to fight. But he's harped on humanity and the curse of slavery, like a damned preacher, until he's pushed us into the chowder."

The volunteer companies, in their sashes and sabers,

took on a new meaning now. All over the North, men were mobilizing, moving toward Washington. *Sign up now and get it over quick. March on Richmond, and we'll be home before the summer's out.* Ranks of three months' volunteers joined up, promising that they'd be back in time to help with the harvest.

On a bright spring morning the Pennsylvania Fifth, the New York Twelfth and the Massachusetts Eighth paraded up the avenue in Washington. Their flags whipped smartly in the fresh breeze, their drums rolled, and bayonets flashed in the morning sun. At the White House gate they wheeled, turning up the drive to pass in review before the President.

Mary stood beside Mr. Lincoln, watching them go by. She saw the faces, young and eager. They wore bright sashes, and many of them smiled broadly as they marched past. Mr. Lincoln did not smile back. His eyes, fixed on them sadly, seemed to be seeing something far away and puzzling.

All along the avenue, windows stood open in the soft spring air. And from inside now and then came sounds of music. Rebel tunes, clear and tinkling, signalling a thin defiance from the Southern ladies at their pianofortes. The strains of "Dixie" mingled with the blare of fife and drum, and the steady clump of marching feet.

But here came an odd-looking company—dressed in gaudy uniforms with red fez caps and pantaloons of vivid blue. The New York Fire Zouaves—a volunteer brigade led by a dashing young colonel who rode before them, his saber drawn. He heard the pianos tinkling—turned and gave an order—and the next moment his corps band struck up smartly.

> Then I wish I was in Dixie!
> Hooray! Hooray!
> In Dixie's land we'll take our stand,
> To live and die in Dixie . . .

The crowd lined along the sidewalk caught the twist, and a roar of laughter went up. The bystanders took up the words.

> Away, away, away down south in Dixie!
> Away, away, away down south in Dixie!

The defiant pianos were silenced. Windows banged shut.

"The North has stolen everything," the southern ladies cried. "Even our tunes."

When the Zouaves marched past the White House portico, Mr. Lincoln's face relaxed for the first time into a smile. They struck up "Maryland, My Maryland." General Ben Butler occupied Baltimore that morning, and Maryland could be fairly claimed.

Mary, looking at the Zouave colonel, recognized young Ellsworth, a lad who had read law for a few months in Mr. Lincoln's office in Springfield. She remembered him pleasantly, as a blond, round-faced boy. Riding past now, he grinned at Mr. Lincoln, and winked broadly. Mary saw Mr. Lincoln's hand raised in salute.

That afternoon there was an informal reception for the soldiers at the White House. Mary stood with Mr. Lincoln, shaking hands, greeting them all. She was a trifle surprised to find them so friendly, so eager to talk. When one of the Pennsylvania lads, in a burst of confidence, told her she looked like his mother, Mary was touched. She promised to write his mother and tell her how well he seemed.

The boy blushed under his freckles. "Ma'd be all perked to hear from you, ma'am," he said. "She didn't think much of my signing up, but Pa said if Old Abe wanted me to fight, I'd best fight. Pa thinks a whole heap of Mr. Lincoln."

Mary looked at the thin young face a moment. "Tell me—how old are you?"

"Going on eighteen, ma'am."

Mary was silent. A fear, swift and cold, brushed against her heart, but she pushed it back.

"I have a son, a little older than you," she said. "I can imagine how your mother felt to see you go."

"Yes, ma'am." The boy looked troubled, then he brightened. "Pa says three months'll be done before we know it though. And I can go home again."

"I hope so," Mary said.

"Oh, sure to." The boy nodded confidently. "Pa says he figured Mr. Lincoln wouldn't've called for three-monthers unless he knew the war'd be finished then. Or maybe sooner, of course."

When the boys had gone, Mary spoke to Mr. Lincoln. Did anyone really suppose the fighting would be over before the summer was out?

Mr. Lincoln hesitated. He was sitting forward in his chair, his shoulders slumped. The talk in Congress, he said, was all of making the war a short one. "They say the South will give in quick enough, once they see we mean business."

"All the same—" Mary said—"I wonder if the Confederate boys are signing up for just three months."

24

THE NEXT DAY WAS SUNDAY, AND ELLSWORTH, THE young Zouave colonel, came to lunch. He was full of talk, at the table, of getting his boys in the "mix-up," and Tad and Willie were entranced.

"What would you do if you saw a Reb coming at you?"

"Shove a bayonet through him—like this—" Ellsworth skewered Tad on the end of a fork, and Willie squealed with delight.

"What will you do with old Jeff Davis if you catch him?"

"Hang him on a sour apple tree."

"What is a Zouave anyway?"

Ellsworth laughed at that. "Ask anyone in Washington —and they'll tell you a Zouave is an Irishman, plus three yards of red flannel sash."

After lunch, in the sitting room, Ellsworth borrowed a carbine from Mr. Stoddard and showed them the manual of arms. They watched the clockwork motions, the boys in high glee, until one *shoulder arms*. Ellsworth was standing too near the south window, and his smart motion sent the muzzle of the gun crashing through the pane of glass. Ellsworth was dismayed for a moment, then he grinned.

"You see, boys," he said, "what we'll do to Johnny Reb."

That night, after Tad and Willie had gone to bed, Mrs. Keckley came downstairs to find Mary. Both the boys were very restless, she said. They seemed feverish. Mary hurried up to their room. They were complaining of sore throats, and when Mary opened the front of their nightshirts she found a bright rash. The doctor was sent for. Measles, he said.

The next day and the next Colonel Ellsworth came to the White House. He made himself entirely at home.

"We seem to have adopted him," Mr. Lincoln said.

"No—he's adopted us," Mary answered.

It was pleasant having young Ellsworth around. He laughed easily, and was so friendly and informal that not even the stiffest-necked members of the staff could help liking him. Cousin Lizzie was charmed.

"I don't know what it is about that young man," she said, "but just having him around makes the house suddenly seem like home."

"I know—" Mary said. "Sometimes I think what we need in this family is a really happy person."

Later, to Mrs. Keckley, Mary confided that it made her feel as though she had her three boys at home again to have Ellsworth with them. She didn't add that she had found herself wishing, more than once, that she could be sure of the same gay affection from Robert that Ellsworth gave so freely.

"I feel as if Ellsworth were my own son," Mary said.

Mrs. Keckley looked up from her sewing with her quiet smile. "It might seem strange for me to say it, madam—but I feel almost as though he were my boy too."

More than once Mary suggested that Ellsworth should make his home at the White House while he was stationed in Washington, but Ellsworth was firm.

"I've got to stick to my boys," he said. "They're such a troublesome lot of Irishmen—if I weren't on hand to apologize for their outlandish behavior, half the company would be tarred and feathered before the week was out."

In spite of all Mary's warnings and scoldings, Ellsworth insisted on going up to visit Tad and Willie every day, and no one was much surprised to hear, after a week of this, that the colonel was confined to his quarters, indisposed. To Mary, who drove to visit him each afternoon, he stubbornly maintained that it was only a little cold he had.

"And what are those spots, pray, that make you look like a strawberry patch?"

Ellsworth smiled apologetically. Just a touch of hives, he said. He always got them with a cold.

Mary fussed over him indulgently, coaxing him to take the medicines the doctor had ordered for Willie and Tad. It was a pity, she said, when a grown man and a soldier had no more sense than to go about catching measles.

On one of the afternoons when Mary had gone to take a hamper of food to Ellsworth, Mr. Lincoln found a slip of paper on his desk. It was a bill from a firm of dry goods merchants in New York, to the sum of two thousand dollars owing for carpeting furnished as per order, installed in the East Room, main corridor, state dining room and staircase in the White House. Mr. Lincoln looked at it for a moment.

"Mr. Hay—"

The secretary turned.

"Mr. Hay, do you know anything about this?"

Mr. Hay studied the bill carefully. He cleared his throat.

"No, sir. Mr. Nicolay must have—"

"Mr. Hay, doesn't it strike you that two thousand dollars is a lot of money just for something people walk on?"

"Well, yes, sir. I—"

Mr. Lincoln looked at the bill again. "You don't suppose they could have made a mistake, Mr. Hay?"

Mr. Hay said, uncertainly, he didn't suppose so. Since Mrs. Lincoln had taken charge of all the decorations and repairs, perhaps she might know. Or possibly Mr. Stoddard—

One of Mr. Stoddard's duties, as junior secretary, was to keep track of the household accounts. He was sent for, and Mr. Lincoln showed him the bill. So far as he could see, Mr. Stoddard said guardedly, the statement was correct.

Mr. Lincoln looked at him in silence a minute. Then he asked whether Mr. Stoddard knew whether any more such bills might be expected.

Well, yes, Mr. Stoddard admitted. There would certainly be others.

"How much will it come to altogether?"

Mr. Stoddard hesitated, glancing uneasily at Mr. Hay. He couldn't say for sure, but judging from the amount of work Mrs. Lincoln had had done, he would guess somewhere in the neighborhood of six thousand dollars.

There was another silence.

"I wish you had consulted me about this sooner, Mr. Stoddard."

Mr. Stoddard's uneasiness grew more marked. Mrs. Lincoln had taken charge of everything, he said. She had particularly told him that Mr. Lincoln was not to be troubled about household affairs.

"I naturally supposed, sir," Mr. Stoddard said, "that you knew what was being done. Mrs. Lincoln seemed quite sure—"

"Yes."

Mr. Stoddard tried again. He understood that it was customary for Congress to appropriate a certain sum at the beginning of each new administration for necessary repairs to the White House. Though in this case, since Mrs. Lincoln had found so much that needed doing, it might be necessary to ask for a larger amount.

Mr. Lincoln smiled. "At a time like this," he said, "with an army to raise and half the country howling about taxes, I hardly think Congress could be persuaded that two thousand dollars for carpets comes under the head of necessary repairs. And for once—Congress would be quite right."

He took the bill from Mr. Stoddard, folded it, and put it in his pocket.

"I still don't see how it could cost so much to fix up a house that looked all right to start with," Mr. Lincoln said. His voice was mild and weary. "But since it was done, I suppose it must have been necessary. When the other bills come in, Mr. Stoddard, will you be good enough to bring them to me? I'll make up the extra myself."

"Yes, sir."

"And, Mr. Stoddard—" Mr. Lincoln's glance was level —"I should appreciate it if nothing more were said of this. It would be too bad—" he rubbed his chin—"to have Mrs. Lincoln upset."

It was useless to hope, however, that any morsel of information that might contribute to the fashionable pastime of criticizing the new administration would remain for long unnoticed. The Washington grapevine was well developed, and within a few days the tea tables and drawing rooms rocked with delight over the story of Mrs. Lincoln's new furniture.

It was a fact, they said, that the impossible Mrs. L. had had a quarrel with the President because he had danced three times at the Inaugural Ball with a certain lady, and had gone off to New York in a huff and run up huge bills which *he* was expected to pay, poor man. Just for spite, mind you. Someone had heard, straight from an usher who had been in the White House for years, that she'd sent back three huge trunkfuls of nothing but lace curtains. Dozens and dozens of pairs—and nowhere to hang them at all. They'd heard Mr. L. went into a towering rage when he found what she'd done—and one of the maids said she wouldn't be surprised if he'd actually beaten her.

It was too shocking, really. Just to fancy anyone spending such sums at a time like this—with the country at war. The secesh ladies shook their heads virtuously. *What* an example for the President's wife to set.

Furthermore, the ladies added thoughtfully, it must not be forgotten that Mrs. L. herself was a Southerner. Mightn't it even be that *that* was the cause of her quarrel with Mr. L.? For all she talked so freely about sympathizing with her husband's politics—war was war. Everyone knew that Mrs. L.'s family was still in the South—that she had three brothers under the Confederate flag. Her youngest brother, Alexander, was a prisonkeeper at Richmond. And mind you, they said, blood is thicker than politics.

Going over her mail with Mr. Stoddard one morning, Mary put down a letter suddenly. "Mr. Stoddard—" she pushed the remaining stack toward him—"will you read the rest of these for me? I—can't stand any more . . ."

Mr. Stoddard glanced up, startled to see tears in Mary's eyes.

"Take them away, Mr. Stoddard." She gave the letters another push. "Burn them—do anything you like—only don't let me see any more, please."

He glanced through a few of the letters, frowning. They were the sort that came every day now. Ugly, anonymous scrawls, most of them—though now and then he came across a carefully written one, no less bitterly vicious because it was written in a neat hand on elegant stationary. He picked one at random and read it through.

Dear Madam,

Who do you think you are? You are only the President's wife, nobody is interested in you, so why don't you stay home and mind your own business instead of trying to get your name in the papers all the time? I read you bought lace curtains for your house, six pairs for every window, and how much you paid for gloves and hats and a string of pearl beads the paper said you paid a thousand dollars for. There are lots of people like me that never had lace curtains at all. We are lucky if we have one pair of gloves and a hat decent enough to go to church in. My husband is gone in the army and my boy too even if he was only fifteen. People like us have to give everything but you don't care so long as you can spend the government money and see your name in the paper. People say you want the south to beat us anyway but don't think you are going to fool us with your *spy* tricks . . .

Mr. Stoddard put the letter aside and glanced at a few of the others. The abuse and bitterness were all too familiar to him. Each morning the President's mail was filled with just such ravings. He looked up and found Mary watching him.

"Mr. Stoddard, why must they write these things? Why do they hate us so?"

25

THERE WAS A WHITE HOUSE RECEPTION PLANNED FOR the last week in April. Mary worked for days over the arrangements, consulting with Cousin Lizzie over the details, ordering the refreshments down from Maillard's in New York. It was her first chance to entertain the Washington ladies, and she meant to show them she knew how to do things properly. The house was done to the perfection of Mr. Montrose's taste. And Mrs. Keckley had Mary's new gown ready.

Watching the preparations, Mr. Stoddard was doubtful. He hoped the party would go well—after Mrs. L. had gone to such trouble. But with the talk that was going around Washington these days, especially in the secesh circles, it seemed there wasn't anything they'd stop at to make things hot for the President. Not that Mr. Lincoln noticed much—he never appeared to care, one way or the other, how people treated him. But it broke Mrs. L. all up to hear him criticized. One thing you had to say for her. Proud and stubborn as she was for herself, she was even prouder for Mr. Lincoln. It would be a shame, Mr. Stoddard thought, if the ladies took it into their heads to be really mean.

On the night of the reception, Mr. Lincoln was late coming down. He'd been working until the last moment, while Mary fumed impatiently outside his study door. She'd sent the barber in to shave him and trim his hair while he worked, and finally Mr. Stoddard was directed to go and warn him that he must dress at once. His clothes were all laid out ready—and Mr. S. was to remind him once again not to fail to put on white gloves.

Mary and Cousin Lizzie were in the East Room when Mr. Lincoln appeared. He stood still a minute, looking around the big room. There were flowers in tall vases, and in the soft candlelight the crystal chandeliers sparkled. The carpet, at which Mr. Lincoln glanced with a new respect, was soft beneath his feet, and the crimson curtains seemed to fill the whole room with rich, living color. Mr. Lincoln raised his eyebrows.

"Kind of dolled up tonight, aren't we, mother?"

Mary came over to straighten his tie, smiling up at him. She wore a new gown of dull-blue watered silk, cut low over her round, smooth shoulders, and with a full skirt sweeping into a train.

"Our cat has a mighty long tail," Mr. Lincoln said, looking at the new dress. "Seems to me some of the tail might have come in handy at the top."

"Don't be old-fashioned, Mr. Lincoln. It's the style to have necks cut low this season. I daresay you'd find nothing out of the way if Miss Chase wore a low neck—or any of the other young ladies." Mary gave his tie a final pat. "There—you look very fine. Now do, for pity's sake, remember to stand straight and not slouch—it looks so undignified. And don't put your hands behind your back while you talk to the ladies. It offends them."

"Well, mother—I'll do my best."

Mr. Lincoln simply must come and peep at the dining room, Cousin Lizzie insisted. It was too, too beautiful. Mary had ordered everything down from New York—caterers and all—for she was quite sure the regular staff would never manage things to suit her. "Don't the tables look lovely? The centerpieces were Mary's idea. All red, white and blue, see? And those flags are made of spun sugar."

Mr. Lincoln eyed the staggering mounds of salads, ices, cakes and pastries. At any rate, he said, he guessed nobody was likely to go home hungry.

"Come, Mr. Lincoln." Mary took his arm. "I hear a carriage."

They stood together by the East Room door, waiting. From the hall outside, the Marine Band struck up a lively tune. There were voices in the corridor. Standing with her hand on Mr. Lincoln's arm, Mary heard the usher's voice, announcing the first guests.

Mary looked up. Her smile, bright and expectant, was full of confidence.

Three gentlemen from the Senate, all looking rather uncomfortable in their dress clothes, shook hands with the President and bowed stiffly to Mary. One of them was saying something, not too clearly, about regretting that his wife had been unable, at the last moment, to come. Between the senator's mumbling and the noise of the band, Mary failed to quite catch the words. She only nodded brightly, and the gentlemen, a trifle red of face, moved on. A large delegation of congressmen came next, then Judge Stevenson who murmured over Mary's hand that Mrs. Stevenson was indisposed and sent regrets.

More congressmen—then a group from the French embassy, among them one woman who was presented to Mary as the wife of one of the young attachés. She was a sallow little creature, all in black, who gazed at Mary out of sad dark eyes and remarked mournfully, in broken English, that it was a charming occasion, and she was enchanted to be present.

Carriages were arriving steadily. The outside corridor was jammed, and the sound of voices rose above the music. Senator This, Representative That were announced, made their bows, and passed quickly into the crowd.

"The secretary of the treasury—Mr. Chase."

Mary lifted her shoulders. Her smile grew a shade brighter. Mr. Lincoln was shaking hands, the two men greeting each other pleasantly.

As Mr. Chase moved on to Mary, she glanced at the next gentleman in line.

"Where's Miss Kate? Isn't she with you?"

Mr. Chase shook his head regretfully. Miss Kate was desolated, he explained, but a headache—at the very last minute. She begged that Mrs. Lincoln would understand, and forgive her for not coming. The secretary's voice was smooth as butter.

For a moment Mary looked at him blankly. She had been on the point of replying quite conventionally when something in Mr. Chase's bland, immobile face made her pause. The next instant, in a stinging, bitter flash, Mary realized what was happening. In the whole roomful of people, except for herself and Lizzie and the dreary little French wife, there was not a woman present. It was Washington's answer to the President and his wife. A colossal, unbelievable snub.

In the sick, unmistakable certainty of what had happened, Mary found herself staring at Mr. Chase's face that swam before her eyes like an absurdly bobbing balloon. Then it steadied—and she saw that he was still waiting, bland and impassive, for her to speak. Mary's smile stiffened, as though it had been frozen. She raised her chin.

"Indeed, Mr. Chase, please be sure to tell Miss Kate that I do understand—quite." She drew her fingers away, keeping her voice carefully bright and even. "It's such a pity though—I can fancy her disappointment at not being able to come. Still—" her smile deepened—"there is one consolation. I'm quite certain Miss Kate will hear all about the party. She's so fortunate in having so many admirers among the gentlemen who are here."

The minutes passed. Minutes of humiliation, sick and cold, while Mary kept her smile fixed and unfaltering, and the ruins of the evening for which she had planned so carefully crumbled slowly about her head. Gentleman after gentleman appeared, shook hands, and moved on. Then suddenly, the usher's voice rang clearly:

"The Honorable Stephen Douglas and Mrs. Douglas."

Mary turned swiftly toward the door. Adele Douglas, her blonde curls smooth and shining, her figure elegant in dull rose brocade, was coming in.

There was a stir—an almost tangible wave of surprise and disbelief—among the guests who stood near the door. They turned to stare, open-mouthed, like boys caught in the midst of a prank that hadn't quite come off.

"My dear Mrs. Lincoln—" Mrs. Douglas took Mary's hand. Her voice, low and clear, carried over the hush. "How charming everything looks."

It was then, for the first time, that Mary found herself weakening. Her knees trembled, and she felt her smile waver uncertainly. But the next moment Mr. Douglas was before her, and she felt his hand on hers, steady and reassuring.

"I'm glad we're not too late," he said. "I was afraid the dancing might have already begun—and I was hoping to ask you for the honor of the first one."

The band had just that minute struck up a waltz, and Mr. Douglas held out his arm.

"May I, then?"

Mary nodded. It would seem odd to dance, she thought, when there were so few ladies. But Mr. Douglas didn't appear to mind. He seemed rather to be enjoying himself, as he escorted her past the guests to the reception hall where the floor had been cleared. She looped her train up, and Mr. Douglas smiled.

"This is quite like old times, isn't it?" he said.

26

COLONEL ELLSWORTH RECOVERED FROM HIS MEASLES IN time to have one more Sunday dinner at the White House before the news came that the Confederates were threatening Alexandria, and he and his Zouaves were ordered to move south. They sailed, that same evening, down the Potomac. Ellsworth was apologetic for the condition of his company. Having been hastily rounded up from the bar at Willard's, and other favorite haunts, some of them were noticeably the worse for wear.

"They'll be all right, though," Ellsworth said to Mr. Lincoln. "It's action they've been spoiling for—and once they get a taste of it, you'll hear well of them, sir." His face, beneath the peaked red cap, looked young and eager.

Mr. Lincoln nodded. "They'll be all right," he said. "I'm sure of it."

Two mornings later, a telegram was delivered to the White House.

Coming in late to breakfast, Mr. Lincoln said in a queer flat voice that Ellsworth was dead. He had been shot in the back and killed instantly by a Rebel innkeeper in Alexandria while he was climbing the stairs to fly the Union flag from the inn roof. He was still holding the flag, Mr. Lincoln said, when he fell.

The news came like a blank, black shock to the others at the table. Willie and Tad burst into a storm of weeping and rushed at their father, burying their heads against him, and refusing to be comforted.

Mary looked at Mr. Lincoln, dazed and unbelieving.

"It can't be true," she said. "It can't be—" Her eyes were on his, pleading. As if he might somehow soften the blow, make the truth untrue. But he only shook his head.

"It's just the beginning of the truth," he said slowly. "I suppose we must learn to get used to it."

It was Mary who insisted that the funeral must be at the White House, and all that day, while the household mourned and Mr. Lincoln went on working, it was Mary who made the arrangements for the service.

Late in the evening, when she had finished everything and went upstairs, Mary saw the light burning under Mr. Lincoln's study door. It was seldom, in these days, that she ventured to disturb him—but after a moment's hesitation, she knocked softly and went in. He was sitting at his desk, a letter before him, and he looked up as she came to stand beside him.

"I've been trying to write to Ellsworth's parents," he said. His face, in the circle of lamplight, was worn and heavy.

Mary saw the last lines he had written. ". . . *to the memory of my young friend and your brave and early fallen child . . . May God give you that consolation which is beyond all earthly power . . .*" While she watched, he signed the letter and laid down his pen.

Mary was silent for a moment, then she said slowly, "Do you know, Mr. Lincoln, when I lived in Lexington there was a doctor in town named Jackson. He used to come to our house often—and I remember how he told us that our Alex made him think of his little brother Jimmy. Jimmy was very like Alex, he said—gay and naughty and always into mischief. I heard this afternoon that Jimmy Jackson was the man who killed Ellsworth." Mary paused. "And then I heard that one of Ellsworth's men had killed Jackson. I suppose in the South tonight they're wanting revenge against the man who shot Jimmy Jackson—and here we're crying murder because Jimmy killed Ellsworth."

Mr. Lincoln sealed the letter and sat looking down at it. "Yes," he said. "And one cry is just like another . . ."

The morning they brought Ellsworth back was mild and sweet. Sitting next to Mr. Lincoln while the funeral service was read, Mary felt the warm breeze that stirred the black draperies she had hung to cover the crimson curtains in the East Room. She looked at the flag-draped coffin, and thought of Ellsworth, going through the manual of arms to amuse Tad and Willie. She remembered the new window pane in the south parlor, with the glazier's marks still fresh on it. She saw this room, thinking how she had fretted over it, wanting so to have it handsome to impress Kate Chase and the other ladies. She remembered the deep lines of tenderness and grief about Mr. Lincoln's mouth as he had sealed the letter to Ellsworth's parents, whom he had never seen. Hearing the words of death, measured and final in the shadowed room, Mary felt a numbing, helpless fear. It was as though a world had splintered at her feet, in jagged, shining fragments.

27

THEY SAID IN WASHINGTON THAT NOWADAYS A MAN HAD to be a Westerner to get anywhere.

"Unless a fellow's been a rail splitter—or at least a hog

caller—he don't stand a show with Abe's gang. And what's Lincoln up to anyway? Playing politics and finding jobs for all his Republican friends while the South steals a march on us."

"These Democrats hold tight to their seats," Mr. Lincoln said. "If the news got out there was a post office being given away at the South Pole the road there would be paved with frozen Virginians."

For three months Washington had watched the northern troops arrive, march through the city, and disappear across the Long Bridge to join the Army of the Potomac. The first enthusiasm for the shining brigades in their brave uniforms had begun to wear thin. All this hoopla was well enough, people said, but what became of them once they had marched south?

"Why don't they fight? We've sent the boys and the money. What's Lincoln waiting for?"

"If we don't get a move on, the war will be lost before we've begun it. They got the boys to sign up for three months—and the time's most out already. Why don't they go ahead and take Richmond and finish up the thing so's they can get back home?"

The generals were after Mr. Chase for more money. But the Treasury was empty, and when the secretary appealed to Congress, Congress said they couldn't raise any more till they had something to show for what they'd spent already. People had no heart for this war anyhow, and unless they saw some signs of action soon they'd lose patience altogether. Chase went back to the Cabinet, and the Cabinet appealed to Mr. Lincoln.

"There's such a thing as striking while public opinion is hot," they said nervously. "Every newspaper and minister and ten-cent orator in the North is howling for a victory."

"Yes," Mr. Lincoln said, "and so is the South."

"But the longer we wait, the better chance the enemy

has to prepare. If you could only persuade General Scott to make some sort of move—just to keep people quiet—"

"Well," Mr. Lincoln said, "I'll try. I'll talk to Scott again, and see what he says."

But Scott and General McDowell, who was commanding the Army of the Potomac, shook their heads.

"Hang public opinion," old Scott said. "What do the fool preachers and congressmen know about a war? Just let us try an attack once—and fail—and then see where your public opinion leaves you."

The general was in his parlor, his gouty leg propped up on a stool. The window blinds, drawn against the hot June sun, let through thin strips of light that lay across the flowered carpet. Mr. Lincoln sat facing him, his tall hat on the floor beneath his chair, his hands resting on his knees.

"McDowell is doing all he can," Scott said, "but the troops they've sent him are nothing more than schoolboys. They act as though the whole business were some sort of holiday—and talk about going home again in a few weeks. It takes some doing to lick boys as green as that into an army—and it takes money too. Tell your damned politicians that."

Mr. Lincoln sighed. "What about the regular army, general? We've been supporting one all these years."

The old man snorted. "The regular army is lined up against us, fighting for the South—the best of them, anyway." He reached out to pour himself a drink. "Better have one with me before you go," he said, as Mr. Lincoln stood up. "Good whisky's the only thing to keep a man alive in weather like this . . . No? Well, I hope you'll excuse my not seeing you to the door. Can't move around much, with this confounded leg."

"That's all right, I can let myself out," Mr. Lincoln said. He stood a moment, looking thoughtful, then he stooped and picked up his hat. "I'll tell them what you've said. I believe you and General McDowell know best—but it's a hard job keeping these fellows from blowing the roof off."

Hearing the outer door shut, the general drained his glass and leaned back, easing his collar. Queer chap, Lincoln, he thought. Not half bad, as politicians went. None of the usual poppycock—and he had the decency to give a man credit for knowing what he was about. He'd never have the stuff to amount to much of a soldier—too apt to shilly-shally around and see two sides to a question. But Seward and Cameron and Chase were fools. Thinking they could run an army from their damned department desks.

The air in the shuttered room was close and heavy. The general shifted a little, grunting at the sharp twinge of pain in his leg. His grizzled chin dropped forward, and his eyes closed . . . He couldn't see that this war they'd cooked up made much sense on either side. You spent your life building up a decent army, and then it split in two and began to fight itself. Sense or not, though, it was war. And war was still a soldier's business, even when you had your own men against you. It was hard to think of them—Jeb Stuart, Jackson, Longstreet, Beauregard, Joe Johnston . . . the best officers that ever came out of West Point. All gone. And you were left in the soup, with a mess of brigadiers who'd never fired a gun and troops so green they wouldn't burn with a fire under them. And the damned politicians.

"The generals say we can't fight without more money, and Congress won't raise any more money without a fight," Mr. Lincoln said to Mary. "I can't tell where the head ends and the tail begins."

"You'd better listen to the generals," Mary said. "I don't trust Chase—or Seward either. They're both jealous of you, Mr. Lincoln. Like as not they're trying to scheme things so that the war goes badly, and you'll be discredited."

"Oh, come now, mother—they're not as bad as all that."

Mary shrugged. "I don't expect you to believe me, though you listen to everyone else's advice gladly enough, I notice. I should think I might talk to you once in a while, Mr. Lincoln. I'm not entirely lacking in intelligence—"

"Why, mother, I never said you were."

"No; but you act it. Which is worse. Let me breathe one word of criticism against your precious Cabinet and you laugh at me and accuse me of being suspicious—"

"Well, you'll admit you're pretty hard on them, mother."

"All the same, I have eyes, Mr. Lincoln. And what I say is true. Everyone knows Chase wanted to be president—and if only you weren't so blind, you'd see that he'd stop at nothing now to take the honor away from you."

"Well, he's welcome to the honor—if he can find any," Mr. Lincoln said. "If he'll just find some way to get us out of this hash."

The last of June melted into July, and the heat grew worse. It hung over the crowded city while Congress stewed and sweated, and the Cabinet met in shirt sleeves, Secretary Welles lifting his beard to fan his neck with a large palm-leaf. They consumed gallons of the iced ginger beer Mary sent up. And still the war hung stalemate.

For Mary, the days were endless. It was impossible to keep the boys quiet. They raced and played and rode Willie's pony until their faces were scarlet with the heat, and when night came they were too restless and exhausted to sleep, and complained fretfully of headaches. Mary worried incessantly. She held long conversations with Mrs. Keckley over the dangers of malaria and typhoid, and the menace of the old sewage canal that wound past the foot of the White House grounds and spread foul smells and disease through the city.

Now that Cousin Lizzie had gone home to Springfield, Mary had no one but Mrs. Keckley to talk to. Mr. Lincoln was busy all day and half the night, and when he came to meals he sat staring at his plate, eating little and hardly seeming to hear when Mary spoke. It was too hot for Mary to go driving, and there was nothing left to do. After the long years of work, with the constant pressure of time at her heels, leisure was like a friend long lost and grown unfamiliar.

As for callers, there were none. The Red Room, which Mary and Mr. Montrose had decorated so charmingly as a place where she would receive visitors, stood empty and unused. Kate Chase and the southern ladies had seen to that. Miss Kate's pointed tongue grew no duller with the passing months, and she had the ear of every important person in Washington. Mary, alone in the White House, had the ear of no one save the President, and he could not always be counted on to listen.

In the confused hate that boiled up everywhere, criticism that had begun as dinner-table gossip was taken up and given the dignity of serious charges. Anything that would make the President look bad was welcomed by nine-tenths of the press, and stories about the President's wife were relished as spicy side dishes to vary the steady diet of vitriol. The President's wife was extravagant. She was vain, ill-tempered, stingy, mean and vulgar. She was a meddler, interfering with her husband's decisions, and playing politics to satisfy her personal grudges. Best of all, she was accused of being a spy. Rumors of her Confederate sympathies, enlarged and glorified, were trotted out and paraded before the country as solemn truths.

It might be a good idea, Mr. Lincoln suggested one day, if Mary were to take the boys and go away for a while. To the mountains or the seashore. Just until the hot spell blew over.

Mary flared up instantly.

"Do you want to get rid of me, Mr. Lincoln?"

No, no. Of course not. He was patient. He'd only thought she might enjoy a little change. Washington was no kind of place in summer—and the boys seemed to be getting all tuckered out . . .

So long as Mr. Lincoln must stay, Mary said, there was nothing, *nothing* that would induce her to leave him. She would be miserable every moment she was gone—knowing he needed her with him.

Mr. Lincoln sighed and said no more.

From that day on, Mary was careful never to complain of anything in Mr. Lincoln's presence. She made light of the weather, and insisted that the boys were thriving on the climate and had never been healthier. No word of the fevers that had worried her so, lest Mr. Lincoln should again suggest her going away. It was a curious fear that made her dread the thought of leaving him. As though she must cling, in the midst of the many pressures that pulled him this way and that, to the little that was still hers. She must hold fast, or else he would be lost altogether.

It was a relief when Ben Helm, Emilie's husband, came for a few days' visit. He brought messages from Emilie and the others at home, and Mary welcomed him eagerly, hungry for news. While Ben was at the White House, Mr. Lincoln offered him a commission in the Union army.

"We need young men like you," Mr. Lincoln said. "And it would be a fine thing for Mother if she could have Emilie here. To tell you the truth, Ben, it's been kind of lonesome since we came to Washington."

Urged by Mary, Ben wavered. He'd like to say yes—but there were some men in New York he'd have to talk to first. Men who had been at West Point with him. Southerners, like himself.

The day Ben left, Mary put her arms around him.

"Try to come back, Ben," she said. "We need you—so much."

A week later Ben's letter came, addressed to Mary. He'd thought it all over. She was please to tell Mr. Lincoln that he was deeply honored by his offer, but now that he had talked with his friends, he couldn't see his way clear to accepting. There was one man in particular, Colonel Robert Lee, who had just resigned his post at West Point to go home to Virginia. "He didn't try to influence me to join the Confederacy," Ben wrote. "Lee told me he is not in favor of secession. He is so opposed to this war that he hopes never to draw his sword in it—but he cannot fight against his own people. Nor can I."

Ben hoped Mary and Mr. Lincoln would understand.

Mary encountered General Scott at the White House a few days after Ben's letter came. His leg was still troubling him and he leaned heavily on his cane.

"I had a young officer on my staff in the Mexican Wars," he said. "Name was Lee. I've just heard he's resigned to go south." The old man was silent a moment, sucking in his cheeks. "Pity we've had to lose him too. He was the best soldier I ever saw." He looked at Mary out of pale, expressionless eyes. "I'm a Virginian myself," Scott said.

28

MARY CAME ACROSS AN UNEXPECTED LETTER IN HER MAIL one morning. Carefully written, on ruled white paper, it said the writer, one Rebecca Orville, would greatly appreciate an interview with Mrs. Lincoln on a matter of business. She hesitated to impose on Mrs. Lincoln's time—which she realized must be crowded—but if it were possible, Miss Orville would be deeply grateful for a few words of "advice and counsel."

Astonished by the novelty of anyone's wishing to consult her on anything requiring advice and counsel, Mary showed the letter to Mr. Stoddard.

"You'd better let me find out who this woman is before you answer," Mr. Stoddard said. "People are trying all sorts of queer tricks nowadays."

"Nonsense, Mr. Stoddard." Mary brushed aside his caution impatiently. "Anyone can see this person isn't planning any mischief." She took the letter. "I shall write today, and ask Miss Orville to come and see me. It can't do any harm, certainly, to hear what she has to say."

The afternoon when Miss Orville was expected, Mary ordered tea served in the Red Room. She was ready promptly at four, pleased with her new mauve silk gown and the prospect of a visitor. At five minutes past, there was a knock at the door and one of the pantrymaids, looking somewhat flurried, presented herself.

Please, there was a woman waiting with a note from Mrs. Lincoln, and what should they do?

What should they do? Mary echoed sharply. Why, show her in, of course. She had left word that a caller was expected. And why on earth, she wondered with annoyance, hadn't Edwards had her properly ushered in, instead of fetching out this creature from the pantry?

"But, Mrs. Lincoln," the maid looked more flustered than ever. "This woman is colored."

Mary looked at her blankly.

"Edwards told her there must've been a mistake, ma'am. He sent her around to the kitchen to wait—"

Mary rallied quickly. "There's been no mistake," she said. "Please bring Miss Orville to me at once."

"In here, Mrs. Lincoln?"

"Certainly."

"But—what shall we do about tea, ma'am? You ordered it served—"

"Serve it, of course." Mary ignored the look of outraged dignity. "Now go fetch Miss Orville—and mind you're civil about it."

A few minutes later a young mulatto woman, quiet and well mannered, was shown in. Mary greeted her kindly, apologizing for the delay and misunderstanding at the door. She talked pleasantly, anxious to put Miss Orville at her ease, but it was entirely impossible to overlook the glaring insolence of the pantrymaid who presently appeared with tea. Without waiting to serve the guest, the maid disappeared, slamming the door behind her.

Mary saw the embarrassment on her guest's face. She saw also that the tea was half cold, and the only refreshments were a few stale-looking cakes carelessly arranged on an ordinary kitchen plate.

"I'm sorry, Mrs. Lincoln," the woman said. "I expect I should have told you more about myself before I came. But I—didn't think you'd be expecting me to take tea—"

Mary rose and handed Miss Orville her cup.

"I'm very glad you could come," she said, smiling. She offered the cakes. "I only hope I'll be able to give you the advice you wanted."

Miss Orville explained that she was a teacher. She was also a member of the colored Presbyterian church on Fifteenth Street, and through the church an effort was being made to supply some sort of school for the Negro children in Washington.

"There are a great many free colored people in the city, Mrs. Lincoln." Miss Orville leaned forward earnestly. "We're respectable people. Quite a lot of us own our own homes, and pay taxes. But we haven't any way of educating our children."

The District had laws, she said, forbidding Negroes to enter any public building, and this included the schools. They had to obey a special curfew which kept them off the streets after ten o'clock at night.

"We try to do as much as we can for ourselves. We have enough teachers—and we've been holding classes for the children in the church. But we're crowded there, and we want to have a regular school building."

They had raised the necessary money, Miss Orville said, but their plan had been blocked by a number of Washington citizens who were objecting to the idea of educating the Negro children. Unless they could get some support from influential people, the whole plan would be lost.

The woman talked well, without either rancor or false humility, and Mary listened sympathetically. She would speak to Mr. Lincoln at once, she promised, and see what could be done.

Miss Orville was grateful, but she seemed rather taken aback by the suggestion. They wouldn't want to trouble the President with their affairs at a time like this—when he had so much important work to do. They had thought perhaps if Mrs. Lincoln would just be willing to mention the school to some of her friends—

Mary smiled inwardly at the picture of herself murmuring the suggestion into influential ears. But she assured Miss Orville that she would do her best. She was pleased and touched by the gratitude in the woman's face as she rose to go.

"My people will always remember your kindness, Mrs. Lincoln," Miss Orville said warmly.

Remembering the difficulty with Edwards at the door, Mary was careful to escort her guest out personally. As they walked through the hall, Mary saw Edwards's glower of disapproval. He climbed down from his stool, and at the very moment when he swung open the front door and Mary turned to shake hands cordially with Miss Orville, a carriage swept up beneath the portico outside and a flunky in mulberry livery stepped smartly from the box.

Mary froze. There was only one carriage in Washington with that livery. It was Secretary Chase, arriving for a meeting of the Cabinet. But it was not at Mr. Chase that Mary looked. She barely saw him as he hurried past her and up the stairs. Her eye was fixed on the carriage outside, where Miss Kate, all in cool white, with a parasol tipped elegantly over her sharp, pretty face, was leaning forward.

And from the gleam of amused astonishment in Miss Kate's glance as the carriage whisked away, Mary knew that the little scene of the President's wife shaking hands with a Negro woman at the White House door had not gone unobserved.

There was no chance for Mary to speak to Mr. Lincoln that evening. The Cabinet meeting dragged on until ten o'clock, at which time General Scott arrived, to stump upstairs and remain closeted with the President for another two hours.

Next morning, when Mr. Lincoln came in to breakfast, he told Mary that a plan of attack against the Confederates had finally been drawn up. General McDowell would move his army against Beauregard at Manassas—while General Patterson held the other half of the southern force in the Shenandoah valley.

"Sherman thinks we're still not ready," Mr. Lincoln said, "but General Scott finally gave his consent last night."

Mary looked at him anxiously. His face was drawn and gray.

"They talk and talk," Mrs. Lincoln said, "and the more they talk, the worse it sounds."

But as the news spread through Washington, it was hailed with delight. The long, dreary delay was over, and the city came out of its midsummer doldrums to celebrate. The voices around the bar at Willard's were loud with bragging.

"We can't lose. Now the fool politicians have quit their wrangling—we're sure to win. We've got more men, more generals, more equipment. The damned Rebels'll run like rabbits once they see we really mean to fight."

The young officers, riding up from the Potomac camps that evening, raised their glasses in a fine spirit of defiance. They had never seen a battle, most of them, but the light of victory shone brightly in their eyes.

"We'll show the measly Graybacks a thing or two," they vowed thickly. "Just let us throw one good scare into them—and they'll kite for home fast enough."

Returning to their camps, late in the hot night, the officers sounded off alarms to see what their troops would do. When they came scrambling pell-mell out of the tents, the officers were doubled up, convulsed by the killing spectacle of the men, half dazed with sleep, brandishing their guns and rushing about with shouts that the Rebs were on them. It was a great success.

The mood of stunning self-confidence that emanated from the plush and gilt interior of Willard's that night only intensified the public conviction that the coming battle was bound to rout the southern armies. People in the streets spoke happily of getting the boys home again. And high time too. July 21st, the day set for the attack, was popularly regarded as the end of the war.

Even old General Scott caught a trace of the prevailing cheer, and admitted things looked promising enough. A smile lighted Mr. Lincoln's tired eyes when he heard that, but Mary shook her head.

"They forget one thing, Mr. Lincoln," she said. "The South is fighting for its life in this war. Our men, most of them, are only fighting because they've been told to."

Mr. Lincoln stood at the window of his study, looking through a glass toward the Virginia hills, low and rolling. From a steepletop in Alexandria the stars and bars of the Confederacy floated defiantly in the breeze.

Mary stood beside him.

"General Scott says our troops are still as green as grass," she said.

"Well, so are the Rebels green, mother," Mr. Lincoln said. He put down the glass with a sigh. "I suppose it will be a contest to see which side is greenest."

With all Mr. Lincoln's attention taken up by conferences over the new developments, Mary still found no chance to bring up the subject of Miss Orville's school.

Meanwhile, wanting to talk to someone, she confided in Mr. Stoddard.

"After all," Mary said, "Washington doesn't seem to regard me very favorably as an ornament to the Capital—so I may as well try making myself useful. I like this plan of Miss Orville's—she's sensible and honest, and I intend to help all I can. I've promised her to come and see the building where they plan to have the school, and then, as soon as Mr. Lincoln has more time, I shall consult him about it. He's quite certain to approve—"

Mary broke off, aware that Mr. Stoddard was frowning in a peculiar way.

"You don't seem very enthusiastic, Mr. Stoddard."

He glanced up, embarrassed. Rather reluctantly, doing his best to be tactful, he suggested that Mrs. Lincoln's taking up such a plan might be awkward. Washington people might misunderstand, and there would be talk.

"Talk?" Mary's brows rose sharply. "There's talk enough anyway, I should think. They can't say worse things of me than they do already, Mr. Stoddard—and this, at least, would have the novelty of being true."

Mr. Stoddard shook his head. This, he said, was different. At a time like this, with feeling running so high, the city was full of people just waiting for a chance to jump on anything to discredit the President. And for the President's wife to sponsor a school for Negroes . . .

He paused. It was the devil and all trying to explain what he meant. With Mrs. L. sitting there watching him, touchy as a firecracker and refusing to see what was as plain as a nose on a face. Of all things, he thought despairingly, for her to have gone and got herself keyed up about.

"They've accused me of being a Southerner and a spy, Mr. Stoddard. Wouldn't this prove that I'm not proslavery?"

Mr. Stoddard hesitated again. "I'm afraid people who circulate such stories aren't likely to be convinced by any sort of proof, Mrs. Lincoln."

"Then what am I to do, pray? Just sit by—and do nothing at all?"

"Well—for the present, it might be best. In these times, one can't be too cautious—"

Whack!

Mary's fist came down on the table between them with a suddenness that stopped Mr. Stoddard short. There—he'd gone and done it now. For all his pains, and trying to be tactful, he'd got her in a wax and no mistake.

"Mr. Stoddard, I will not hear that word *cautious* again—" Mary's eyes blazed. "Every fool in this city talks of nothing but being cautious. You sound like Mr. Lincoln, forever saying we must go slowly."

"Mrs. Lincoln, *please*—" Mr. Stoddard glanced uneasily at the door. "You may be overheard—"

"I haven't the slightest doubt I'm being overheard, Mr. Stoddard. Every word I utter in this wretched house is overheard—with servants peeping and spying at the keyholes for some new gossip to spread all over town. And then you talk to me of caution. I've tried your precious caution, Mr. Stoddard, and what has it got me? Nothing but hatred and lies. Spiteful, vicious lies about me—about Mr. Lincoln—even about my children."

"Yes, yes—I know." Mr. Stoddard mopped his forehead. "I realize it's been most trying. But we can only be patient, Mrs. Lincoln—and try to understand . . ."

"Mr. Stoddard—do for mercy's sake stop trying to soothe me." Mary's voice trembled with fury. "You talk to me as though I were ill—or out of my mind. I shall thank you to remember that I'm neither. I tell you, Mr. Stoddard, I know quite well what I'm saying. I'm sick of caution. Sick to death. Ever since I came into this house, I've heard nothing but that hateful word. I must be cautious—I must be careful—I mustn't do this or that for fear of being misunderstood. I can't go into a shop to buy a new dress without being accused of extravagance. I must hold my tongue and smile no matter what lies they spread about me. I daren't read the letters from my own family because they happen to live in the South and I'll be called a traitor. I'm spied on and talked about in my own house—but I can't discharge a servant who is insolent to me for fear of having more vile stories spread about me. And then you tell me I must be patient and try to understand—" Her voice broke bitterly. "You are the one who doesn't understand, Mr. Stoddard. How can I be patient when I'm humiliated every day of my life? I'll go mad if I keep on this way—doing nothing—afraid to speak or move. I'm practically a prisoner in this house."

"I know—I know, Mrs. Lincoln. Believe me, I see how difficult it's been, but still, you must think of your position—"

"My *position!*" Mary flung the word back at him furiously. "My position is a laughingstock, Mr. Stoddard. Washington has seen to that. They've hounded me and made a fool of me, until you and the others pity me. You talk about me behind my back—oh, don't deny it, Mr. Stoddard, I know the things you say. Don't you think I read the letters my son Robert writes to me? Asking me to be more careful, more discreet, because there has been so much talk. What do you think I care for my position when my own son is ashamed of the lies he hears about me? And you dare to sit there telling me I must think of my position. You're a young fool, Mr. Stoddard. A blundering, self-important fool!"

Mary sank back in her chair. The anger died out of her in a shuddering wave, leaving only misery. She covered her eyes, feeling the tears against her fingers, helpless and shaming. And through the spinning emptiness she could hear Mr. Stoddard's words. His distressed apologies. He was so sorry—he hadn't meant to say anything that would upset her. She must try to calm herself, not to allow herself to get so overwrought. No matter how unreasonable he thought her, Mary realized, he must try to make amends now. He must cater to her, humor her, give in to her. Not because he had an ounce of affection or respect for her—but merely because she was Mr. Lincoln's wife, and so she mustn't be offended.

She dropped her hands.

"It's quite all right, Mr. Stoddard," she said. Somehow, she felt, out of this ridiculous and shameful scene she must manage to show him she wasn't an utter fool. She stood up, shakily, and smiled at him, a smile that bit deep in the corners of her mouth.

"You see—there's no reason to be alarmed, Mr. Stoddard. I'm quite myself."

She began to gather up her letters, fumbling at them, cramming the edges into an even pile. At the door, she turned to look back. Mr. Stoddard was standing at the table.

"About the plans for the school, Mr. Stoddard—I mean to go ahead just as I said. After all, I gave my word to Miss Orville—"

Mr. Stoddard bowed stiffly.

"Very well, Mrs. Lincoln."

She closed the door. Crossing from the Red Room, past the dour glance of Edwards, Mary moved swiftly. She went up the stairs, her head held carefully high. And the full sweep of her stiff blue gown hid the trembling of her knees.

The Union attack was set for Sunday morning, at dawn.

It was convenient, having the date and hour posted in advance. For half of Washington, it appeared, was making plans to drive down the night before and be on hand to watch the show. It was worth going twenty miles, after all, to see the Union victorious. "Southern chivalry will bite the dust," they said. "Watching the Graycoats run will be a treat for sore eyes."

By sundown on Saturday all the preparations had been made. Senators, judges, congressmen, and lesser dignitaries had marshaled their carriages for the drive. Newspaper correspondents, sightseers, and assorted visitors in the city had besieged the local stables for hired hacks—and, after one last round for luck at Willard's bar, were off to battle. All that night the Long Bridge over the Potomac rumbled beneath the carriage wheels, and by morning Washington was practically a desert. Everyone who *was* anyone had gone.

It would never have done to leave out the ladies. They were as anxious as any to see the fray—and nearly every party had its quota of crinoline skirts and gaily ribboned bonnets. The ladies obligingly squeezed themselves into corners to make room for the loaded picnic hampers at their feet, and they set the sultry night air ringing with their gallant cries.

"On to Richmond!"

Tad and Willie, kept awake by the brave shouts of the departing company, grumbled bitterly at being left out of the fun.

"But *why* can't we go, mamma? Papa is the President—and we want to see the Johnny Rebs run too."

That night McDowell and Sherman sat late, talking with their lieutenants. The tent flaps were pinned back to let in the faint breeze, and the candles flickered, throwing shadows on the grave faces bent above the maps.

On the far side of Bull Run Creek, beyond its yellow, muddy banks, were Beauregard and Jackson, Longstreet and Joe Johnston.

The moon, rising late, shone clear. High and impartial, it floated through the night, making the tents bright where the soldiers lay, turning restlessly in a half-sleep, waiting . . .

29

THE SABBATH MORNING BROKE, HOT AND RED.

All day, in Washington, the telegraph wires clicked, bringing news. McDowell had attacked, and things appeared to be going well. The plan was working like a charm. By three o'clock that afternoon, Mr. Lincoln rose from his desk. He went to find Mary.

"Well, mother, it looks as though they've pulled it off." He stuffed the latest batch of telegrams into the pocket of his gray coat. He might walk down to General Scott's house, Mr. Lincoln said, and see what he thought of the news.

Mary was waiting at the front window when Mr. Lincoln came back.

"Well?" she looked at him closely. "What did Scott say?"

"He said it was damned hot." Mr. Lincoln sat down and pulled out a red cotton handkerchief to wipe his face. "But he admitted things look pretty favorable."

There seemed to be a lull in the telegraph messages.

"I guess the worst is over, mother," Mr. Lincoln said. "Why don't you order up the carriage? A breath of air might do us both good."

They drove for an hour, and everywhere in the streets the people seemed in high good humor. Some of them waved as the President's carriage passed. Now and then there was a voice raised in cheerful greeting.

"Good luck, Abe!"

"Hurray for Lincoln and our side!"

Mr. Lincoln smiled and waved back, answering the cheers.

"Our stock seems to have gone up, mother," he said.

When they came back to the White House, Mr. Nicolay was waiting on the front steps. He came forward at once, with an odd expression.

"Mr. Lincoln, may I have a word with you?"

A moment later Mr. Lincoln turned back to Mary. "Seward was here while we were gone," he said. "He's over at the War Office now. I think I'll just walk over and see what's up."

Mary felt a twinge of alarm. "It's bad news, Mr. Lincoln—" She put her hand on his arm. "I know it is—don't try to hide it from me—"

"Now, mother—" he patted her hand consolingly—"it's no use getting all fired up. Seward didn't say there was anything wrong. Most likely he's just got some bee in his bonnet he wants to tell me about. You and the boys better go ahead with supper. I'll be as quick as I can."

But there was an uneasy note in Mr. Lincoln's voice that troubled Mary. All through supper, while the boys gabbled noisily about the news of the battle, she was listening—waiting for the sound of Mr. Lincoln's step.

By eight o'clock, when it was time for the boys to go to bed, he still hadn't come. Willie was teasing for a story.

"Mother, you *said* you would. You *promised*, if we won the fight today you'd read us extra—"

Mary looked down at Willie's flushed face. He and Taddie had been up since dawn—and she had been too preoccupied to notice how long they had stayed outdoors, racing in the sun. They were both fretful and keyed up, after the excitement of the long day.

"Please, Willie, you and Tad go to bed like good boys. I—" Mary paused, glancing at the door. She thought there was a footstep. But it was nothing. "I'll read to you tomorrow. And I'll play with you all day—truly I will."

"But, mamma, you said *tonight*. You *said*—"

Mary bit back a quick jab of impatience. Hastily, before Taddie should start to cry, she promised that Mrs. Keckley could read. "You can tell her I said she might."

"As long as we want her to, mamma?" Taddie's eye, never slow to catch a bargain, brightened artfully. "Until we go to sleep, mamma?"

"Yes, I suppose so—if you'll only go quietly now."

As the boys rushed upstairs, Mary followed slowly. She ought to be more firm with them really. They were getting so out of hand. But it was difficult, with the house always filled with people, and hours so irregular. Hearing Mrs. Keckley's voice, calm and reassuring, and the door close, Mary turned into her sitting room. She stood a minute, grateful for the silence, but it was stiflingly hot in the room, and her head ached, with a dull, insistent beat. She pressed her hands against her eyes.

Where *was* Mr. Lincoln? Why didn't he come? Surely he couldn't have forgotten that she was waiting . . .

She turned abruptly and went to the wardrobe, to fetch out a bonnet and gloves. There wasn't any reason to stay here. She could send for the carriage and drive awhile. It was barely dusk, and out of the house at least she could breathe.

As the carriage turned down the avenue, Mary leaned back and closed her eyes. There—it was better now. The heaviness, the vague uneasy feeling was gone. The sound of people's voices and the smart clatter of traffic on the cobbled street were comforting. She drew a long breath, and opened her eyes.

They were nearly at the corner in front of Willard's Hotel. A crowd was gathered there, grouped about the door, and they seemed to be listening to a man who was calling something and waving a paper. Mary glanced curiously. It was odd that the man should shout so. She bent forward, trying to catch the words, but they were lost in the noise and confusion.

Everyone seemed to be shouting now. But it couldn't be good news that made them act like this, Mary thought. The faces she saw looked angry and frightened. Suddenly a woman screamed, close by the carriage. Mary turned, and saw the woman throw up her hands.

"*They're coming—the Rebels are coming!*" The woman rushed out into the street, her arms waving, her bonnet half off. "*They're marching on the city—and we'll all be killed—murdered . . .*"

Still screaming hysterically, the woman barely missed being struck by Mary's carriage. The coachman managed to swerve just in time, but the startled horses plunged, lurching the carriage so that Mary was nearly thrown out. There were more voices now, rising shrill and panicky.

"We're lost—they've beaten us—"

"Our troops are routed—"

"They're marching on us—we'll be killed—"

"We'll all be killed—"

The carriage heaved again. The coachman, caught in the sudden, milling rush, struggled to quiet the horses and steer them clear of the crowd. But it was already too late. Someone had recognized Mary—and they were closing in around her, screaming and shaking their fists. Jeers and hoots rose in a frightening chorus.

"There she is—look!"

"There's Mrs. Lincoln!"

A rough-looking man, bolder than the rest, pushed his way through the crowd and leaped onto the carriage step.

"Lincoln's to blame for this!" The man pushed a hairy face close to Mary's. "He'll pay for it—just wait and see. We'll make him pay—see if we don't—"

Mary shrank back, clutching the seat, her hands clammy, her eyes wide and unflinching as she stared into the man's sweating, leering face. She could feel his breath, fuming with whisky. She saw the coachman turn—saw him raise his whip—but she managed to speak in time, and at her sharp command, he lowered the whip.

The man still clung to the step, pouring out a stream of black abuse.

Suddenly a girl at the edge of the crowd brandished her fringed parasol. "Hurray for Jeff Davis!" The girl's voice rose defiantly. "God is on the side of the South!"

For a moment the crowd's attention was diverted from Mary as they turned on the girl, trying furiously to howl her down. But she was instantly surrounded by Rebel sympathizers. A tall gentleman flung his hat into the air. "Three cheers for Beauregard. Old Beau has knocked the damned Yankees into a cocked hat."

"The South has won—"

"*Down with the South!*" Another gentleman seized the tall Southerner's topper and drove his fist through it. "There's your cocked hat for you."

In the brawling confusion, the coachman saw his chance. He wheeled the horses, and whipped them up. The carriage swayed perilously, then righted, and the next instant they were clattering up the cobbled street while the howling melee died in the distance. Only the burly man, shaken loose from the step when the carriage turned, followed a little way, still shouting.

"She's a dirty spy. Lincoln's wife's a spy . . ."

And then he too was left behind.

Old Edwards had been dozing on his perch by the door when Mary came in. She stared at him, blinking in the sudden light after the dusk outside.

"Has—Mr. Lincoln come yet, Edwards?"

Yes, a few minutes ago. He'd gone upstairs with Mr. Seward and Mr. Cameron. There was to be a Cabinet meeting, Edwards said. He was looking at Mary, moved to curiosity for once by the sight of her white face.

"Are you all right, ma'am?"

Mary nodded. Her knees were like water, and her hands shook as she tried to straighten her hat, but she managed to turn toward the stairs. Once her hand was on the banister, she felt safer. She paused, gathering her strength.

Edwards was still watching, puzzled. She must have heard the news, judging from the look of her. Or else seen a ghost. He'd never thought to see her like that—her, with her proud eye and her head always in the air, as if the ground were too poor a thing to give a glance to. He followed a little way, thinking she might need a hand—and when she was halfway up, he remembered to call after her.

"Mr. Lincoln said to tell you when you came in, ma'am —there's nothing to worry about."

It was nearly one o'clock when Mary heard the door of the Cabinet room open, and the sound of the departing gentlemen's steps. She went out into the corridor, and waited until Mr. Lincoln turned back from the head of the stairs alone. He didn't seem surprised to see her standing there, still dressed. He only looked at her.

"What is it, mother?" His voice was cold and lifeless.

Mary hurried to him. "Mr. Lincoln, I had to see you. I had to know. Is it true what people are saying? The dreadful things—that we've been beaten?"

"Yes, it's true. We lost today."

"But the things they said, Mr. Lincoln—I was out on the street and I heard them. The people were so angry—

so frightened. They said we'd been ruined—that we'd lost everything. They said our army was routed and the men were deserting—"

"We don't know yet," Mr. Lincoln said. "We don't know just how bad it is. But I don't believe we're ruined. We made a mistake, it seems . . ." He paused. "God knows what that mistake has cost. We must try to find out now how to keep from making more."

"Mr. Lincoln, how could it have happened? How could everything have gone wrong so suddenly? You said yourself—General Scott said, this afternoon—"

He shook his head slowly. "They did their best," he said. "McDowell did the best he could."

"How do you know that, Mr. Lincoln? How can you be sure? You take things so on faith." She must shake him out of this lifelessness somehow, Mary thought. Make him listen. "Don't you see, Mr. Lincoln? They could have tricked you into this failure. Because they hate you—because they want to make the people blame you. They *are* blaming you, Mr. Lincoln. The people I saw tonight—they were saying you'd have to answer for this. They said terrible things."

"Yes, I know." He paused a minute. "Well, when the news is bad, I suppose they have to blame someone."

"But why must it be you, Mr. Lincoln? Why must you let them put everything on you?"

He came closer and put his hands on her shoulders.

"You're all tired out, mother," he said. "You'd better go to bed and try to get some sleep."

It was no use. He hadn't even heard her. He'd listen to the others, trust the others, believe every word they said. But when she spoke, he didn't even hear.

"What about you, Mr. Lincoln? You're tired too."

"I'll wait up awhile. There may be more news."

For a moment more she stood looking up at him, wanting so to reach him, to say something that would ease the sadness that lay deep in his eyes. But there was no way . . . She only made things worse. She turned away.

Passing the study door, she saw Mr. Nicolay standing by the desk, waiting. He held a sheaf of telegrams in his hand. Glimpsing his face, opaque and expressionless, as she passed, Mary wondered how much he had heard. Everything, no doubt.

On the threshold of her room, she turned to look back along the empty corridor. The study door was shut.

30

IN THE MORNING MARY WOKE TO SEE THE RAIN. A GRAY, listless rain that fell like a chilling curtain after the days of heat. She got up and dressed, smoothing her hair into place, and crossed to Mr. Lincoln's room. The door stood half open, and she saw the bed untouched.

Down the hall, in front of the study, Mr. Hay was standing guard. He touched his lips warningly as Mary came near.

"Mr. Hay, where is Mr. Lincoln?"

"In the study—sleeping. People have been coming in to see him all night, and he insisted on staying up to talk to them. They'd come back from the fight—and he wanted to hear what they could tell him."

"You should have called me, Mr. Hay. He ought to have had something to eat—"

Mr. Hay had seen to that. He had ordered up coffee and eggs at five o'clock.

"But surely he can't be warm enough. Sleeping on that couch—it's turned so cool. He'll need a blanket, Mr. Hay."

Mr. Hay had attended to that too. He had fetched a quilt from his own room and put it over Mr. Lincoln.

Mary bit her lip. She looked over Mr. Hay's shoulder, at the closed door. Then, slowly, she walked back to her room.

By nine o'clock the cavalcade of visitors had begun

again. All that day it kept up, steady and monotonous as the rain. Congressmen and senators, the sightseers who had started out so confidently to the battlefield were back now—their eyes wide, their voices hoarse, as they described the horrors they had seen. The utter rout of McDowell's army. The stampede on the field. The disordered, panic-stricken retreat.

They were full of indignant stories. Of officers lashing their men, trying to force them back into line. Of deserters, throwing down their guns and running wildly off the field into the woods.

In awestruck tones the gentlemen told how narrowly they had managed to escape with their own lives. Their carriages had been all but wrecked by the deserting wretches who had cut loose from their regiments and were crowding the roads north.

Sitting at his desk, Mr. Lincoln heard the accounts, breathless and dramatic. "I congratulate you, gentlemen," he said dryly, "on winning the race."

By late afternoon the returning stream of carriages had stopped—and the soldiers, on foot, began to straggle in. Their boots, still caked with Virginia mud, left tracks on the new stair carpet as they filed up to Mr. Lincoln's office. The stories they had to tell were briefer. After walking twenty miles, they hadn't much breath left to shout.

The fight had been going all for the North, they said, until midafternoon. Then something had happened—no one could quite tell what. But the enemy had taken a new hold—begun rushing them. And before they could re-form to counterattack, Jackson's troops had been on them. They came like a gray wave—with a yelling that was like no sound they'd ever heard. The Union officers had done the best they could—some of them, anyway—but the men were running wild. Companies had got broken up, and everybody was too scared to pay much attention to orders. And those confounded carriages that had come down from Washington—cluttering up the field—and the ladies screaming blue murder. It had been a mess.

Mr. Lincoln sat at his desk, listening. Listening to anyone who would come in and talk. Listening to excuses, explanations, stories of the long trek back to the city. Of roads jammed with men who were lost or who had deserted, retreating helter-skelter through the night—of the carriages, forcing their way through, refusing to stop and pick up those who had fallen by the way. Stories of wounded men who had walked all night long, supported by their comrades . . . Listening . . .

Coming downstairs into the front hall that afternoon, Mary found a group of soldiers who had just left the President's office. They were standing by the door, looking out at the rain. Seeing their wet coats and muddy boots, and the exhaustion in their faces, she paused and asked where they were expecting to go. They turned, staring at her dumbly.

They didn't rightly know, one said, shuffling his cap. Nobody seemed to know just what they were supposed to do.

"But there must be some place for you," Mary said. "They must have made some arrangements."

The men shook their heads, looking at each other uncertainly.

"I guess we can find some place, ma'am."

Mary hesitated, then she turned toward the corridor.

"Come with me," she said, and led the way to the East Room. "You can make yourselves comfortable here. I'll have a fire built, so you can dry your clothes, and see about some food right away."

Within an hour there were kettles of soup and coffee boiling on the big ranges in the kitchen, and Mary was supervising trays, having them sent up to the East Room. One of the soldiers had told her there were more men outside, lying on the benches in Lafayette Square across the way, and she had sent Mr. Stoddard over to find them, and bring as many as would come back with him. They had come in, rain soaked and dazed with fatigue, and been sent to the East Room.

When she went up again, Mary found the men silent, grouped about the fire. A few were perched gingerly on the edges of the brocaded chairs and sofas, but most were sitting on the floor. They stared uncomfortably as she came in. One or two stood up. But none of them spoke. When the food was brought, they ate and drank hungrily, in silence.

Most of the men had taken off their wet coats, and Mary saw that a few had wounds they had bandaged clumsily themselves. She hurried upstairs to find Mrs. Keckley, and together they ransacked the linen closets for old sheets to tear into strips. But when they took the bandages down, it was to Mrs. Keckley that the men turned. Mary was puzzled to notice how easily the men talked to Mrs. Keckley, and how their smiles died and they lapsed into uneasy silence again whenever she approached. But on the whole she was relieved to leave the dressings to Mrs. Keckley's capable, experienced hands—while she went to the kitchen again to see about fresh coffee.

On one trip, she met Mr. Stoddard in the hall.

"Mr. Stoddard, if you're not too busy, would you give me a minute? Some of the men are so tired, they've fallen asleep. And they really ought to have some covering. I'm going to fetch some blankets. If you could help me carry them down—"

"Certainly, Mrs. Lincoln, if you wish it." Mr. Stoddard's tone was stiff.

Mary glanced at him sharply. What on earth could have got into him to answer like that? Surely he wasn't offended by such a simple request. Then she remembered that they hadn't seen each other since the unfortunate discussion about Miss Orville and the school. Good heavens, it wasn't possible he was still harping on a little misunderstanding—and at a time like this. But evidently he was waiting for her to say something. Mary smiled.

"Mr. Stoddard—"

He turned.

"Mr. Stoddard, I've been meaning to speak to you. Naturally, I'm sure you realize that any—" she hesitated, still smiling—"any differences of opinion between us are not to be taken personally. For my part, I'm quite sure your advice the other day was entirely well meant."

Mr. Stoddard bowed. "It's very generous of you to see it that way."

Mary went on smoothly, while she gathered up the blankets. As a matter of fact, she said, she had talked over the matter with Mr. Lincoln—and while he was *quite* in sympathy, he felt that she had better not undertake any active part in the school until Miss Orville's plans were more definite. Possibly in the autumn, Mr. Lincoln had said. She had written to Miss Orville and explained.

"So you see, Mr. Stoddard, you were quite right after all." Mary laid the last folded blanket on the pile in Mr. Stoddard's arms and smiled up at him again, briskly. There—she thought. Surely he would see now that she bore him no grudge for their little quarrel. She was on the point of starting toward the stairs to go down when she caught something in Mr. Stoddard's glance that made her hesitate.

It was an odd look about his eyes. A look that was half amused, half pitying. He might have looked at Taddie like that, she thought, when Taddie had been naughty and willful and was trying to make amends by being extra good. Mary lifted her chin. She must look haggard and badly, she thought suddenly. She'd slept so little the past two nights—in the rush this afternoon, she'd had no time to tidy herself. She pushed back a loose strand of hair from her cheek.

"Will you take the blankets please, Mr. Stoddard?" Her voice was stiff and even. "And tell Mrs. Keckley I shall be down presently."

"Yes, Mrs. Lincoln." The look vanished from Mr. Stoddard's eyes, leaving them blandly impersonal again.

He stood aside to let her pass, and she swept by quickly, her chin still high—not looking back.

Another night passed, and still there was no sign of a Rebel invasion. Washington relaxed. Not a single citizen had been murdered in his sleep.

People came out of the first hysterical shock of defeat, and took time to look around and get mad. What, they demanded indignantly of each other, had gone wrong with the glorious Army of the Potomac? The army that had boasted so loudly the night before the battle? The army that was in pieces now—scattered and disgraced? Somewhere, they said darkly, there must be a scapegoat in all this—and they meant to smoke him out.

Congress and the Cabinet said it was the generals' fault. The generals, soothing their smarting pride, howled back that it was the meddling politicians who were to blame.

And Lincoln.

Where was Lincoln in all this? they demanded. Lincoln wouldn't say yes and he wouldn't say no. While the air was thick with hurtling brickbats, Lincoln sat tight, refusing to come out and say who had been to blame.

"For mercy's sake, Mr. Lincoln, why don't you stop all this argument?" Mary said impatiently. "Admit that the Rebels fought too well for us—and be done with it."

But General Scott thought otherwise.

"It wasn't Beauregard and Jackson who beat us," the old man said to Mary. "It was our own blockheadedness. Too many cheers ahead of time." He rubbed the silver head of his cane gloomily. "People think they can win a war just by yelling loud enough they're going to. Now they've found they're wrong—and they want to chop off a few heads to make themselves feel better. McDowell's will be the first to go—though he doesn't deserve it. And Patterson's too. If anyone's to blame, it's me—for being fool enough to let them talk me into a fight when I knew we weren't ready. But they'll never think to take my head off. It's too old and tough to give them any satisfaction."

"Do you think Mr. Lincoln was wrong?" Mary asked. "Do you think he ought to have tried to make them wait longer?"

"Of course he was wrong. The politicians are always wrong." The general thumped his stick. "All the same, though, Lincoln's man enough to own up to his mistakes—and that's more than the others will ever do." He looked at Mary in silence for a moment. His eyes, under grizzled brows, were cold and tired. "Lincoln might learn," he said. "He might turn out to be a pretty good president. Only—try to keep him from taking these things too hard. He's got a long way to go yet."

31

IN THE WEEKS THAT FOLLOWED, MARY OFTEN FOUND herself remembering the old general's words. It all happened just as he had said it would. McDowell and Patterson were in disgrace. And still the grumbling, the endless hue and cry of criticism went on.

"Why don't they do something? They got us into this war—and now they sit and talk—and get us nowhere."

The more they railed, it seemed, the less Mr. Lincoln was willing to commit himself to any policy. Floods of conflicting advice poured in on him. Hour after hour, week after week, he sat in his study listening.

"In the name of heaven, Mr. Lincoln, what more is there for you to hear?" Mary said. "You listen to every Tom, Dick, and Harry who wants to air a crackpot scheme. You take every word your Cabinet utters as though it were graven on tablets of stone."

"Well, mother, they're the best men I knew how to pick. I have to trust someone."

Mary leaned toward him. "Then trust yourself, Mr. Lincoln."

He looked at her for a long moment. Then he sighed. "I wish to God I could."

"Stop listening to everyone who says you are wrong, Mr. Lincoln. Stop blaming yourself for everybody else's mistakes. You're the President—you're the one they elected. The whole country is looking at you—"

He shook his head.

"I know it, mother. I wish they'd look some other way."

Robert came home in August, after a month in Springfield. He said little about his visit there, except that everyone was well, but Mary could gather clearly enough from Elizabeth's letters the shocked fascination with which they dwelt on every shred of criticism against Mr. Lincoln.

Robert said little about anything, for that matter, except to tell his father he'd been thinking seriously of enlisting. Half his class at Harvard had gone already, he said, and it looked queer for him not to.

Mr. Lincoln looked at him thoughtfully. "You haven't mentioned this to your mother, have you, Bob?"

Well, not exactly, Robert said. He'd tried leading up to the subject once or twice, but she hadn't been encouraging.

"No, I expect not." Mr. Lincoln sighed. "Your mother's been upset lately. Things have been pretty hard on her, I guess, since we came to Washington." He hesitated, weighing a paperknife in his hand. "I know it's asking a good deal, Bob, but I'd appreciate it if you could kind of let this thing slide for a while. Maybe later—your mother might get more used to the idea."

Robert shrugged. Later might be too late, he said. The war might be over.

Mr. Lincoln smiled. "I guess there's no call to worry about that, Bob. From the looks of things, I'm afraid you'll have plenty of time. Only—" he looked up quickly—"don't tell Mother I said that, will you?"

Robert was careful not to mention the matter again, but Mary was uneasy. The last day before he left for Cambridge she asked him to promise her not to enlist.

"It's your father I'm thinking of, Robert. He has so much to trouble him these days—it wouldn't be fair to add another worry."

Robert was silent.

"When you've finished your education there will be plenty of time to talk of enlisting. And besides, you're not strong enough—"

"Oh, mother—for heaven's sake."

"Well, it's true, Robert. You've always had a delicate chest—ever since you were a baby. You know what dreadful colds you get. And if you were off in camp somewhere during the winter, I shouldn't have an easy moment." She put her hand on his. "Please, dear, promise me you won't think about it any more."

"I should think you might realize how it makes me look," Robert said. "With my own father calling for volunteers—I can't join up because my mother says I have a weak chest. It makes me feel like a fool."

"Oh, Robert—" Mary's eyes filled with tears—"how can you speak to me so? When I'm asking it for your father's sake—" her fingers tightened.

"All right, all right, mother. I've promised—isn't that enough?"

Mary pulled away her hand quickly. Her world, rocked for a moment with fear, came back to its precarious balance. She wiped her eyes.

"Yes, dear." Her smile quivered. "If you've given me your word, Robert, that's enough."

The nights were the hardest times now. With the late summer heat hanging over the city, Mary couldn't sleep. Hour after hour she lay staring into the stifling darkness. She would get up suddenly and cross to the boys' room, only to find them sleeping. But down the corridor she could see the crack of light under the study door.

Dear heaven, what could Mr. Lincoln be doing so late? She would tiptoe down and stand listening. Sometimes there was no sound, but often she could hear his steps, slow and even, moving back and forth, back and forth.

There was one night when she opened the door without knocking and went in. Mr. Lincoln turned to look at her. He was standing by the map rack before the mantel, his dark hair rumpled, his eyes ringed with weariness.

He stood waiting for her to speak, but now that she was here, Mary wondered what it was she had meant to say. She pushed one of her thick braids across the shoulder of her blue robe.

"I—couldn't sleep, Mr. Lincoln."

"I know, mother. Neither can I." He stood facing her, his shoulders drooping.

"I thought perhaps—if I could talk to you—"

But there wasn't anything to say, really. After a moment, Mr. Lincoln sighed.

"I wish things were easier for you, mother," he said. "Maybe if you had gone back with Robert—and stayed a few days in New York—"

Talking to Mr. Stoddard one morning, Mary had a sudden idea. The trouble with them all, she said, was that they had had no company for such a long time.

"Why shouldn't we plan a dinner for next week, Mr. Stoddard? Just for the Cabinet members and their families. I believe a party would do us good."

After the long dull drag of summer, it was nice to have something to plan for again. Mrs. Keckley was making up a new gown for Mary. A patterned white silk, sprigged with small bowknots of cornflower blue.

On the morning before the dinner, Mary tried on the frock for a last fitting. While Mrs. Keckley knelt beside her, pinning and snipping, Mary talked more cheerfully than she had in weeks. A thunderstorm the night before had broken the heat, and now a steady rain was falling, freshening the baked earth and washing the trees so that the leaves hung dark and glistening.

Tad and Willie, pleased by the novelty of a rainy day, were playing checkers on the sewing-room floor.

Mary and Mrs. Keckley discussed the plans for the dinner. Mary had decided to make it a larger affair. There were so many people back in the city—and it seemed a pity to go to all the trouble with only the Cabinet to enjoy it. She'd had to have the caterers from New York anyway, for there was simply no trusting the kitchen staff to do a dinner up in proper style—and besides, it saved so much wrangling and argument to have everything brought in from outside.

"It will do Mr. Lincoln a world of good," Mary said. "He needs cheering up—and he always enjoys a party, though he does fuss so ahead of time over having to dress for it."

She lifted one arm, so that Mrs. Keckley could adjust the waistline.

"What do you hear from your son these days, Mrs. Keckley? You told me he was in Tennessee, didn't you?"

Mrs. Keckley drew a basting shorter, stroking the gathers carefully with a pin. No, her son was in Ohio.

"Could you turn just a shade, madam? There—that's right."

Of course. Ohio. Mary remembered now. "I hope he's well?"

"Quite well, thank you." Mrs. Keckley tipped her head, considering the placing of a pin. "He's in the army now."

"Really?" Mary looked down in surprise.

Mrs. Keckley nodded. "He enlisted two months ago—in Ohio." She hesitated. "They put him in a white company —even though he told the officers his mother was colored. He says they're very good to him."

"I should think you must be very anxious about him."

Mrs. Keckley nodded again, quietly. Just at first, she said, she had been disappointed to have him interrupt his schooling. But now she was more used to the idea.

"When I told Mr. Lincoln, he said I ought to feel very proud. He said—" Mrs. Keckley paused, smiling a little—"that we must all learn to be anxious in these times. And then, of course—I'd expect my son to do whatever he thought was right, no matter how I felt about it."

"Yes," Mary said. "Yes, I suppose so." She turned to look into the long mirror. "It looks perfectly lovely, Mrs. Keckley. It's really a beautiful dress."

"Thank you, madam. I'm sure Mr. Lincoln will think it's very becoming. He always seems to admire you in that shade of blue."

Mary smiled at her reflection.

"I hope you'll let me know when you have news of your son," she said.

"Indeed I will, Mrs. Lincoln. It's kind of you to be interested."

Mary watched Mrs. Keckley stoop to brush the silk ravelings from her neat black skirt. She seemed to take it calmly enough, Mary thought. Her only son two whole months in the army—and she'd gone about quite as though nothing had happened, never even troubling to mention it. But then, it only went to show that with some people feelings never ran very deep.

From the look of things, Mary reflected, the dinner was starting out extremely well. She looked down the long table, lit softly by the candles in the wall brackets of the state dining room, and smiled graciously at Mr. Seward on her right. He was actually looking quite agreeable for once. His sharp eyes and long nose seemed less noticeable than usual. Perhaps Mr. Lincoln wasn't so wrong about him, after all.

Mr. Chase, on her left, was bland and impassive. She saw him eying the centerpiece, a concoction of white sugar doves and icing roses, topped by a gilded eagle with spread wings and lowered head who glared at the guests ferociously.

Catching Mr. Chase's glance, Mary smiled. "You approve, I trust?"

Mr. Chase touched his lips with his napkin. "It's—most original, I'm sure."

Mary was pleased. Mr. Chase was looking at the soup, which had just been put before him. Let him look, she thought confidently. There was nothing he could possibly criticize in terrapin flavored with sherry. Nor, for that matter, would he find any fault with the rest of the dinner. The caterers had seen to that. Mr. Seward, less tentative by nature, was already consuming his soup with evident relish.

Conversation generally was going well. Looking down the table, Mary saw that Mr. Lincoln was telling a story. At the laugh that went up when he finished, Mary smiled. She'd been right to think a party would do him good. She hadn't seen him look so cheerful for weeks.

"Miss Kate seems to have positively thrived on our wretched weather," Mary said to Mr. Chase. "She looks charming tonight."

It was after the entree that the general spirits showed signs of sagging. If only it hadn't turned so miserably hot again. There was no fault with the dinner, surely, but in the stifling closeness it was discouraging to face course after course of rich food. There were beads of perspiration on Mr. Chase's high forehead, and Mr. Seward stared at the raddled remains on his plate as though his tussle with stuffed breast of guinea hen had left him quite exhausted.

Mary was casting around for a new topic to begin when suddenly the voice of a senator, midway down the table, boomed out.

Had anyone ever heard of anything more outrageous, the senator demanded, than the uppityness the free Negroes were treating the city to lately? You wouldn't believe it—but there had even been some sort of scalawag notion of the Negroes of setting up a free school for themselves.

The general lethargy, stirred by the senator's vehemence, gave way to a flurry of murmurs.

"Absurd," said someone.

"Too, too preposterous."

There was a pause, then the delicate voice of Miss Kate, cool and drawling, came clearly down the table.

"Do tell us more, senator." Miss Kate bent toward him encouragingly. "I'm sure Mrs. Lincoln will be interested." Her smile, flicking Mary's glance for an instant, was sweetly barbed.

"Why—" the senator looked surprised—"the thing was overruled, of course. The whole scheme was proper foolishness—cooked up with the idea of wangling a slice of money out of honest taxpayers, I daresay. No decent sort of backing. The authorities put an end to it quick enough. It just goes to show, though, what sort of wildcat notions get started nowadays. As if we don't have enough trouble with free niggers, without educating them to make more." The senator leaned back, evidently rather pleased with his mot, though it was plain from their expressions that a number of the guests felt he had gone somewhat too far.

"Personally," Miss Kate said, "I'm inclined to disagree with you, senator. I'm frank to say I believe Negroes have their rights, quite as other people have. But I'm certain we all admit that there are limits. I mean to say—" her glance brushed Mary's again—"one is hardly expected to invite Negroes to take tea with one. Don't you agree with me, Mrs. Lincoln?"

For an instant, while everyone turned to look at her, Mary could feel her cheeks flaming. She saw the long row of faces, waiting expectantly, and the centerpiece with its sugar roses that had begun, ever so slightly, to melt. She was aware of Miss Kate's smile—languid and challenging.

"I'm not so sure, Miss Kate," Mary said. "Judging from some people who *are* asked to tea in the best Washington circles—I think one might do a great deal worse."

Miss Kate's smile remained serene. "That's very witty, Mrs. Lincoln; and, I'm afraid, all too true. But quite seriously, I wonder if we aren't making a mistake to let the Negroes feel that this war is being fought for them. In all fairness to them, I mean. One wouldn't want them to get an exaggerated sense of their importance." She turned to the other end of the table. "Do you think I'm right, Mr. Lincoln?"

Mary saw Mr. Lincoln look at Miss Kate. Mary held her breath, waiting for his answer. He mustn't fail her now—he wouldn't . . .

Mr. Lincoln took a slow breath. "It seems to me, Miss Kate, that's kind of like worrying in the middle of a tug of war, for fear the rope might get to feeling too important. I guess it's important, all right—but whichever side wins, I don't know that the rope gets much fun out of it."

It was only a little after eleven when Mary went upstairs. The party had broken up early—the guests had made polite excuses about the heat and the possibility of another thunderstorm, but it was plain enough that they were anxious to escape. After the incident at the dinner table, conversation had been strained and difficult, and Mary, watching the party slowly crumble into boredom, had felt helpless to revive it.

She climbed the stairs slowly, too tired to care that the dinner had been a failure. A headache, that had begun dully early in the evening, had grown into a drumming throb of weariness.

She was half way down the hall when a sudden sound from the boys' room made her pause, frowning. They must surely have been asleep long ago—but no—there it was again. A curious moaning sound, low and strangled. In quick alarm, Mary opened the door just in time to see Taddie hurl himself off the foot of his bed with an ear-splitting scream of laughter.

The table lamp was lit, showing the wild disorder of the room. The sheets were dragged off the beds, a chair was upset, and Taddie in his nightshirt danced furiously up and down over the prostrate form of Willie.

"Boys!"

Taddie turned, his eyes blazing with excitement. "We're playing war, mamma. Look—Willie is dead now. He's a Johnny Reb, and I've shooted him dead. Be dead, Willie—you're *dead.*"

Willie, on the floor, writhed convulsively, emitting another series of strangled groans. "O-oo—oh, I'm dead. Help, help—I'm dead—"

"Look—Willie is dead!" Tad's scream was ecstatic. "Now I'm going to shoot his head off with a big cannon." He leaped onto the bed and took aim. "BANG BANG BANG. Look, mother—"

Mary put her hands over her ears. The sound of Taddie's shouts pierced her aching head like a knife. Suddenly, in his agonized twistings, Willie's foot caught the leg of a table that held a vase of flowers and sent it crashing to the floor.

Mary made a quick move. She reached Willie, yanked him to his feet, and boxed his ears soundly. And then, just as Willie's outraged howls were added to the din, Mr. Lincoln appeared in the door.

"Papa!"

Both the boys hurled themselves on Mr. Lincoln.

"Papa—papa, Mother *hurt* Willie." In a burst of sympathetic wails, Taddie buried his head against his father's knees. "She *hit* Willie—and she hurt him, papa—"

Mr. Lincoln lifted Willie in his arms. The boy clung to his shoulder, sobbing.

"Hush, Willie." Mr. Lincoln's voice was mild. Over the boy's head, he surveyed the room. The stripped beds, the upset chair and table, the broken vase and scattered flowers.

"Well, mother—" a tired smile touched the corners of his mouth—"it looks as if the war has reached us at last."

Mary pressed her hands over her eyes, shutting out everything.

"Willie broke the vase." She could hear her voice, muffled and childish. "He broke my favorite vase. I can't stand it. I can't stand any more. I can't—I can't . . ." Misery broke over her, shaking and helpless. She turned and left the room, stumbling blindly over the hem of her gown.

When Mr. Lincoln came into her room, Mary didn't look up. She lay face down across the bed, the new blue and white dress crushed beneath her.

"The boys are all right now, mother," Mr. Lincoln said after a moment. "I got them to bed and called Mrs. Keckley. I told her things had got a little upset. I reckon she'll know what to do."

Mary didn't answer.

"Willie was sorry about the vase. I don't suppose he meant to break it." Mr. Lincoln paused. "I guess all the fuss over the party was too much for you—in this weather—" His voice was kind, a little puzzled.

Mary said nothing. In the silence she could feel him standing beside her. There had been a hundred times, she thought dully, when she had lain awake in the night, alone, and wished she might look up and find him like this. Times when she wanted to talk to him, to try to reach through the lonely, frightening bleakness. But now that he was here, there seemed to be no words to tell him what she had wanted to say. No use trying to speak of the long nights, and the dreads that came like shapeless mists. No use to ask for comfort. No use, even, to speak of the party that had gone so flat and wretched. She might have liked to thank him for standing up for her, answering Miss Kate. But he wouldn't have understood. He'd only say she was imagining things.

She lay still. Let him think it was nothing but the heat—and being tired that made her like this. It was no use . . .

He waited a minute longer.

"Well, you'll feel better tomorrow, mother, when you've had a good sleep."

He bent down and touched her shoulder. Then he went out, closing the door carefully behind him.

Next morning at breakfast, when Mary said she had been thinking of taking the boys north for a few weeks to Saratoga Springs, Mr. Lincoln looked surprised. After all, Mary said, the early autumn was the pleasantest time of year to travel. Saratoga wouldn't be too crowded, and she might try the waters. On the way home, they could stop a few days in New York. The shops would be showing their new fall things—and perhaps Robert could come down and join them for a visit . . .

But when the moment came, a few days later, to say good-bye, Mary clung to Mr. Lincoln weeping.

"I can't go, Mr. Lincoln. Please don't make me. Mrs. Keckley can take the boys. But let me stay with you—please. I'll be better, I promise—"

She heard his voice, mild and surprised.

"Why, mother, there's nothing to feel so bad about. I thought you wanted to go. You and the boys will have a fine time—and you'll be home again before you know it."

On the train, Mary leaned back against the seat. They were pulling out of the station, through the flat, bedraggled outskirts of the city. She sat motionless, lulled by the steady clack of the wheels. As they gained speed, rolling north, and the low green hills began to appear, she straightened up.

At the Springs, where the nights were cool, she could surely sleep. And when they came back, she thought, everything would be different. She could try again. Yes, of course . . . things were bound to be better. They needn't stay away very long. Only until she was rested. And then she could begin again . . .

32

IT WAS LATE OCTOBER BEFORE MARY CAME HOME TO Washington. The weeks had passed quickly, and it was pleasant at the Springs. Pleasant to be waited on, to take the boys driving every afternoon on the smart promenade past the United States Hotel with its famous millionaires' piazza where Commodore Vanderbilt sat, and young Jim Fisk with kiss-curls on his forehead. It was pleasant to dress every night for dinner, and be pointed out when she entered the big dining room with its round tables and rose-shaded candlelight. To hear voices and music and laughter, and no talk of war. And to sit on the verandah in the mornings, after taking the waters, while the boys went pony riding, and listen to the latest hotel gossip. Gossip about Jim Fisk and Mr. Astor and Madame Jumel with her wigs and parasols and laces and airs. Gossip that had nothing to do with Washington.

At first Mary had worried a good deal about Mr. Lincoln. But he wrote often and assured her that, while he was missing them sadly, he was delighted to hear that she and the boys were enjoying themselves, and he was getting on all right. The only sad news he sent was the information that Mrs. Keckley's son had been shot in a skirmish with Rebel troops on the Tennessee border, and had died a few days later, of a fever that had developed from the wound. Mrs. Keckley had borne the loss with courage and fortitude, though it was an overwhelming blow—and she had begged him not to tell Mary, for fear it would mar the pleasure of her holiday. But he had thought she would want to know.

Mr. Lincoln was at the station to meet them the night they arrived in Washington. Seeing him come down the long platform toward her, Mary was struck, even before they were close enough to speak, by the change in him. Surely he looked older—she hadn't remembered how stooped his shoulders were nor how deeply the lines were set around his mouth. But he looked well, though he was even thinner, and there was a new firmness, a kind of toughening, she felt in him at once. And she saw that he smiled more readily, in spite of the anxious look that never quite left his eyes.

He was glad to have them home again—pleased to find Mary so rested and well.

"You look very grand in your new feathers, mother," he said, admiring the bonnet she had bought in New York. He swung each of the boys up to his shoulder, pretending to groan over their weight. There was nothing in his manner to show that Mr. Lincoln remembered the strained and difficult circumstances under which they had parted, and for once Mary was grateful for his ability to act as though the past simply didn't exist. Driving up the avenue, Mary felt excited and pleased. Everything seemed new, and she kept turning to look at Mr. Lincoln beside her, conscious again of the subtle difference in him.

Not until they reached the White House, and she saw the familiar countenance of old Edwards, gnarled and glum, did Mary realize she had come home again to Washington.

It wasn't long before Mary discovered that Mr. Lincoln wasn't the only person who seemed to have changed while she was gone. There was a new spirit in the city—a sort of settling down to the grim business of war, that showed itself in a hundred ways. Social feuds and scandals were no longer of paramount interest, having been abandoned for the moment in favor of the far more diverting pastime of armchair strategy. Everyone, it appeared, had become a military expert overnight, and conversation nowadays was all of encampments, platoons, maneuvers, bivouacs, and such.

"Washington," Mr. Lincoln said, "has decided to accept the war, after all. Even in the best families."

In its new phase of patriotism, the city was inclined to view the President with a more tolerant eye. Except for a few unregenerate cave dwellers, even the Southerners forgot their hatred and distrust of the black Republicans.

The first evening she and Mr. Lincoln went to the theater together, Mary was astonished to see the audience rise and cheer when they stepped into their box. Mr. Lincoln leaned over to whisper in her ear.

"You see, mother, what fine folks we've gotten to be these days."

At lunch one day a visiting gentleman from New York spoke feelingly of the selfless spirit the Capital women were showing.

"It's an inspiration," he said to Mary, "to see the way you ladies have devoted yourselves to war work. Miss Kate Chase tells me she's given up entertaining entirely to do hospital nursing this winter. I understand she makes a point of driving down into Virginia regularly to visit the camps and take supplies for the men. It's that sort of spirit, Mrs. Lincoln, that will do more than all the generals' speeches to give our soldiers the courage to fight and win."

Mary's smile was thoughtful.

The next morning, ordering the carriage, she drove to the military hospital and offered her services, and from that day she went regularly to do her share of rolling bandages, distributing candy and tobacco, and writing letters home for the soldiers.

One new element of Washington life which Mary found puzzling was the overwhelming public confidence in General McClellan, the new Commander of the Army of the Potomac. McClellan was young. He was handsome and dark, with a fiery eye and a great reputation for fearlessness. And his penchant for galloping up and down the Washington streets on a spirited black horse seemed to instill in everyone a profound conviction that the savior of the Union had been revealed at last. A rash of McClellan badges and pennants appeared everywhere—in lapels, on hatbands, and even proudly adorning ladies' muffs and tippets.

When Tad and Willie played soldier now, they wrangled bitterly over which one should have the honor of being "Little Mac."

Mary was curious. "Besides looking very well on a horse," she inquired of Mr. Lincoln, "what has this General McClellan done to make himself such a hero?"

Mr. Lincoln was as taken as everyone else with Little Mac. McClellan, he assured Mary, had a good head, firmly screwed on. There would be no more rushing into battle half cocked, as they had at Bull Run. The new commander had laid his plans before the President and the Cabinet, and informed them that he was building the largest and best armed and trained military force that had ever been raised in the course of history.

"Well, at least," Mary smiled, "your McClellan doesn't seem to be troubled with false modesty. What does he intend to do with this remarkable army? Is it to fight with —or only to look at?"

The army would strike, Mr. Lincoln said gravely, when in McClellan's estimation, the moment was ripe. And not before. The one thing he has insisted upon is plenty of time.

"And I have personally promised that he shan't be hurried," Mr. Lincoln said.

Mary pursed her lips. "I can only hope, Mr. Lincoln, that General Beauregard will be equally considerate."

For one thing at least, Mary was grateful. She saw that Mr. Lincoln had come out of the long, slow process of making up his mind about who should run the war. His tone was no longer hesitant. Once and for all, he had shown the politicians the door—and Congress, having reluctantly abandoned its fond dream that the war could be waged without parting with either money or authority, had heaped both on the President and sat back, with a sigh, to let him use them as he saw fit.

"It's kind of surprising," Mr. Lincoln said, "to find how many people would rather be driven than drive themselves. I guess maybe horses are luckier than we realize."

"We have a novelty in office seekers today, mother," Mr. Lincoln said one morning. He handed Mary a letter dated from Springfield. Ninian Edwards had written to say that he had suffered severe business losses during the past months, to put it plainly. Was there, Ninian wondered, any possibility of an opening in a government appointment for which Mr. Lincoln would think his qualifications suitable? He hesitated to ask for favors, but at Elizabeth's suggestion he ventured to write.

Mary looked up from the letter. "What do you intend to do for him, Mr. Lincoln?"

"Whatever I can, I suppose."

A few days later Mary inquired whether an appointment had been found, and learned that Ninian had been offered a captain's commission, in charge of commissary distribution for the Springfield area.

Mary raised her brows. "I daresay Springfield will have plenty to say when they hear that, Mr. Lincoln."

Sure enough, the following week brought a letter from Ann, the first Mary had had in a long while. Everyone in Springfield was amazed, Ann said, to hear that Ninian had received a commission. It was very wonderful for *him*, of course, and for poor Elizabeth, who had surely had *much to bear*. As for Ann herself, she was delighted. But all the same, she couldn't help wondering how those outside the family would regard it. There were those, certainly, who would think it odd—coming from the President to his own brother-in-law.

"There are times," Mary said, putting away Ann's letter, "when I'm afraid I don't think any more highly of my sisters than they do of me."

From Elizabeth, Mary heard nothing at all—an omission which she didn't fail to comment on when writing to Cousin Lizzie.

Cousin Lizzie hastened to reply, soothingly.

> . . . I am *sure* Elizabeth means no slight or lack of *gratitude* in not writing, dear Cousin Mary. But I must be honest and tell you that your sisters have felt, since you went to Washington, that you have been so preoccupied with the pleasures and duties of your *position* that you have rather lost touch with the old ties

which in the past held you so *devotedly* together. For my part, I feel that this is *entirely natural* under the circumstances, and I have said so plainly on a number of occasions. But you know for yourself how *firmly* dear Elizabeth clings to an idea once she has formed it. I am sure, however, that in spite of this little misunderstanding, your sisters regard you with as much affection and esteem as ever. Even Mr. Lincoln is beginning to be highly spoken of here. Only a few nights past I heard Judge Harris observe, at a dinner, that Mr. Lincoln's ability to fill the office of President gave him the same sense of *wonder* and *admiration* that Dr. Samuel Johnson experienced while watching a dancing bear. (I do hope I have got this *right*.) I did not altogether understand the reference, but it was greeted with so much approval by the company that I am passing it on to you, knowing you will be pleased, and doubtless you will know what it means, dear Mary, as you are always so *clever* . . ."

On one of her visits to the hospital wards, Mary noticed a thin young man whose cot was placed next to the wall, a little apart from the other beds. He was a Confederate lieutenant, she discovered, who had been wounded and captured at Bull Run and sent to the hospital to recover from a fever. The other soldiers were kind enough to him, but Mary saw the wistful look in his eyes when he watched the visitors who came to the ward, and she took special care to stop by his bed for a word whenever she could.

The young man was friendly and likable. In the course of their conversations Mary found that he came from Atlanta and had known Ben and Emilie Helm there. Being an officer, and well connected, he had a good chance of being sent back to the South in one of the customary exchanges of prisoners—but he confided to Mary that he was worried for fear the exchange would come too late for him to reach home in time to see his mother, who was very ill and not expected to live.

Touched and troubled by the young man's anxiety, Mary spoke to Mr. Lincoln. Wasn't there something that could be done to hurry the boy's transfer?

Mr. Lincoln was doubtful. He had a pile of letters with just such appeals waiting on his desk for cases just as urgent.

"But this is different, Mr. Lincoln. This boy is a friend of Ben and Emilie's. If you could just see him—if you could hear the pathetic way he speaks about his mother—"

"I know, mother. I've talked to dozens like him." Mr. Lincoln sighed. "I wish I could send them all home to their mothers—but these things have got to be done in a military way. And I don't like to ask McClellan for special favors, when I know he's doing the best he can."

For a few days Mary let the matter rest, but it was hard to forget the young lieutenant's thin face and the haunting expression in his eyes that lost a little more of hope each time she saw him. Suppose it were she who was dying, and Robert was a prisoner somewhere in the South—waiting to come to her . . .

One morning when she walked through the ward, Mary found the young man up and dressed. He was leaving the hospital the next day, he said. He didn't know where they were sending him. He wanted to say good-bye and thank her for being so kind. He said nothing more about his mother, or his chances of reaching home. But when Mary left the hospital, her mind was made up.

Military procedure or no military procedure, she meant to see that General McClellan heard about the boy's case. It was no use, she knew, to appeal to Mr. Lincoln any further. But at least she could go to the general herself. And since there was no time to lose, she told the coachman to drive her to the War Department.

General McClellan sent out word that he would receive Mrs. Lincoln at once. The arrival of the President's wife, unannounced and alone, caused a stir of curiosity in the offices, but Mary was too intent on her errand to notice the stares that followed her progress down the corridors to the general's office.

McClellan waited at the door. It was the first time they had met, and the general, with a great show of gallantry, bowed low over Mary's hand and expressed himself as deeply honored by the unexpected visit.

She had come, Mary explained at once, to ask a favor. Quite unofficially.

The general bowed again, sweepingly, and begged her to be seated. Anything in his power, he said, was hers to command. She had only to speak.

Mary had scarcely been prepared for such a flowery reception. While she told about the young lieutenant, the general sat facing her, his dark face frowning and intent, his finger tips drumming nervously on the desk. When she had finished, he looked up.

Such cases, he said, involving the exchange of military prisoners were subject to hard and fast rules. There was no room in official regulations for exceptions, however urgent the personal circumstances behind them might be. But—

Here he paused, rising dramatically.

"It is the duty of a soldier, Mrs. Lincoln," he said, "to exercise discretion when and where he feels it indicated. In view of your interest in this young man, which has impressed me deeply—and your willingness to vouch for the truth of his story, which I cannot doubt—I am inclined to feel that this is a case deserving of the utmost consideration. I shall do all I can to see that this prisoner's transfer is executed at once."

Mary rose. She was extremely grateful. She hoped that General McClellan would forgive her for coming so impulsively . . .

"Not at all. Not at all." The general made a deprecating gesture. "You have no need to apologize, dear madam, for your generosity in seeking help for this unfortunate boy. Indeed, I wish there were more such examples of unselfishness and humanity in the world today." He paused, sighing heavily. "We soldiers are generally supposed, I fear, to be mere machines of efficiency. But we are not without hearts, Mrs. Lincoln. And I assure you that no stone will be left unturned in my effort to see that your request is granted."

The general bowed one last time, and they parted.

It was lunchtime when Mary reached home, and Mr. Lincoln was just coming down the stairs. She smiled at him so warmly that he looked surprised.

"Is something up, mother? You look like the cat that just swallowed the canary."

Hearing the homely twang in his voice, Mary remembered the pompous, florid accents of General McClellan. She looked at the wrinkles in Mr. Lincoln's rusty black coat, and the lean breadth of his shoulders—and she thought of the general, small and elegant and dapper, with his carefully brushed pompadour, his polished boots that shone like mirrors. She tucked her hand in Mr. Lincoln's arm, smiling up at him.

"I was only thinking," Mary said, "how glad I am to see you, Mr. Lincoln."

Writing his daily letter to his wife in Cincinnati, General McClellan was careful to include an account of Mrs. Lincoln's visit. He had given in to the Lady President, he said, as everyone must—and she had gone off feeling that she had wheedled a great favor out of him. He might have told her she could have spared her pains—that her young lieutenant's exchange had already been arranged and would have been accomplished quite as promptly without her interference. He had thought it hardly politic for one in Mrs. L.'s position to take up the cause of a Confederate, in view of the rumors one heard (very likely quite unfounded) of her southern sympathies. But one hesitated to offer advice, however sound, to a lady of such *decided* mind. He had found her somewhat overbearing in manner.

though civil enough—and knowing her reputation for vanity, he had been careful to treat her with *great* deference, which he could see pleased her—and she had gone off flattered and delighted, convinced that she had charmed him into submission!

33

IT WAS A REGULAR THING NOWADAYS FOR VISITING REGIMENTS to be entertained at the White House. One afternoon, chatting with a group of Massachusetts volunteers, Mary discovered that a number of them were former Harvard students. Oliver Wendell Holmes, Jr., was among them, a slight, soft-spoken lad with a good wit and admirable manners, and a handsome boy who was a grandson of Paul Revere. Some of them, Mary learned, had recently left their classes to join up. Delighted at finding someone who could bring news of Robert, Mary began to question them eagerly—when suddenly she realized from a twist in the conversation that they were speaking of the possibility of Robert's being in the army soon.

Holding tight to the teacup in her hand, Mary went on talking. As though nothing out of the ordinary had been said, she spoke of the weather, of the New England climate, of the prospects for a Union victory. But when the guests had gone, she went at once to find Mr. Lincoln.

Had Robert, she asked sharply, said anything more about this absurd notion of joining the army? He couldn't have meant it, of course. He'd given her his word before he went back to Cambridge. But with these other boys rushing off so recklessly—with so much talk of enlistments—he might have been influenced in spite of his promise.

"Has he written to you, Mr. Lincoln?"

Mr. Lincoln didn't answer for a minute. His glance was fastened on something outside the window and he seemed unaware of Mary's agitation.

Not waiting for him to speak, Mary heard herself rushing on. Robert couldn't go now—he mustn't. There was his education to finish—and the boy wasn't strong enough for army life. And besides, it wouldn't be fair—Robert would be in far greater danger than the others, being the President's son . . .

While she spoke, pleading and angry, piling up excuses, Mary was conscious all the time of the truth, dark and terrifying, that hid beneath her words. If Robert was to go, she knew the fears would come back. The fears that came at night and whispered: "*This is the price. This is the price you must pay. This is the price . . .*" But surely the price had already been great enough. It needn't begin all over again.

"You must forbid Robert to go, Mr. Lincoln."

He turned from the window. "Robert is a grown man, mother. He has to decide for himself—just as these others did."

"Robert isn't the only one to be considered. There are other reasons—"

"There are always other reasons, mother. It's always like this—in all the homes these boys come from."

"Yes—yes, I know, Mr. Lincoln. But this is different—"

Mr. Lincoln shook his head. Mary had seldom seen him look so stern.

"No; it's not any different, mother," he said.

Alone in her room later, Mary tried to write to Robert, but halfway through the letter she stopped and tore the sheet in two. There must be some other way to stop him, she thought. She remembered how easily General McClellan had granted her request for the young lieutenant. She would wait, and watch her chance. A word dropped to the right person, at just the proper moment . . . She would wait . . .

The opportunity came sooner than Mary had expected. General Scott was being retired, and there was a dinner for him at the White House. McClellan was there, and Mr. Cameron, the secretary of war. Old Scott was one of the few men in Washington whom Mary respected, and she was troubled and genuinely sorry to see him go. It was McClellan's doing, she knew, to force his commander in chief out, but when she had said so to Mr. Lincoln, he shook his head.

"There can't be two heads to an army," he said, "and Scott is old—and sick besides. McClellan says he can handle things better if he's not interfered with, and he knows what he's about. The people trust McClellan."

"Yes," Mary said, "they trust him because they know nothing about him except that he looks well on a horse and boasts that he can win the war. They call him the little Napoleon—" She shrugged. "It will take more than a few photographs of McClellan with his hand inside the front of his coat to make a Napoleon of him, Mr. Lincoln."

But General Scott showed no resentment. At the dinner, seated next to Mary, his grizzled countenance looked merely sleepy and impassive while McClellan held forth, with a great display of energy and courage, on his plans for the future of the army.

When Mary told him he would be sadly missed in the Capital, the general roused himself and turned to look at her.

"It's kind of you to say so. But I can't say I'm sorry to go. They've given me everything I could require for my last days—even a successor."

Mary saw him glance down the table. She wondered what thoughts lay behind his heavy eyelids as he watched McClellan, frowning and important, more conscious of his gold braid than ever.

"I only hope," Mary said, "your successor will be worthy of you."

The old man looked at McClellan a moment more,

fixedly and without expression. Then he sighed—a sigh that was half a yawn.

"I'm too old for anything," he said. "Even opinions."

During the course of the evening, Mary found the chance for a few minutes' private conversation with Mr. Cameron, and brought the subject around to the matter of Robert's enlistment. Being careful not to put too much of a point on it, she let him understand that she and Mr. Lincoln were opposed to Robert's leaving college for the present. They hesitated to interfere directly—boys at that age were so headstrong and anxious to show their independence—but if Mr. Cameron would be willing to use his influence, she was sure Mr. Lincoln would be grateful. A judicious word in the right quarter? Perhaps Mr. Cameron had already heard something of Robert's intentions?

Mr. Cameron was evasive. He could make no promises . . .

But Mary was satisfied. She felt certain at least that the secretary of war would take steps to see that Robert was not allowed to enlist without her knowledge. Doubtless, she thought, Mr. Cameron and the others would have their private opinion of her for wanting to keep her son exempt. But she didn't grudge their scorn. It was a small enough price to pay for keeping, a little longer, her truce with fate. The fears would not come again, for a while at least. For a little while . . .

At four o'clock one rainy morning in November, General Scott left Washington. He had received the thanks and tribute of Congress and the President, and he was free to go. General McClellan came to see him off, muffled in a heavy cape—dramatic as always as he clattered down the avenue in the pitch dark and the beating rain.

Surrounded by his cavalry officers, sneezing and shivering in their dripping uniforms, McClellan stood in the drafty station, trying not to show his impatience to see old

Fuss and Feathers on his way. General Scott shook hands with them all. He puttered about, seeing to his luggage, sending courteous wishes to Mrs. McClellan and the baby. He was too old and weary to be hurried.

With General Scott gone, McClellan was in full swing. Mr. Lincoln spoke to him anxiously one day.

"We have put a terrible lot on you now."

McClellan smiled quietly. "I can do it all."

Once, when the President had been kept waiting two hours for an appointment with McClellan, Mr. Hay protested the general's cavalier behavior.

Mary was quick to chime in. "It's perfectly true, Mr. Lincoln. No matter how much you admire McClellan, you'll admit he treats you as if you were nothing more than an old grandma."

"Well, maybe so, mother. But this is hardly the time to be standing on points of etiquette. I'll hold McClellan's horse if only he'll bring us a victory."

Christmas came, and Tad and Willie hung their stockings over the mantel in the south parlor.

The first snow fell, thin and wet, over the camps where McClellan's army waited. There had been another victory for the South at Ball's Bluff—but in comparison to Bull Run it had seemed only a mild setback. Surely soon McClellan would be ready to begin. But McClellan still called for more time, and troops and money and supplies poured down from the North—to disappear across the Potomac into silence.

All quiet along the Potomac, some people said. All *too* quiet, if you asked them. But for the most part they were still content to pin their faith to McClellan's star.

The weeks went on, and winter settled in. The country waited.

And Mary held, from day to day, her truce with fate.

34

DURING A RAW AND SUNLESS FEBRUARY, MARY CAME home from a morning at the hospital to find that Willie was feverish and had been put to bed by Mrs. Keckley. She hurried upstairs. Willie was sitting up, a red wool sock wrapped round his throat, entertaining Taddie with a long, excited story about a little lame robin who couldn't fly south when the other robins did and would have starved and frozen except for the sparrows, who brought him food and gave their feathers to make him a warm cover.

Taddie caught Willie's cold, and for several days Mary was hardly out of their room. She read to them, rubbed their chests with camphor, dosed them with sassafras tea, and scolded Tad for hopping out of bed in bare feet.

"I'm afraid poor Taddie has taken it the worse of the two," Mary said anxiously. "He's like Robert—these things always go to his lungs."

Taddie was a troublesome invalid, complaining loudly of his woes when he felt badly and bursting into irrepressibly high spirits the moment he showed signs of improving. Keep them quiet, the doctor had told Mary, and they'll be all right in a few days. But there was no keeping Tad quiet. He squirmed and fussed and bounced until by evening he had brought on the fever and coughing worse than ever, and at night he slept fitfully, half waking to fling off the covers, so that Mary had to get up half a dozen times and tuck him in again.

One night, when Taddie had been crying and restless, Mary sat by the bed stroking his hot forehead and told him stories until he fell asleep. When she rose, stiff and chilled, to go back to bed, she paused to bend over Willie and was surprised to find him wide awake, looking up at her.

"Do you feel badly, Willie?"

He shook his head.

"I was just listening to the story you told Tad," he said.

Unless Taddie was better by morning, Mary told Mrs. Keckley, she meant to have the doctor again. But when he woke, the fever was broken. Mary sighed with relief. By afternoon both boys were so much improved that she went for an hour's drive—breathing the misty winter twilight air gratefully after nearly a week of being indoors.

That evening at dinner Mary spoke cheerfully to Mr. Lincoln about the White House reception planned for the following week. It was to be the largest affair of the season. All the diplomatic corps was invited, and the Marine Band was to play for dancing. It was lucky, Mary said, that Mrs. Keckley had finished her new dress before the boys got sick.

Two days before the reception Taddie was up and out, quite well again. But Willie, who had seemed so much less ill, was still in bed. His cold was better, but he remained white and listless. Mary questioned him anxiously. Was he in any pain? No. Was there anything he wanted? Willie hesitated. Nothing special, he said, only it would be nice to see his pony.

"So you shall, dear." Mary was touched by the politeness of the small voice. So unlike Taddie's stormy demands. "Tomorrow morning, if you're better, Papa will carry you to the window, and Taddie can ride the pony right onto the lawn where you can see him."

That night Mary was wakened by Taddie calling, and she hurried across the hall to find Tad sitting up, huddled in his nightshirt, staring at Willie's bed.

"Something's wrong with Willie, mamma. He keeps saying funny things and when I talk to him he doesn't answer."

Willie was awake, but when Mary bent over the bed his eyes looked strange and unfocused, and he muttered something thickly as he pulled away from her touch. His skin was dry as hot paper.

"Is Willie very sick, mamma?" Tad leaned over from his bed. "Will he have to take medicine again?"

Mary went to call Mrs. Keckley. They stood together looking down at Willie in the shaded night light.

"It may be only the fever working out of him, madam. I've seen it act this way—and then in the morning it may be quite gone." Mrs. Keckley's voice was calm and reassuring. "Let me put Taddie in the guest room, and I can stay here and watch. I'll call you if there's any change."

In the morning the fever had not gone. The doctor came, and Mary stood watching while he looked at Willie gravely. The cold had gone into the lungs, he said. There was not much they could do but watch and wait.

At the doctor's words, heavy and guarded, fear plunged sharply into Mary's heart. She looked at Willie. He twisted fretfully, trying to say something, but his voice was choked and unfamiliar. Through a rush of tears Mary bent and gathered Willie in her arms, begging him to speak again—to tell her what he wanted.

Over Mary's head the doctor looked at Mrs. Keckley. He cleared his throat. It might be best, he said, to have a nurse for Willie. Then Mrs. Lincoln would have some chance to rest. And in a case like this, it was often better for the mother to stay away as much as possible. The slightest emotion, however natural, could often be most upsetting.

Mary looked up quickly. "I won't have a nurse. I won't have some stranger coming in. No one understands Willie as I do—no one else knows how to take care of him . . ."

The doctor stood up and closed his bag. Well, he said, they'd see. He would come in again, toward evening.

When the doctor was gone, Mary still knelt by the bed. Willie was quieter now, his eyes closed in a drowsy stupor as she smoothed the tangled hair back from his forehead. They were trying to push her away, she thought. Trying to shut her out. But she wouldn't let them. Not when Willie needed her.

Late in the afternoon Mr. Lincoln came in and sat an hour by Willie's bed, watching, speaking very little. Later, when they went down to dinner, Mr. Lincoln told Mary that the afternoon before Willie had first taken cold he had gone out to ride his pony and had wandered too far and got caught in a drenching rain. Mr. Lincoln had seen him come in, but had promised not to tell, for fear he might be scolded.

"Poor little fellow—he was punished much worse than he deserved, after all," Mr. Lincoln said.

Mary flared at him, stung by the thought of their keeping the secret between them. "You had no right not to tell me, Mr. Lincoln. If I had known—I could have taken care of him at once. And this never would have happened—"

"No, mother. If Willie were going to have the fever, he'd have it. There isn't any use thinking after a thing has happened we could have made it different."

Mary shook her head impatiently. "That sort of talk is humbug, Mr. Lincoln."

"Well, mother, all the same—I believe it."

A little past midnight Mary hurried into Willie's room. She had wakened from a heavy sleep, fancying she heard Willie call. But he lay quiet, and Mrs. Keckley was asleep in Taddie's bed. The night light threw vague, twisting shadows on the wall. There was no sound but the hoarse breathing from Willie's bed.

Pausing in the corridor, Mary saw the door of Mr. Lincoln's bedroom ajar. She looked in. He was sitting by the lamp, still dressed, and reading.

"Mr. Lincoln, I'm so frightened about Willie—" Mary stood on the threshold, her long braids over her shoulders. She drew her blue robe closer, shivering. "There must be something we can do, Mr. Lincoln. Isn't there something?"

She spoke almost timidly, feeling for a moment as though she was one of the strangers who came to Mr. Lincoln, asking him for help in their troubles—trusting him, somehow, to reach out and make things right. In that moment she had forgotten that he was her husband—forgotten that he was a prophet in his own house.

Mr. Lincoln got up from the low rocker and took off his spectacles.

"Come in, mother," he said.

They faced each other in the circle of lamplight. In the night silence they were like strangers, and yet closer than they had come in a long while, without obstacles or barriers. Mr. Lincoln talked. He spoke matter-of-factly. There was nothing momentous in his words—no magic wisdom. But hearing his voice, Mary was quieted. In the stillness of the room, in the simple words and the plain, worn face—she felt for a few minutes the strength that had given comfort to so many.

At the doctor's insistence, next morning, a nurse was sent for. Mary made no protest. When the woman arrived, she watched Willie lie back, quiet under the sure, impersonal touch. She saw how docilely he took the spoonfuls of barley water he had refused from Mary.

All day Mary hovered in and out of the sickroom, unwilling to quite give over to the new nurse. Downstairs, meanwhile, the caterers were getting ready for the reception, spreading the long tables, clearing away furniture, taking charge in the kitchens. The florists' men arrived, bringing garlands of laurel and tubs of potted palms for the East Room.

Mr. Lincoln said it might be better to postpone the reception until Willie was better. But Mary shook her head.

"It's too late to change now," she said wearily. "We must go through with it somehow. If we cancel the invitations it would only make more talk."

By evening, when it was time for Mary to dress, the doctor had come again—and for the first time he said Willie was better. Mary went in one last time before going downstairs, to find him sleeping. His breathing was easier, and his cheeks felt cooler to her touch.

The nurse stood by the bed. The shaded light fell softly on the ice-blue satin of Mary's gown and caught the gleam of pearls at her throat and wrists.

"You look very handsome, ma'am."

Mary fancied she caught a trace of resentment in the woman's voice. No doubt she, like so many others, thought it out of place for the President's wife to be entertaining in satin and pearls while just beyond the river an army lay camped in the snow, without enough blankets to protect them from the damp and freezing night.

"This is the only reception we have had all winter," Mary said quickly. "I wish we needn't have had it at all—but even in wartime the President is expected to entertain for the foreign diplomats."

"Naturally." The nurse smiled faintly. She leaned down with a possessive gesture to smooth the sheet over Willie's shoulder where Mary's touch had disturbed it. "I only hope the noise of the dancing won't be too loud. It would be a pity—when I've coaxed the poor lamb into such a nice sleep."

Mary bit back a sharp answer. She glanced again at Willie's face. It wouldn't do to let herself resent the woman when so much depended on her. She wouldn't resent anything—ever again, Mary thought suddenly—if only Willie would go on being better. It was the old feeling again—that she must bargain with fate—that all fortune must be paid for with an equal measure of misfortune.

She turned to the nurse, forcing a smile. "There won't be any noise. I gave orders this morning that we're not to have the music."

Plainly, the evening was a success. The embassy guests were elegant and gay, and light voices mingled with the rustle of fashionable silks and brocades in the palm-filled East Room. Mary felt the weariness drop away from her as she saw the approving glances of the gentlemen who bent over her hand.

Even the Washington ladies appeared to be too occupied in discussing other matters to find time for criticism. A year of war had made the old sport of hating the administration seem tame and outworn. Kate Chase, in pale lemon-yellow lace, that set off the flame of her red hair, paused a moment in the receiving line to ask kindly for news of the sick boy.

Mary was touched and grateful. Later, when she saw Kate deep in conversation with Mr. Lincoln, and noticed how attentively he listened and the way he laughed at her sallies, Mary only smiled, pleased to see him enjoy himself.

It was two in the morning before the last guests were gone, and Mary and Mr. Lincoln went upstairs together. Mr. Lincoln took her arm.

"Well, mother, it was a nice party. I was proud of you tonight."

Mary looked up. The compliment, so rare from his lips, added the last drop to her full cup. Still together, they looked in the door of Willie's room. Several times, earlier, Mary had left the party and come up—and twice during the evening she had seen Mr. Lincoln go upstairs. Willie still slept quietly, his head turned to one side, the long lashes shadowing his cheeks. The nurse, wrapped in a woolen comforter, drowsed in her chair by the night lamp.

Mary bent to touch Willie's hand, and straightened again, meeting Mr. Lincoln's eyes. The moment, full and sweet, hung between them like something shining and unfamiliar. Moving carefully, almost fearfully, lest the trembling perfection break, Mary turned and tiptoed from the room.

35

THE DAY AFTER THE PARTY WAS GRAY AND COLD, AND Mary stayed at her desk in the morning, writing letters, while downstairs the men carried away the extra chairs and dismantled the long tables. Willie wakened late, rested from the long sleep, and when Mary went in he smiled a little, and asked if he could have his pussy please, to sleep on the bed.

"Of course you may, dear. I'll send Taddie to fetch her from the kitchen."

But when Mary brought the kitten in, the nurse frowned. She didn't hold with animals in a sickroom, she said. They poisoned the air and carried all manner of disease, and the doctor would surely disapprove. Besides, the child was not to be excited. It might bring on the fever again.

Mary hesitated, torn between resentment of the woman's officious manner and a reluctance to offend her. But seeing the light in Willie's eyes as he reached out for his pet, she hadn't the heart to disappoint him.

"Just for a little while," she said, holding the kitten down for Willie to stroke the gray fur. She glanced at the nurse apologetically. "Surely it can't do any harm—when it pleases him so much."

The nurse, rustling her starched apron, made no reply. Later she took care to point out to Mrs. Keckley that, First Lady or no First Lady, she wasn't accustomed to having her authority in the sickroom questioned.

By afternoon the sky had cleared, and the sun came out, warming the air with the false mildness of early spring. Willie was sleeping again, his arm wrapped contentedly around the curled-up kitten, and when Mr. Lincoln found an hour free from appointments and suggested a drive, Mary felt safe in going.

It was dusk when they came home. The sun had vanished, leaving a chill in the sharp wind. Edwards, opening the door, stepped back quickly to avoid the cold draft. Mrs. Keckley had brought down word from the nurse, Edwards said. Mrs. Lincoln was to go upstairs directly she came in.

Mary knew at once that Willie was worse. He had wakened with a chill, the nurse said, immediately after

Mrs. Lincoln left. And now the fever had taken a queer turn.

"I don't like the looks, ma'am. I shouldn't be surprised it's going into the typhoid—"

Mary knelt by the bed, still in her coat and bonnet. She pulled off her gloves, rubbing her hands to warm them before she touched the flushed, blazing cheeks. This mustn't happen. It couldn't—not now. Not now. She spoke to Willie, coaxing him—but there was no light in the dull eyes that stared back at her.

"If you don't mind, ma'am—I really think you shouldn't try to rouse him. He ought to be left quiet, until the doctor sees him. We've sent for him—just now—"

Mary turned, sudden anger blazing in her voice. Why had he only been sent for now? Why not at once—an hour ago?

"Well, ma'am, I hardly liked to be giving orders, with you out of the house. But Mrs. Keckley said she'd be responsible—"

It was another hour before the doctor came—an hour while Mary hung over the bed, while she felt the strength drain out of her with every moan, every restless spasm that racked the small, worn body. She hardly knew when the doctor had gone again, and Mr. Lincoln came in to stand at the foot of the bed, for a long while, in silence. Much later, when they came and helped her to her feet to lead her across the hall to her own room, she followed numbly, only partly aware of Mrs. Keckley helping her undress, holding a cup of hot milk to her lips. Alone in the darkness, when they had left her to sleep, Mary lay still. She hadn't noticed when they tiptoed out, or felt the icy stiffness that crept slowly over her. She only knew that Willie was dying—and that this, at last, was the price.

After the third day the fever subsided. Willie lay motionless, his round cheeks shrunken so that he looked strange and wax-like. He no longer looked up when Mary came to the bed, nor seemed to hear when she called him—

pleading through the tears that choked her, begging him to listen.

Living the hours blindly, hardly knowing day from night, Mary hovered between her room and Willie's. At intervals, conscious of the doctor's voice speaking solemnly of courage, she struggled to push back the anguished tide. When they said she must either control herself or else be forbidden to come into the sickroom, she would promise to be quiet. But the tide would rush over her, and she was flung with helpless, shaken fury against the fate that would take her child and would not be denied.

Mrs. Keckley watched by the bed during the times when the nurse slept, and Taddie was left to roam the house disconsolate. There was nowhere for him to go—nothing to do that wouldn't make a noise and disturb Willie. He wandered into his father's study and amused himself pulling colored pins out of the war maps and making paper hats out of the piles of letters stacked on the desk. There was a meeting of the Cabinet one afternoon, and Taddie crawled under the long table. He was an Indian in the forest, and the circle of black-trousered legs were trees through which he peered cautiously at Pussy, who was a skulking, stealthy enemy. At length Mr. Lincoln pulled Tad out and took him on his knee.

"It's hard on a little fellow, having to keep so still," Mr. Lincoln said to the gentlemen.

Dozing one night, in her chair by Willie's bed, the nurse roused to a faint sound from across the corridor. She straightened—jerking her eyes open. If that was Mrs. Lincoln again, coming with her tears and wild talk . . . The door opened softly, and it was Mr. Lincoln who stood there, tall and sad.

He came near the bed, and stood watching.

The nurse left him there, and when she came back presently, he hadn't moved.

"I've fixed some hot tea, sir. Why don't you take a little? It might do you a speck of good."

"Thank you." Mr. Lincoln took the cup. "I believe maybe it will."

He stood holding it, not drinking.

"This is the hardest trial of my life," he said, speaking low. "I wish I knew why these things must come."

"Perhaps to make us better, sir."

He looked up. "Do you really think that?"

"I know it, sir. I lost my own two children, and then my husband. But I can't feel bitter. It was God's hand that took them, and I've learned to love Him all the more."

He still looked at her. "Did you always feel like this?"

"No; not for a long while. But blow after blow came—and then I began to learn."

For a long while he didn't speak.

"I'm glad you told me," he said finally. He handed back the cup.

"But you haven't taken the tea, sir. Would you like some fresh?"

"No. But I'm grateful all the same."

The next day, when the doctor came, he spoke to Mr. Lincoln. It would be better, the doctor said, if Mrs. Lincoln were not to be with the boy.

"It seems hard, I know; but the nurse tells me she disturbs him—" The doctor coughed. "I'm afraid, with all the strain, Mrs. Lincoln is not quite herself . . ."

Mr. Lincoln nodded. "We must try to remember how hard this is for her."

From her room across the corridor Mary listened late into the night. Toward one o'clock she heard the door of Willie's room open and shut, and then the sound of Mr. Lincoln's step. Up and down. Up and down. She had heard him walk like that in the nights after the news of battles. He had grieved then for other men's sons—now it was for his own. Up and down. At the sound, Mary felt a swift, unreasoning resentment. In her own sorrow, sharp and immediate as a knife plunge, it hurt her to know that he had grieved as much for the others as he did now for his own. That he would always mourn so—for all who must die.

She went to the door and called him.

"Mr. Lincoln—Willie is dying. I know it. I must go to him."

He answered patiently. She was worn out and overwrought. There was nothing she could do for Willie. It was best to leave him with the nurse.

"The nurse," Mary said. "The nurse is a stranger, Mr. Lincoln. A woman we never set eyes on until a few days ago. Why should I have to listen to her? Let her tell me whether I can see my own child." She was silent for a moment, brooding and wretched. "Mr. Lincoln, I don't trust Willie with her. I don't like her eyes—the way she stares at me. There's something queer about her, I tell you. I won't have her alone with Willie—I won't—"

She made a move toward the door, but Mr. Lincoln held her back. He would stay with Willie, then. He could call Mrs. Keckley.

"Go back to bed, mother. Try to rest."

When Mary wakened later there was no sound in the darkness. She crossed to Willie's door, and stood listening a moment. Then she knocked, and heard Mr. Lincoln's answer.

"Mr. Lincoln, may I come in now?"

He opened the door and took her arm, not saying a word. He was still dressed, and Mary saw Mrs. Keckley sitting beside Willie. The nurse, busy at the bureau where the medicines were kept, did not turn as Mary went toward the bed. She sat down next to Mrs. Keckley. Willie's hand lay outside the covers, but she made no move to touch it. Holding herself very still, trying desperately to do right, Mary watched Willie's face—listening for the breath, hoarse and shallow, that stirred his parted lips.

She was still there, motionless and dry eyed, when Willie died.

The thin gray light of dawn was at the windows when Mr. Lincoln came into Mary's room. Remembering the first night of Willie's illness, she turned to him—looking through the helplessness of pain for the strength and comfort he had given her then. But now, searching his face, she found none. There was a dry sound in her throat, and suddenly, beyond her will, she heard the sound of her weeping. Through her tears she could see Mr. Lincoln facing her as he had that other night. But there was no strangeness in him, no mystery or strength. She saw only her husband watching her helplessly.

"Go away, Mr. Lincoln!" Mary flung herself blindly back against the pillow. "You don't understand—you never can. Go away and leave me—"

"Mary—Mary, why do you torture yourself this way?"

"You can't know what this is to me, Mr. Lincoln . . . You can never know . . ."

There was no way, she knew, ever to make him see. To make him understand that Willie's dying had been her fault. Part of her fate. The price . . .

On the morning of Willie's funeral, Mary was in bed, too ill to go to the service. Mrs. Keckley was to stay with her. Before he went downstairs, Mr. Lincoln came in, wearing the black coat that had been new for his inaugural. He sat by the bed a few minutes. The lines were drawn sharp around his mouth, but he sat quiet, his hands resting on his knees.

Mary closed her eyes, shutting out the sight of him. In the utter calm of his silence she felt reproached for the tempest of her own grief. If either of them could have spoken, she thought wretchedly, there might have been some help. But there was in his dark face a remoteness that held her off. It was a wall against which her tortured spirit bruised itself in vain.

After a while Mr. Lincoln stood up.

"There were people outside the house this morning, mother," he said. "Some of them were kneeling—praying for us. They tell me that all over the country, when they heard the news, people prayed for us."

A bitter cry broke from Mary's lips.

"What good can their prayers do us, Mr. Lincoln? They can't help Willie—nor us—"

"No, I suppose they can't, mother. All the same," Mr. Lincoln said, "I'm glad they prayed."

36

THE AIR WAS MOIST WITH THE SMELL OF SPRING WHEN Mary was able to be out again. She moved absently through the days, dressing herself, going through her mail with Mr. Stoddard, reading aloud to Taddie. In the pleasant afternoons, when Mr. Lincoln ordered the carriage, she drove with him along the road that led by the river's swollen, muddy banks, where the willows had begun to put forth shoots, pale and green in the mild sun. She tried to talk, to smile, to come back to the life that those around her seemed so intent on offering.

"You must think of Mr. Lincoln," they said. "You still have Taddie—and Robert. You must be brave. There is so much left. So much ahead . . ."

She listened to them, feeling only emptiness. They couldn't know that a world could die, leaving only bitter shadows. And in the emptiness, like a brooding ghost, she saw her own failure. Even in her sorrow for her child she had failed again, somehow—so that they whispered about her, shaking their heads.

There was no escaping. Even in the privacy of grief the limelight shone on her, bright and cruel. She was trapped, bound irrevocably to the bargain she had made. The fate she had struggled so to win turned now and mocked her. And there was no going back.

The snowball of the war rolled on, piling up its burden of defeat and misery, of treachery and jealousy and strife. There was trouble now between the new factions that wrangled and bickered for control. They were opposing McClellan more and more openly. He was slow, overcautious—worse even than old Scott had been. They complained to Mr. Lincoln, and Mary saw him harried and worried until it seemed his shoulders must break beneath the weight of malice and confusion heaped on him.

Only from the West was there any good news. A man named Grant had captured Fort Donelson from the Rebels. Later Mary heard that her brother Sam had been killed in the fighting, on the Confederate side.

Seeing how, in spite of all his anxiety, Mr. Lincoln still had time to be patient with her, Mary tried to respond. In little ways she tried to meet his kindness. But the strange listlessness that held her did not lift. She would look up, sometimes, out of a long silence and find his eyes on her, watchful and troubled. They were together more than in a long while, talking of everyday things, of old times in Springfield—of anything that would not touch on the soreness of grief. They were friendly, considerate of each other—affectionate.

But all the while, beneath the surface calm, Mary felt the dark gulf of silence widening between them. In the first days after Willie's death there had been no way to speak. The language of their suffering was so different that it seemed hopeless. And now, as the silence lengthened, it was like a wedge—forcing them apart, driving deeper day by day, making them strangers who could only try to cover the loneliness with cautious phrases.

When summer drew near, Mary spoke of taking Taddie away with her. He ought to be out of the city—to have other children to play with.

Mr. Lincoln suggested Saratoga. They had enjoyed it last season. But Mary shook her head quickly.

She thought of the familiar hotel rooms—of the piazza

where she used to sit and watch the path for the boys to come back after their pony ride. She remembered their kind Polish waiter in the dining room who always smuggled extra lumps of sugar from the kitchen for Willie to take to the brown and white pony. It was unbearable to think of meeting the people she had known the year before. Their sympathy, however kindly meant, would be like a knife in the rawness of her heart.

"No," she said, "I don't think the waters agreed with me after all. Perhaps we might try the seashore this time. Some quiet place, where no one knows us—"

"Well," Mr. Lincoln said, "whatever you think best, mother."

One afternoon Mary and Mrs. Keckley were in the sewing room, going over Taddie's clothes and getting them ready to pack.

Mary had finished lengthening the sleeves of an Eton jacket. She sat twisting the silver thimble on her finger for a minute, watching Mrs. Keckley's head bent over her stitching.

"You know, Mrs. Keckley," Mary said, "I was just thinking. You've been so kind to us since we came here—I feel now as though we couldn't get along without you. I hope you're not too lonely—being so far from your own people."

Mrs. Keckley looked up. "I never think of being anywhere but here, Mrs. Lincoln," she said. "I feel as though I belong with you."

Mary hesitated, turning the thimble. Then she said slowly, "I wonder sometimes these days how you bore your trouble so bravely when your son was killed. It must have been very hard for you—and yet you never complained. I'm afraid we must have seemed not half sympathetic—"

"No, I wasn't brave at all, really. There were times, in the first weeks, when I felt as if I couldn't go on living—" Mrs. Keckley bent her head lower over her sewing. "I don't believe I ever could have gone on—if it hadn't been for

Mr. Lincoln's kindness. But when he talked to me—he seemed to understand everything and to comfort me so . . ." She was silent a moment. "I can never forget what he did for me."

Mary said nothing. She was thinking how often she had heard these same words. From soldiers she talked to in the hospital—from the wives and mothers of other soldiers who had been killed. *I can never forget how Mr. Lincoln gave me the courage to go on. . . . Mr. Lincoln helped me when no one else could. . . .* It was a strange and bitter thing that he could give comfort so freely to these others, and yet for her, he had none. They were the ones who could still come close to him—the strangers. But when she searched for their path, Mary knew that somehow she had lost the way.

There was a pleasant-faced young woman Mary had engaged early in the year to take charge of the household supplies. The woman worked well, minded her own affairs, and fitted into her position so unobtrusively that beyond an occasional glimpse of her hurrying along the upstairs hall with an armful of fresh linens, Mary was seldom conscious of her presence in the house.

One afternoon the woman brought a tea tray to Mary's sitting room. Bessie, the chambermaid, was ill, and there was no one else to carry up the tray.

Mary thanked her, adding pleasantly that she hoped the woman was finding her work agreeable.

"Very satisfactory, thank you." The reply was prompt and courteous. She touched the tea tray, straightening a corner of the embroidered cloth. "You have such beautiful linens, Mrs. Lincoln, it's a pleasure to take care of them. I noticed a snagged thread in your lace tablecloth when it came up from the laundry this morning, and I took the liberty of mending it. I hope you don't mind—Honiton tears so easily and it would be a pity to have it spoiled."

Mary glanced up in surprise. It wasn't usual for a servant to recognize Honiton. She noticed that the woman's hands were soft, and the nails carefully trimmed and buffed. She made no comment, but, coming into Mr. Lincoln's study a few mornings later, when he was out of the house, Mary was startled to find the woman standing before the rack where the war maps hung.

She turned as Mary entered, making an excuse about having come in to see whether the curtains needed laundering, and left the study quickly. That afternoon, Mary spoke to Mr. Lincoln.

"I don't like the way that woman acts, Mr. Lincoln. She's always snooping about, making excuses to come into our rooms."

So long as the woman did her work well, Mr. Lincoln said, he couldn't see any reason for worrying.

"Just the same, I don't believe she ever worked as a servant before she came here. I don't trust her, Mr. Lincoln."

"Now, mother, there's no use imagining things. The woman's decent and well behaved. And she's got a nice face—"

"A nice face—" Mary shrugged. "Do you suppose, Mr. Lincoln, there are no women with nice faces who might be in sympathy with the Rebels? I believe that woman came here deliberately to spy on us—and I mean to find out who she is."

A trip to the woman's room in the servants' quarters revealed nothing, but the next day Mary was informed by Mrs. Keckley that the woman had gone. She'd packed her things the night before, and simply walked out—without a word to anyone.

"It does seem strange, madam, when she took such pains with her work."

Less than a week had passed when Mr. Stoddard showed Mary an item in the newspaper. A woman, calling herself Edith Connell, had attempted to take a position as chambermaid in the home of the secretary of state. Having become suspicious of the woman's manner and appearance, Mr. Seward ordered her to be investigated, and the woman had been identified as the widow of a Confederate officer who had been killed at Bull Run. Arrested and taken to the Old Capitol prison, she admitted that she had recently been employed by Mrs. Lincoln as a servant. Sufficient evidence in the form of letters and maps had been found in her possession to convict the woman as a spy.

"I don't know whether Mr. Lincoln ought to be told about this," Mr. Stoddard said. "I haven't mentioned it—"

"Then don't." Mary handed back the paper.

There was no use, surely, in burdening him with another worry, now that the danger was past. And besides, Mary had learned long ago that there was never any satisfaction in saying "I told you so" to Mr. Lincoln.

A week before Mary left for Narragansett, Adelina Patti was in Washington. Mr. Lincoln had heard Patti sing once, at a concert in New York, and had met her afterward at a reception. Rather hesitantly, he asked whether Mary would care to invite Patti to the White House.

Mary knew he was making another effort to distract her. She smiled at him, trying to rouse herself from the listlessness that still hung over her empty days. "I could send around a note, I suppose, and ask her for tea—if it would please you, Mr. Lincoln."

The afternoon Patti came, Mary was late coming downstairs, and she found her guest in the East Room talking to Mr. Lincoln. Mary paused a moment on the threshold. She had dressed carefully, taking extra pains with her hair, and for the first time since putting on mourning she had added a touch of white to the throat and sleeves of her gown. It would please Mr. Lincoln, she knew. She saw him look up, and the anxiousness lift from his eyes as she came forward, smiling, to greet her guest.

Patti was charming. Slender and very young, she wore wine-colored silk, and a tricorn bonnet of ostrich plumes that curled around her fresh, pretty face and dipped over one shoulder.

It was the first time in weeks that Mary had entertained

a stranger, but Patti was so friendly and unaffected that the conversation went easily, and Mary found herself joining in, laughing with Patti at Mr. Lincoln's stories.

When tea was finished, Patti smiled at them. "I've had such a lovely time," she said simply, "I should like to do something to thank you. I can't tell clever stories, as Mr. Lincoln does—" she spread her hands—"but if it would please you—I can sing for you."

Seeing Mary's smile of pleasure, Patti crossed to the gilt piano. Against the yellowed keys her fingers looked very white and slender as she began the rippling accompaniment to a Mozart aria.

From her place by the tea table, Mary watched. She sat quiet, listening to the lovely voice that rose and swelled until it filled the room as effortlessly as the late afternoon light that streamed in the long windows. The light fell on the crimson curtains, on the graceful curve of the singer's throat—on a bowl of deep-red roses that stood on the piano. It shone on Mr. Lincoln's face, lined and weary, and on the stiff folds of Mary's black silk dress.

The song ended, and Patti paused—letting her hands rest on the keys. Then, more softly, she began again. "The Last Rose of Summer" . . . Her young voice was full and tender on the melody; when it was done, the sweet notes died in the silence.

Mary had left her chair and gone to the window. She stood looking out across the lawn, her back to the room, and she did not turn when Patti rose from the piano. She heard Mr. Lincoln saying something in a low voice, and then Patti's soft exclamation of dismay.

They knew she was weeping, Mary thought—even though she had made no sound. She could hear them now, going toward the door. Still she did not turn. Mr. Lincoln would make her excuses . . . and they would go out, thinking she had wept because of the song—and Willie. They would be understanding and considerate, and they would pity her. But they couldn't know that she wept for something more. For a sadness she could not understand—for the bitterness of a world gone hopelessly wrong.

37

THAT WAS THE SUMMER OF COLD HARBOR, AND LATER, IN August, of the second disastrous battle at Bull Run. At Cold Harbor the Union troops had been within sight of Richmond—and for a few days there was hope in the North that a victory was coming at last. It was the furious onslaught of Stonewall Jackson's brigade that turned the tide, at the end, and McClellan's advance into Virginia was ended.

The North, accustomed now to defeat, took the news with glum, stoical calm. But Mary, hearing that General Lee had taken command of the Confederate armies, remembered what Old Scott had said. *There was an officer named Lee who fought with me in the Mexican War—he was the best soldier I ever saw.*

"It still goes badly with us," Mr. Lincoln said. "The lessons of war are hard to learn. But with God's help, we will learn them yet."

Mary, home from the summer at the seashore, had been dismayed to find that even in the bitter weeks while the army of the north was being beaten back, steadily and relentlessly, the politicians and the generals were intent on their old jealous game of wrangling for power and blaming each other for each new failure.

"It seems to me, Mr. Lincoln," Mary said, "that one good general could help more than God just now."

"I expect he could, mother." Mr. Lincoln sighed. "But until we can lay our hands on the right man we'll have to struggle along with the Almighty."

Less than a week after Mary's return came the news of Antietam. There, at last, was a victory for the North—but they learned too late that McClellan had succumbed to one of his fits of caution at the crucial moment and let Lee and Jackson escape with their exhausted troops and retreat to safety unpursued.

Coming down late to dinner after a meeting of the Cabinet, Mr. Lincoln sat staring at his plate.

Mary watched him anxiously. "They've been at you again, Mr. Lincoln," she said. "I can tell from your expression."

"Well—partly at me, and partly at each other. And between times they were picking on the generals. Altogether, it was quite a day."

"Truly, I don't know why you stand for it." Mary put down her fork. "If I were you, I shouldn't put up with their carping another day."

"I don't know what else I can do, mother. I can't very well stay away from the Cabinet meetings—the way Seward does when things don't go to his taste."

"*Seward—*"

Mr. Lincoln smiled, in spite of his weariness. "The way you say that name, mother, makes it sound as if there were no worse word in the English language—unless maybe it would be the way you can say *Chase*."

"Or *McClellan—*" Mary said, and suddenly they were both laughing.

Mr. Lincoln took a piece of bread and buttered it slowly. The laughter died out of his eyes, leaving them puzzled and thoughtful.

"They want me to throw out McClellan," he said. "They've got up a petition—and this time Stanton says he means to fight it to a finish."

Mary looked up quickly. Months before, when Cameron had resigned and Mr. Lincoln had appointed Stanton as the new secretary of war, she had been indignant.

"For pity's sake, Mr. Lincoln," she had demanded, "must you forever pick men who despise you? Stanton has snubbed you and talked against you for years. Mr. Stoddard says he's actually heard Stanton refer to you as a gorilla."

"I know, mother. But if I were to choose only my admirers for the Cabinet, I might not have enough to go around."

"But Stanton of all people, Mr. Lincoln. He's sure to make more trouble—I don't believe he has the slightest respect for your opinion."

Mr. Lincoln had looked at her with unexpected firmness.

"I have a great deal of respect for his opinion," he had said. "And that's enough."

The appointment had worked out surprisingly well, but Mary had remained unconvinced by all of Stanton's dogged efforts to cut through the paralyzing lengths of red tape and put some action into the war. She found him personally quite impossible—rude and irritable, and so charged with his own importance that he held forth at a dinner table as though he were giving orders on a battlefield.

"He's a detestable boor," Mary had said, and she clung to her opinion without wavering until a day, shortly after Willie died, when she had encountered Mr. Stanton unexpectedly on his way to Mr. Lincoln's office. She hadn't supposed he would even notice her, but to her surprise he stopped and took her hand, and spoke to her with such gentleness and understanding that she was astonished.

"Mr. Stanton told me about his little daughter Lucy who died," she said later to Mr. Lincoln. "He's a strange man, I think—but I shall never see him again without remembering the way he spoke to me—and the look in his eyes."

In the times when they had met since, Mr. Stanton had been as irascible and hard-shelled as ever, but Mary never forgot his moment of tenderness, and never again spoke a word against him.

Hearing now that Stanton was determined at last to

put a hatpin into McClellan's bumbling mismanagement, Mary took hope. If anything could ever shake Mr. Lincoln's faith loose from the Little Napoleon, it might be Stanton who could do it.

But Mr. Lincoln was still doubtful. "I don't see how I can put McClellan out now," he said. "Three of our other generals are already dismissed for inefficiency—and McDowell is so distrusted he says himself he can't hope to command his men again. If we fire McClellan, there's no one to take his place. Besides, I've heard that McClellan is the only one of our generals the Rebels have the slightest respect for. They say Pope is a fool—and worse than that, no gentleman—and they call poor old Burnside 'the Tortoise.' But they admit McClellan takes watching."

Mary sighed. "Well, that's something in his favor, I suppose. If he can't be respected by his own side, it's nice to think that at least the enemy approves of him. Still and all, Mr. Lincoln, it's a sorry picture."

As they walked out of the dining room, Mr. Lincoln patted her shoulders.

"Don't give up yet, mother," he said. "I guess all this is like a book on religion I read once. The first chapter was called *Hell*, and the second was called *Hell Continued*."

Mr. Lincoln went up to Sharpsburg to have a look at McClellan's headquarters, and see for himself what was going on.

"Everything was in fine order," he reported glumly to Mary when he got home. "McClellan keeps his camp neat as a whistle. All the guards wore nice white gloves, and they bowed me in with wonderful style. The men say Little Mac is a demon on etiquette. He makes his sentries polish their boots every morning and stand as straight as wooden soldiers—" He paused and sighed. "Sometimes, I'm afraid, they're just about as harmless."

But Mr. Lincoln had enjoyed being with the men. There were some Rebel prisoners in the camp, and he had talked to them too.

"They were fine-looking boys," he told Mary. "I was afraid they might bear me a grudge, but they seemed glad to have me come in and shake hands."

Several of the captured soldiers had been members of Stonewall's brigade, and Mr. Lincoln had asked them questions about their commander.

"The most surprising thing they told me," Mr. Lincoln said, "was that Jackson makes his soldiers kneel down and pray with him—and they don't mind doing it." He rubbed his chin thoughtfully. "I'd swap all the supplies in the Union army for one general who could do that."

The best the Union could do was to spin their wheel and try a new one at the top. Less than a week after Mr. Lincoln's return from the camp, General McClellan was relieved of his command, and old Burnside, whose only claim to distinction was that he trimmed his whiskers in a novel way, seemed to be the only successor whose record was so uneventful that everyone could agree on him.

"It seems a pity," Mary said, when she heard the news, "that we must choose our commanders by default."

The winter set in early. As the days grew short, and the sun shone pale over the gray, frozen ground, the hopes for a northern victory congealed like the mud in the rutted streets. With only old Burnside to look to, people said, the chances for a surprise move against the Rebels seemed mighty thin. More than likely, by the time Burnside stirred himself to action, *they'd* be a good deal more surprised than the South.

In December, after a week of cold, mean rain, Burnside did finally attack at Fredericksburg. But Lee and Jackson rallied and refreshed by the long interval since their retreat from Antietam, carried the day.

A pall of gloom, lead-cold as the winter sky, hung over Washington. For three days after the battle, the wounded poured into the city. The hospitals overflowed, and those who could not be cared for at once were left, on stretchers or huddled on park benches, to wait until places could be found for them.

Since Willie's death, Mary had given up her work at the hospital. She went back now, hoping to find some place where she could help, but after so long an absence it was difficult. People brushed past her, too busy and tired to stop and find something for her to do. It was all very different from the leisurely mornings when she had rolled bandages and scraped lint—and there had been only a few patients in the wards. Now there was no time to stop by the beds and talk, to read aloud and help the men write letters home. Now there was only ceaseless, confusing activity. The rows of beds in the wards were long since filled, and men lay on the floor, in the corridors—any place where a few feet of space was available. Only the most desperate cases were treated at all.

After a few hours of being jostled about, of feeling in everyone's way and being sickened by the sights and sounds of pain she was powerless to help, Mary gave up.

On the way up the avenue the carriage came to an abrupt halt, delayed by a train of wounded which had just arrived. Mary looked out. Dear heaven—not more men when there were already so many, and no place left to care for them. She leaned forward, looking out at the ragged, shivering procession. They were being unloaded from the springless ambulances that had brought them over the miles of rutted roads from Fredericksburg. Unloaded, like so many head of butchered cattle, to lie in the cold, the stretchers lined in rows across Lafayette Square.

There was a woman, Mary saw, in a long gray cloak, moving among the men. She had a wagon of supplies drawn up in the street, from which she carried blankets and food and water. Followed by two rough-looking orderlies, she went from stretcher to stretcher, bending briefly over each one. One of the orderlies, following close behind, carried a basin and sponges. Mary saw how the woman washed the mud from the men's faces, caked and frozen as hard as turtleshells. She watched the woman's motions, calm and skillful. There was no time for sentiment, no lingering over the wounded. The woman moved swiftly, like a tireless and experienced angel, speaking little. A word here and there, a low request to the orderly. The eyes of the men followed her progress with silent patience.

Watching, drawing her fur mantle closer against the biting wind, Mary was appalled by the sight of so much suffering. She would have liked to get out, to do something to help—but the spectacle of so many made her shrink back, feeling futile. Vaguely she thought that Mr. Lincoln would never have sat still, as she was doing. He would have been out, in a moment, among the men—talking to them. But it was a language Mary did not know.

She spoke to the coachman, telling him to turn back and take another way around the square. . . . But in that moment, her eye was caught by a young soldier who lay with his face turned away, on a stretcher by the edge of the park. There was something in the line of his cheek, in the way his dark hair fell over it, that was so startlingly like Robert that Mary felt her heart leap.

In an instant her hesitancy was forgotten. Giving a quick order to the coachman, Mary got out. Unmindful of the raw wind that whipped her skirt, or the curious stares of the men, she knelt beside the stretcher, on the frozen ground, looking down at the wounded boy. There was no blanket over him, and she saw that he had one leg shot away. The stump was wrapped in clotted bandages. As Mary leaned over him, he turned his head weakly, and opened his dark eyes for a moment. In spite of the cold, his face burned with fever, but there was no delirium in his gaze, only an expression that wrung Mary's heart with its hopeless patience. The boy's eyes closed again, and he lay still, not even shivering. From under his long lashes, so like Robert's, silent tears rolled down his cheeks. With the tenderness she would have given her own child, Mary took her handkerchief and wiped the tears away. The boy didn't move or look at her again.

Mary stood up. She looked around for a moment, dazed, and found herself staring into a circle of curious faces. She heard a young soldier standing near her whisper suddenly, "That's Lincoln's wife—"

The men watched in silence while she hesitated, not knowing where to turn to get help for the wounded boy. The lad who had recognized her stepped forward, touching his cap. He had one arm in a makeshift sling, and a patch of bandage on his forehead.

"Is there something I can do for you, ma'am?" he asked politely.

Mary looked at him. "I must get a blanket for this boy here," she said. "It's so cold—"

The soldier stared at her, not seeming to understand. He said something about all the others who lay in the wind, with no blankets either—but Mary didn't listen. She saw the woman in the gray cloak coming toward her. The woman didn't seem to notice Mary. She was dipping slices of bread into a bowl of whisky, bending over each man in turn to feed him. When the woman was near enough, Mary spoke.

"Please," she said, "is there anything you can do for this boy? He's very badly hurt—"

For an instant the woman's eyes met Mary's, direct and unemotional. She showed no slightest sign of recognizing the President's wife. She turned to look down at the soldier.

"If he could just have a blanket," Mary said.

"There are no blankets." The woman's voice was low and well bred. She spoke matter-of-factly, as though repeating something she had said a great many times before. "I'm afraid there's nothing I can do until they send me help from the hospital."

The woman moved on, calm, unhurried, and Mary was left. She glanced around once more. There must be someone, surely, who would do something . . .

A slight stir behind her made Mary turn, and the next moment she was face to face with a tall, dark-haired gentleman who gazed at her with an expression of astonishment.

"My God, Mrs. Lincoln, what are you doing here?"

It was Senator Sumner, very elegant and dapper in black broadcloth and beaver hat.

"Mr. Sumner, I'm so glad you're here—" Mary felt herself sway slightly against the firm grip of his hands on her shoulders. "You'll help me, won't you? Please—?"

"Yes, of course. Of course—" The senator's glance took in Mary's tearstained face, and her streaked, muddy skirt where she had knelt on the ground. And the stares of the men gathered about. "You must get back to your carriage, Mrs. Lincoln. I'm afraid all this is too much for you—"

Feeling herself led toward the carriage, Mary pulled back. She tried to explain about the boy. That she must help him.

But there was nothing, Mr. Sumner said, that they could do. When the poor fellow was only one among so many . . . They were at the carriage. Perhaps, Mr. Sumner suggested, if Mrs. Lincoln was alone, he might ride back with her. It was only natural that she should be upset by such harrowing sights . . .

Mary looked back one last time. The boy lay perfectly still, his eyes closed. If only he hadn't looked so like Robert . . . With a shuddering sob she turned and let Mr. Sumner help her into the carriage.

They were almost at the White House drive before Mr. Sumner spoke. "I'm sorry," he said. "But there was really no way we could help—"

Mary nodded. She felt drained, utterly weary—aware only of the swaying motion of the carriage and the cold wind that seemed to go through her in numbing waves.

"Was the boy—someone you knew, Mrs. Lincoln?"

"No. Oh, no."

There was a silence. Mary was vaguely conscious of something uncomfortable in the senator's glance.

"I thought perhaps—" he said, "since the poor fellow was in Confederate uniform—"

Mary turned, her eyes blank. "Was he?" she said. "I—didn't notice—" She paused a moment. "I don't wonder, then, you hurried me away, Mr. Sumner. It must have been quite awkward—"

The senator cleared his throat. Mary looked at him steadily. She saw the slight frown between his eyes—and his look of relief as they drew up before the steps.

"Mr. Sumner," Mary said, "that woman in the long cloak who was helping the men. Who was she?"

He turned in surprise. "That was Miss Barton. Didn't you recognize her?"

Mary shook her head. She had heard of Clara Barton—but she had pictured a very different sort of person from the woman in gray, with her quiet, genteel voice.

"A remarkable woman—no doubt of that," Mr. Sumner said. "A good many think she has no business following the army as she does—no place for a woman, going right in the thick of a fight. But she's as persistent as a horsefly, they say. Generally gets where she intends to, I daresay—no matter who tries to stop her."

Long after she had left the carriage, with orders that Mr. Sumner was to be taken back to the Capitol, Mary was thinking of Miss Barton—remembering the cool, level eyes that had held hers for a moment. There was something in the memory of that glance that was troubling. As if, somehow, she had been weighed in an impartial balance—summed up, and found wanting . . .

On a Sunday morning, early in March, Mary was driving home from church. Taddie, sitting beside her, pointed excitedly to a train of army wagons jogging up the avenue ahead of them.

"Are they going to a fight, mamma?" Tad craned his head for a better view. "Look—there's a lady in that wagon. Do ladies go to fight too, mamma?"

Mary followed Taddie's glance. Seated in the back of a canvas-covered ambulance, dressed in a gray cloak and a bonnet neatly faced with white, was a woman. Mary recognized the placid, gentle features she had seen on the winter's afternoon after Fredericksburg.

"That's Miss Barton, Tad," she said. "She can go with the soldiers because she's a special person."

Taddie looked interested. "Will she have a gun, and kill Rebels?"

"No—she's a nurse. She'll take care of the soldiers who are hurt in the fighting, and try to make them well again."

"She won't try to make the Rebels well, will she, mamma?"

"I expect she will—if any Rebels fall prisoners on our side."

"Why?"

"Because she's a nurse—and a nurse's work is to take care of sick people, no matter whose side they fight on."

"But I thought we wanted all the Rebels to be dead . . . " Taddie was puzzled. "Bad people should be dead."

"Rebels aren't bad, Taddie. They're people—just like us."

"Do they have little boys at home? Just like me?"

Mary nodded. "Just like you."

"Will the little boys be sorry if their papas get killed?"

"Yes—very sorry."

"Then why do we shoot them?"

"Because we're at war. They are fighting us because they believe in things we think wrong."

"Do they think they're wrong?"

"No."

"Will they think they're wrong if they get killed?"

"Oh—I don't know, Taddie. Perhaps not. It takes years and years sometimes for people to realize they were wrong."

Taddie was silent a few minutes. The wagon train ahead had slowed to a stop, and as their carriage turned out to pass, Mary caught a closer glimpse of Miss Barton. She leaned forward, half hoping for some sign of recognition on Miss Barton's face—but there was none. Miss Barton was looking straight ahead, her gloved hands folded in her lap as decorously as though she were going for an ordinary drive. If she were aware that the President's carriage was passing by, there was nothing in her expression, serene and bland, to show it.

That afternoon, Mary was in her sitting room, looking through a new copy of *Leslie's Weekly*. Taddie had gone for a drive with Mrs. Keckley, and Mr. Lincoln had been in his study working since dinnertime. The house was very still.

Turning the pages of *Leslie's* idly, Mary stopped as the sight of her name caught her attention. Tucked modestly between the close of a story dealing with the lurid adventures of a wronged but virtuous heroine, named Lady Violet d'Astonga, and an article dealing with the rules of discreet conduct for young widows was an announcement, chaste and simple, devoid of comment or explanation:

The reports that Mrs. Lincoln is in an interesting condition are untrue.

Mary smiled wryly, thinking of Grandmother Humphreys. No lady's name, she used to tell Mary, would ever be seen in print except on two occasions—once when she was married and once when she died. In the event of a breach of taste against any lady in this regard, Grandmother Humphreys always added serenely, the lady's nearest male relative was under moral obligation to shoot the editor.

Turning to the back of the magazine, Mary found the usual account of social events in Washington, gushingly transcribed by a correspondent who signed himself "Debonair."

At a recent gathering of the Capital *élite*, the most notable event was the appearance of Mrs. Lincoln, only lately emerged from the period of mourning following her tragical bereavement. It was observed by this humble scribe that the First Lady looked to be in excellent health, and she resumed her *rôle* as reigning queen of Washington society with her customary graciousness and vivacity of wit. Entering upon the arm of our noble President, Mrs. Lincoln presented to admiring eyes a spectacle of *regal* elegance. Gowned, as always, in the very height of the *môde,* she wore a handsome creation of heliotrope brocade, its *décolletage* gracefully modified by a mantle of black lace. The lace, which was the most exquisite and costly *point de Venise,* we understand was purchased by Mrs. Lincoln at the establishment of *A. T. Stewart's* during a recent shopping expedition to the marts of Gotham.

In these times of melancholy distress, it is indeed a heartening sign to observe that the First Lady does not allow the pessimism of the hour to deter her from her gracious duty in brightening the Capital scene with the fashionable *toilettes* for which she is justly famous. Such a display of courage cannot fail to sound a note of gallant and patriotic cheer amid the pervading gloom . . .

Mary closed the magazine and crossed to the window. She stood a long while, looking down through the dusk, while her fingers toyed aimlessly with the edge of Mr. Montrose's lace curtain. Once she might have been pleased by the account in *Leslie's.* Once she might even have taken pains to send a marked copy to Elizabeth . . .

Watching the wind that rocked the bare trees, making them a swaying pattern against the darkening sky, Mary wondered suddenly where Miss Barton was by now. It was curious how persistently, during the day, the image of Miss Barton had come back. It must be cold and uncomfortable to be jounced along in a springless ambulance, with no more than a canvas top to hold out the wind, Mary thought. But still—Miss Barton was going somewhere. Somewhere where she was needed . . .

Mary turned back into the lighted room, and took up the magazine with a vague sigh.

"*Such a display of courage . . .*"

38

ON AN APRIL MORNING TADDIE WOKE EARLY AND bounced out of bed to go to the window and look at the weather. This was the day—the wonderful, exciting day when, right after breakfast, they were to start out—he and Papa and Mamma—to visit General Hooker's headquarters. General Hooker sounded like a fine person. Fighting Joe Hooker, they called him, and he was the new general of all the Army of the Potomac. They were going to stay a whole week in the camp, living in tents like the regular soldiers, eating in the barracks and watching drills. And they were going down the river by boat.

Looking out the window, Taddie was dismayed. The whole sky was full of swirling snow—fat white flakes that fell like cotton on the grass that was already beginning to show bright green. Mamma would surely say they couldn't start out in snow. She'd say it was damp, and they'd all catch their deaths, and wipe her eyes the way she always did when she thought of Willie. She'd want the trip to be postponed—or, worst of all, she might say Papa was to go on alone without them. One way or another, Taddie thought, Mamma was certain to make a fuss.

But no.

At the breakfast table there was only a little talk about the storm, and Mamma, looking cheerful and nice, said it was sure not to last. Snow in April couldn't mean much, and they'd start as planned. Taddie curled his toes with happiness. Papa smiled too, though not as cheerfully as Mamma, and he said all right, they'd do just as Mamma wanted.

It was still snowing when the carriage pulled up at the front door. There had been a last wild argument with Mamma in the hall, over whether Taddie must wear his overcoat and scarf, and many warnings about racing around and getting overheated before going out in the damp air. But Papa, coming down the stairs at the last minute with Mr. Hay following with three more papers to be signed, cocked an eyebrow at Taddie.

"You'd better do as Mother says, Tad, or we shan't get to go at all."

Papa hiked up one knee and signed the papers for Mr. Hay. And they were ready.

Safely started, squeezed in the seat between Papa and Mamma, Taddie squirmed around to wave at Mrs. Keckley on the steps. He'd bring her a pair of Rebels' ears, he shouted back, for a present. Mamma hushed him sharply, but with a face that showed she didn't really mean it, and Taddie settled back content. The round, fat backs of the horses were steaming under the wet snow, and when they got to the dock the air was still thick with white flakes that fell into the gray river and disappeared.

The boat was wonderful. Full of little rooms with beds like shelves, and men who jumped around obeying orders and didn't seem to mind how many questions Taddie asked. They went slowly down the river, and when it got dark they decided to put into a cove and wait for morning. Taddie got to sleep on a shelf-bed in one of the little rooms.

By morning the snow had stopped, and when they reached camp in the afternoon all the officers came out to meet them. General Hooker, who looked big and rather fierce, Taddie thought, made a great to-do when he met Papa, and kept talking all the time in a loud voice, as though afraid to stop. Every now and then the general would look at Mamma in a worried way, and he would break off what he was saying to Papa about taking Richmond and say he hoped Mamma would find everything to her liking, and if not please to say so.

But Mamma, smiling, seemed pleased with the three tents that were ready for them. She said the wooden floors, which Taddie found disappointing, would keep out the damp. Taddie and Mamma would share one tent, Mamma said, and Papa could take another—and the third was where they would eat. It seemed rather hateful—Taddie had hoped to sleep with the soldiers, or at least with Papa, but Mamma shook her head firmly.

Once they were settled, General Hooker wanted Papa to come out right away and look over the camp, and he said Tad might come along. There was a special horse ready for Taddie to ride, and he clumped along beside Papa, who looked taller than ever on a rawboned gray, with his legs dangling down the sides and his plug hat sticking up like a chimney. All the men they met seemed friendly and nice, coming out to shake hands—and once they were safely out of Mamma's hearing, General Hooker talked more and louder than ever. He said a great deal about how they were going to Richmond in short order, and when he described what they would do to the Rebels, he used wonderful words that Taddie felt sure Mamma wouldn't approve in the least. Papa talked very little, but he listened and watched everything while they rode along.

The next morning, when General Hooker asked Papa what he would like to do, Papa smiled.

"Well," he said, "Taddie here has got an idea he'd like to see some Rebels. If it would be possible, general, we'd appreciate it."

General Hooker looked surprised. He scratched his chin a minute and said he guessed they might manage. They rode down to the river and along the bank a little way; then the general pulled in his horse and pointed across to the other side.

"There they are, son."

Taddie felt a jump of excitement—but when he looked where the general pointed, all he could see was some men in gray coats on the opposite bank. Several were standing together, at the top, leaning on their guns, and there was another, sitting cross-legged on the ground, reading a newspaper. They certainly didn't look very dangerous.

Papa got off his horse and helped Taddie down, and took him by the hand. Taddie could see that Papa was watching just as curiously as he was. Just then the sitting-down soldier on the other shore jumped up and began to run down the hill toward them. Taddie's hand tightened in Papa's—but the next minute the soldier stopped, and after he had stared at them a moment, he suddenly pulled off his cap and waved it. Then he kited back up the far bank and said something to the other Graycoats—and they all turned and began to wave too.

Taddie simply couldn't understand it. Even from so far away he could see that the men weren't looking the least bit fierce, but friendly and smiling. They were Rebels, all right—he could see their silver buttons shining in the sun. But it was all very strange, standing out in the open like this. Taddie had expected they might have to hide, and peek at the enemy from behind the trees.

"What are they waving for?" Taddie asked.

General Hooker said he guessed the pickets had recognized Mr. Lincoln. "More than likely they knew you were coming down to the camp," he said to Papa. "When things are quiet for a few weeks, it's hard to keep the pickets from going back and forth to each other's lines. They have orders forbidding it—but they're forever swapping tobacco and newspapers, and I wouldn't be surprised if those boys had heard about your visit, Mr. Lincoln."

Taddie looked up at the general, still puzzled.

"If they know who Papa is," he said, "why don't they shoot him?"

The general frowned and didn't answer, but one of the Union pickets standing near Taddie spoke up quickly.

"Why, they wouldn't do a thing like that," he said. "Those are fine fellows over there."

Papa had taken off his hat and was looking across at the men with a queer expression. He put up his hand—and right away they waved back again. Taddie tried it—and they waved at him too. He could hear one of the men calling something as they turned to get on the horses. It was hard to catch the words across the distance, but it sounded like *Hello, Abe*—

Riding back to camp, Papa kept on looking as though he were thinking about something—and Taddie noticed that he was quieter than ever when General Hooker began to tell again how they'd skin the Johnny Rebs and hang them on the apple trees when they got to Richmond.

Taddie guessed Papa must have been secretly a little disappointed, as he was, to find the Graycoats quite so tame.

On the third evening of the visit there was a special dinner planned for Papa and Mamma—and all day Taddie stewed and worried for fear Mamma wouldn't let him stay up for it. But when the time came, Mamma never said a word about bed, and only reminded Tad to be sure and come in a half hour before to get clean and put on his best serge suit. Mamma was dressed up herself, in a gray dress trimmed all over with shiny braid that Tad thought very pretty. She didn't scold, or make him stand still while she fixed his tie and brushed his hair down flat with water —and when he was ready she hugged him and said he was a good boy and not to forget his table manners or ask the officers too many questions. It was funny, Taddie thought, how cheerful Mamma always got when they were away from home.

When Mamma saw how they had fixed up the long tables for the dinner, she smiled at General Hooker and told him she'd hardly expected such a fine party. The general smiled too, and said he was pleased that she liked it—but Taddie noticed that his face seemed quite red, and he pulled at his collar every now and then, as though it were too tight.

There were tin cups at all the men's places, and while they ate, an orderly kept filling the cups from a brown bottle. Papa's cup seemed to be the only one that never needed filling—but he picked it up politely every time the general or one of his staff thought of another toast to someone, even though, when the men drank *Burn Down Richmond* or *Hang Lee* Papa only touched his cup, and Taddie thought he looked sorry and not quite pleased about something. General Hooker seemed to enjoy these toasts most of all, and he emptied his cup each time, while his face got redder and his collar tighter, and he talked to Mamma more loudly and politely than ever.

They had oysters to eat, and steak and fried potatoes, and for dessert stewed peaches with a wonderful thick yellow cream that came out of cans and didn't taste nearly as good as it looked. Taddie was just finishing his peaches, feeling quite full, when a sudden commotion behind him made him turn—and he saw the orderly, who had put down the brown bottle for a minute, carrying in a huge iced cake, decorated with ten fat lighted army candles. The orderly put it down in front of Tad.

Mamma stared in astonishment. How in the world, she asked General Hooker, had he found out that tomorrow was Taddie's birthday?

Well, it wasn't his doing exactly, the general said. It was General Sickles who had reminded him of the occasion.

At the mention of General Sickles the look on Mamma's face changed slightly—but she turned to thank him, and General Sickles stood up and bowed very low, looking pleased with himself, and came around the table to Taddie.

"You must do the honors in military style, my boy," General Sickles said. He drew out his sword and handed it to Taddie, who was puzzled at first, until the general told him he must use it to cut the first slice of cake—and steadied his hand with a grip that was none too steady itself. "Make a wish now—" General Sickles's voice was loud and cheerful, though Taddie wondered why it sounded thick—as if he had already taken a large mouthful of the cake. "Make a wish for victory—for the finest army in the world—the Army of the Potomac!"

The cake was sliced and passed around. The tin cups had somehow, in the interval, got filled again—and now there was a toast to Master Tad, and a great many very cheerful remarks while the orderly came back, this time with a military cape, and a pair of regulation army boots with silver spurs.

"Compliments to Captain Tad—from Fighting Joe and his staff!"

Taddie thought his eyes would drop out with astonishment and delight. He must put on the cape at once—and the boots over his own shoes. He stamped them, and felt the spurs jingle. Then, while he was still standing, General Sickles unbuckled his own sword belt and fastened it around Tad's waist.

"There you are, my boy." General Sickles drew himself up, with only a little waver, and saluted smartly. "Captain Tad—salute your commander in chief." He whirled Tad around by the shoulders to face Mr. Lincoln.

"Look, papa," Taddie said. "I'm a real soldier, papa—*look*—"

Papa sat quiet, saying nothing, smiling at Taddie.

The next day was set for the big review. Starting early in the morning, the whole army—troops and horses and guns—was going to parade down a long field, and Papa had said Tad might wear the new cape and sword and boots and sit beside him on his horse.

It was fun at first, watching the columns of men march past, and the big cannon trundling along the bumpy ground. But there did seem to be a great many, all looking very much alike, and even the bands seemed all to be playing the same tunes. Taddie had a hard time to keep from fidgeting, and he was glad, after a while, when Papa came and helped him down from his horse and took him over to the carriage to sit with Mamma.

"If you and Tad get tired," Papa told her, "you can drive back to camp and rest awhile."

Surely, Mamma said, the review must be nearly finished—there couldn't be many more soldiers left in the whole world after all that had gone by. But Papa shook his head, looking over at the wide meadow where the regiments were standing crowded together in close formation.

"It does seem like a terrible lot," Papa said. "But General Hooker tells me there's nearly half left to come."

While Papa walked back to his horse, a new company came slowly past, marching to the roll of drums, their flags whipping smartly in the breeze. Taddie sank back on the carriage seat, and Mamma put her arm around him.

"You're not getting too worn out, Taddie?" she asked anxiously.

Taddie pulled himself up straight, frowning. It always worried Mamma to have him act quiet.

"Of course not. I wanted to stay with Papa—only it gets so tired where I sit."

On the trip home, after the first hour or so, Taddie found that the time went awfully slowly. The boat, somehow, wasn't half so exciting as it had been coming down. It looked so much smaller, for one thing, as though it must have shrunk during the time they were away, and no one, Taddie thought, seemed very much interested in talking to him. Mamma had gone straight down to the cabin to rest, and she told Taddie he wasn't to bother people or go outside on deck where it was misting and damp.

For a time Taddie wandered around, wishing dismally they were home again so he could play with the goats. They'd had to send away Willie's pony because every time she saw it Mamma would begin to cry, and Papa had bought the goats to make it up to Taddie. Taddie was glad, really, because he liked the goats ever so much better—but he was careful never to say so to Mamma, who surely would have cried again.

He wished now he could hitch the goats to their red wagon and make them clatter down the cobblestone drive. But they were still hours away from home, and in the meantime Taddie went to look for Papa, finding him in the little parlor on the top deck, his long legs stretched out in front of him, looking out the window at the slow-passing shore with the expression on his face that Willie used to say made Papa look as if his brains were racking. Mr. Brooks, a friend of Papa's who had come along on the trip home, was there too, smoking a segar.

Taddie climbed on the arm of Papa's chair, hoping for a story, but Papa only put one arm around him absent-mindedly and went on talking to Mr. Brooks.

"There's a good deal to be said for General Hooker, I suppose," Papa was saying. "He's kept the army in good shape during the winter—and there's something I can't help liking about him. All the same—I'd feel better if he and Sickles didn't spend so much time talking about Richmond. It makes me think of a farmer and his wife I knew out in Illinois. They were set on building a new barn, and they saved up for it and talked about nothing else till they had enough money to start. But they couldn't agree what color the roof should be—and they spent so much time arguing about it that they finally fell out and got divorced, and the barn never got built at all."

Papa was quiet for a while, looking out the window again, then he turned around to Tad. "Well, what did you think of the trip, Tad? Did you have fun?"

Taddie nodded, but not very enthusiastically. "Yes," he said, "only I wanted to stay longer. General Sickles said he was going to let me help shoot off a cannon, only we had to leave too soon. And I think," he added thoughtfully, "I'm beginning to have kind of a stomach-ache."

Papa smiled, and leaned over as if he were going to tell a secret. "To tell you the truth, Taddie, I think I have kind of a stomach-ache myself—only I don't suppose we'd better mention it to Mother—or she'll blame it on too much excitement. Personally, I think a little excitement is worth a stomach-ache now and then, but Mother can't see it that way."

"It was good to get away awhile and rest," Papa said to Mr. Brooks after a minute. "Only it seems sometimes as though nothing ever quite touches the tired spot."

Late in the afternoon, when the boat came in sight of Washington, they all went out on deck together. Mamma stood by the rail watching. The smile that had been on her face almost all the while during the trip was gone now, and she pulled her cape tighter and shivered.

"When I look at Washington," she said to Papa, "it frightens me. I feel as though the city were full of enemies—waiting for us."

Taddie looked up, expecting to see Papa laugh at such a queer remark. But Papa didn't look at all like laughing. He only nodded slowly.

"I reckon our enemies are like the poor, mother," he said. "We have them always with us."

Which was certainly, Ted thought, queerer than ever. The Rebels were the enemies—and certainly *they* weren't in Washington. And when Papa had stood on the river-bank and looked across at the Graycoats, he hadn't said a word about enemies, but had taken off his hat instead, and waved as though they were friends. It was all peculiar, but grownups were so often odd—and it didn't matter really because the boat was getting ready to dock and they were nearly home. Taddie gave a hop of anticipation. His stomach-ache was gone—and there would be time before supper to go out to the barn and see the goats.

39

THAT YEAR, WHEN THE HOT WEATHER CAME, THE whole family moved out to a cottage on the grounds of the Soldier's Home. It was near enough for Mr. Lincoln to ride the three miles down Vermont Avenue to the office every day, and far enough out of town to discourage most of the White House callers and to be a breath cooler than the simmering city. Robert was coming to join them later, for his vacation.

There was space for Taddie—and the goats—on sloping lawns, and shade from the cedars and poplars. And from the porch Mary could look across the city lying at the foot of the long hill, its border outlined by the curving band of the Potomac. Sitting with Mr. Lincoln and Taddie, in the evenings, under the bright-starred summer sky, Mary was peaceful and at ease. There was no music, no rose-shaded candlelight at dinner, no diverting parade of fashionable carriages as there had been at Saratoga—but there was something in the brown frame cottage and its narrow, rather shabby rooms that made Mary feel that she had a home again.

Leaning back in a low rocker, Mary would look up at the sky.

"Look, Mr. Lincoln, there's the Small Dipper. And see, over the top of the cedar there, how bright Venus is tonight—" Mary couldn't remember noticing the stars before in Washington. "I always forget, from year to year, how many stars there are in summer."

"And how many mosquitoes." Mr. Lincoln reached down to slap his ankle. "Still—I'd rather have mosquitoes than office seekers. There's one advantage in a mosquito—you can sometimes swat him."

Mr. Lincoln had been worried at first for fear Mary would find the long quiet days tedious—but for the first time since Willie's death, she was beginning to seem really like herself.

In the still country nights, she found that she could sleep again—and when she woke it was no longer to a sense of misery that made her want to push back the new day. Little by little, the cold shell of numbness that had clung so long about her heart was eased. She began to get up early in the mornings, surprised to find herself rested and the leaden heaviness in her head gone. They had brought only Mrs. Keckley and one general servant to run the household. Mary went often into the kitchen—not formally, to inspect, as she did in the White House—but to consult leisurely with Jenny over the dinner. To discuss whether last night's roast might have been browned the least bit more, whether the man who brought their supplies was giving full weight on the butter and meat.

One day, to show Jenny just how Mr. Lincoln liked his dumplings made, Mary put on an apron and cooked the fricassee herself. That evening at dinner, Mr. Lincoln looked up in surprise.

"I haven't tasted anything like this since Springfield, mother. Jenny must be improving."

After that Mary put on the apron more often. She helped Mrs. Keckley make the beds and sort the linens, and tidy the upstairs. It was strange, she sometimes thought, how the things that had seemed like fretting shackles in Springfield could give her such a sense of peace and comfort now.

At first, on the evenings when Mr. Lincoln was delayed in town and came home hours late for dinner, Mary tried sending Taddie up to bed as usual. But he begged so touchingly to be allowed to stay up for Papa, that she began to yield more and more often. It was partly to avoid ending the day with the nerve-shattering tears of one of Taddie's stormy scenes, but more, really, because it was easier to be with Mr. Lincoln when Tad was there too. His presence seemed to hold back the queer barrier that had never quite broken down between them since the night Willie died.

Without ever speaking of it, Mary realized as the weeks went by that she and Mr. Lincoln were depending on Taddie more and more. He protected them from something—she never knew quite what it was—that they dreaded when they were alone. So Tad went everywhere they went. He sat between them when they drove in the evenings, through the summer dusk, and he took his place, importantly, at the dinner table.

To Taddie it was a windfall. Never to be hushed or told to run out and play. Not to be left with Mrs. Keckley while Papa and Mamma drove off together. And to have his endless flow of conversation and questions listened to with flattering attention. Mamma hardly ever seemed to say any more that he must leave her alone because her head was aching. And Papa, instead of offering him a fifty-cent piece to be quiet for a while, let him talk as much as he pleased and gave him the fifty-cent pieces besides. Whenever he came and climbed on Papa's chair now, Papa would draw him onto his knee and hold him there, while he sat reading, or talking to Mamma over Taddie's head.

Mrs. Keckley said one morning, "I'm afraid Taddie is getting to be a very spoiled little boy, Mrs. Lincoln. He doesn't mind me as he used to, and lately he refuses to stay with me at all. Even when you and Mr. Lincoln have guests he simply insists on going down to dinner."

"Well, let him come then," Mary said. "It pleases Mr. Lincoln—and I can't see that it does Tad any harm."

"But when we go back to town, madam, if Taddie thinks he must be included in everything, it's sure to make him very difficult."

"Yes, I know—" Mary sighed. "I used to think discipline was the most important thing with children—but lately I've wondered sometimes whether we oughtn't to let them just be happy while they can." She paused a moment. "After all, the time seems so short—for any of us—"

Mary was careful not to question Mr. Lincoln for news of the war when he came home in the evenings. Ever since General Hooker's long-heralded attack had been defeated at Chancellorsville, there had been nothing but gloom and uncertainty.

"They're after me to change commanders again," Mr. Lincoln said, "but I won't do it. We've been enough of a laughingstock for the South already without playing 'Going to Jerusalem' with our generals."

Instead of asking how the day had gone, Mary would watch by the front window when it was time for Mr. Lincoln to come. Seeing him ride up the long curving drive, she could judge from the droop of his shoulders whether the news had been bad again. And if he looked too dejected, she would call Tad and send him running down the drive. The weariness in Mr. Lincoln's face never failed to lighten then, as he got down from his horse and let Tad ride the rest of the way up to the porch steps where Mary waited.

It was Mr. Lincoln who did the questioning.

"Well, what's the news today, mother? Did Tad catch us a fish from the brook for our supper?"

By the first of July, in spite of all Mr. Lincoln's resolution, the wheel had turned again. Fighting Joe was down and General Meade had taken his place.

"I don't know what we can expect from Meade," Mr. Lincoln said. "I'm afraid to get my hopes up any more."

On warm afternoons the soldiers from the hospital barracks across the lane would walk on the grounds. Taddie followed them for hours, listening with spellbound attention to their endless stories of the battles they had seen. There was one soldier in particular Tad attached himself to. The man had a gunshot wound in the knee, and he would come and sit on the cottage steps, his game leg stuck out stiffly, his cap pushed back on his head while he whittled boats and whistles for the boy.

One day, when a thundershower broke in an unexpected downpour, Mary asked Taddie to invite his friend in. The man came into the parlor, uneasily at first, leaning on his cane. But when he saw the tea and cakes Mary had set out by the fire, his lean face brightened.

"It's been quite a spell since I sat down in a real house, ma'am," he said.

The shell in his knee was a souvenir of Chancellorsville, he told Mary.

"It was one of Jackson's men that got me," he said, rather as though the distinction had been an honor. "Our company was about a mile behind the line, waiting to go up and reinforce General Hooker, when all of a sudden

Jackson's men came on us like a clap of lightning. They'd come around through the woods and got us from the side and back. I never did hear anything like the yell those men let out, ma'am. Before we hardly knew what'd hit us, it seemed like half our company was down, and the other half scattering all over the field with those yelling Rebs everywhere. I never saw anything like it."

The man stopped suddenly, and sat staring into the fire. Taddie squatted before him.

"Tell me—" Mary stirred her tea—"did the Confederates feel as badly as we heard they did when General Jackson was killed?"

He nodded slowly. "It was that same night, about two hours after dark. I and a lot of others that'd been hurt were still on the field, pretty much where we fell. There were some Rebs there too—I remember one of them was lying near me. He'd been hurt pretty bad, but he could talk—and it seemed like all he wanted to talk about was Jackson. When the word came round that Stonewall had been shot by one of his own pickets who'd taken him for a Union scout—that boy next to me just wouldn't believe it. I guess none of us believed it at first. We'd all got so we thought that nothing could ever happen to Jackson . . ."

"But—it could," Mary said.

"Yes, ma'am; it could." The man rubbed his game knee, easing it. "There's been a lot of talk about how bad we came off that day—but I don't know. I don't believe the Rebs'll ever fight again the way they did for Jackson. It's like that boy said to me that night: 'Stonewall's men would've followed him to the devil,' he said, 'and he knew it.' It makes an awful difference when men can feel that way."

Mary nodded. "Still—they have brave generals left," she said.

"Yes, ma'am—and so have we. Plenty of them. But Jackson was different. Lee's army will fight for him—and die if they have to. And so will our army for their generals. But when they lost Jackson, the South lost something more than their best general . . ." He hesitated, shaking his head. "I guess I can't put it rightly, but you wait, ma'am. You'll see what I'm driving at sometime . . ."

A few nights later Mr. Lincoln was very late coming home. Tad had begged, as usual, to wait up—but when it got to be eight o'clock and still no sign of Mr. Lincoln, Mary said they'd have to eat without him. By nine they were out on the porch again, and after another hour of waiting, Mary coaxed Tad upstairs, silencing his fretful insistence that it was *not* late and he was *not* sleepy by telling him she was going to bed herself.

When Taddie was settled, still protesting, Mary crossed to her room and undressed. She turned the lamp down and went to sit on a low chair near the window, where she could look down on the drive, shadowed and empty beneath the full, high moon. The night was breathless. There was something queer in the air—an ominous waiting in the night stillness. It might be going to storm.

It was like the summer night Mary remembered long ago, when she had waited for Mr. Lincoln in the little parlor of the Globe Tavern. The night before Robert was born—when she had been so frightened—and then so hurt and angry when Mr. Lincoln said he had just been playing checkers. She smiled to think of being so afraid—only now—an icy thought contracted her heart—now it was different. She had something to fear now. Only last week Mr. Brooks had told Mr. Lincoln he oughtn't to take the long ride out from town alone at night. Mr. Lincoln had laughed, but then, seeing Mary's face and Mr. Brooks's earnestness, he'd said soberly:

"There's no use being afraid. If they are going to shoot me, they will. No matter if I wear an armored vest and take a dozen men to guard me."

Mary leaned closer to the window, straining her eyes down the road. If only something would move—even a wind to stir the leaves—anything to break the stillness that was like death . . .

Suddenly, splitting the silence, came a shout from Taddie's room.

"There's Papa!"

Mary's eyes flew wide. She had seen nothing—but in that moment there was a sound of horse's feet crunching on the gravel—and there, quite surely, something *had* moved. Emerging from a patch of deep shadow was Mr. Lincoln's tall hat.

Relief burst like a bubble in Mary. Her nerves, loosed suddenly from the taut suspense, jangled irritably. She was angry because Mr. Lincoln had come so late, because Taddie was still awake. She was angry at Taddie for crying out so that it had frightened her—angry at herself for letting the fear dissolve her into this foolish, helpless trembling. She crossed the hall swiftly.

"Taddie—"

He was out of bed and at the window, hopping up and down and squealing. "Papa's here—I can see Papa—Papa's come!"

"Get back into bed, Taddie. You cannot see your father tonight. I won't permit it."

Even as she spoke, it was too late. There was the step, slow and heavy, on the stairs—and the next moment Mr. Lincoln was at the door and Tad had flown at him, scrambling up on him, throwing his nightshirted arms around his father's neck.

"Well, well, well—" Mr. Lincoln seemed astonished by Tad's noisy embrace. "What's all this rumpus about?" He put Taddie down and went to sit down on the bed while Tad tore around the room like an Indian, shouting.

Mary felt her lips tighten with exasperation. "Mr. Lincoln, really, you must not encourage this child's absurd notion of waiting up for you to come home. Do you realize that it's past midnight—and he's not had a wink of sleep? He'll work himself into a fever going on like this—"

Mary stopped. As well cry for the moon, she thought,

as expect Mr. Lincoln to listen. Taddie, suddenly quiet, came over and climbed meekly into bed.

Mr. Lincoln pulled the sheet over him. "There now, Taddie, are you ready to go to sleep?"

Taddie burrowed his head contentedly. "Yes, papa."

"And no more fidgets?"

"No, papa." Taddie's smile was angelically obedient.

"That's a good boy, then . . . Good night."

Outside the door, Mr. Lincoln turned. "I think he'll be all right now, mother."

"I haven't the slightest doubt of it. Now that he's had his own way and stayed awake to see you—when I had expressly forbidden it. You've no idea what he can be like when you're not here, Mr. Lincoln. Perverse and willful—and yet you act as though I were to blame for scolding him."

"Why, no, I don't, mother—"

"But you never see how naughty and spoiled he is. He defies me, and gets himself worked into a perfect state—and then, the moment you come, he behaves like an angel."

Mr. Lincoln sighed. "Well, let him be good while he can, mother. I wish we all had something that would turn us from sour into sweet as easily."

They crossed the hall, and Mr. Lincoln dropped down on the bed. Mary, turning her back for a moment to adjust the lamp, was startled, when she turned back, to see how badly he looked. He sat hunched forward, his elbows on his knees, and in the light his face showed ashy pale.

"Mr. Lincoln—" She went to him in quick alarm. "You're not ill?"

He shook his head. "We had the news today," he said. "It seems Meade carried it off all right at Gettysburg."

"You mean we won?"

"We lost three thousand of our men," he went on, in the same flat tone. "And they tell me the South lost even more." He was silent a moment, staring down at his hands, pulling the knuckles until they cracked, one by one. Suddenly he looked up, with such haunted misery in his eyes that Mary was frightened. "How long is it going on like this?" he said. "How much more of this killing have we got to stand?"

The words burst from him as though wrung out of pain past bearing. For an instant more he stared at her, and in that brief moment there was no barrier—no guard. Mary looked straight into his eyes, seeing the tortured doubts. She tried to speak—searching for the word that would say she understood—but the long habit of restraint was too much, and she could only look at him in silence. For the first time now, dimly, she saw how it must have been for him when Willie died and she had longed for comfort. How he must have been held by her grief, locked by it, as she was now by his.

Mr. Lincoln stood up. "Well," he said, "it's good news. Stanton and the others are all set up—and the newspapers have gone wild. They all say this must be the turning point against Lee—and I suppose they may be right." His voice had dropped back to normal. Calmly, quite as though nothing out of the way had happened, he took off his coat, and slipped the watch from his vest pocket. He wound the watch with its small brass key, and laid it on the dresser. "I'd better see about locking up downstairs—I didn't think of it when I came in."

When he came up again, Mary was in bed.

"Mr. Lincoln," she said, "I'm sorry I said the things I did—about your spoiling Taddie. I didn't mean them." She watched his face, half hoping to see some sign there that he knew she really wanted to say more—wanted to tell him, somehow, that the moment between them hadn't been lost.

Instead, he looked around in surprise.

"Why, that's all right, mother," he said mildly. He bent down to blow out the lamp. "I know you have a lot of things to trouble you nowadays."

Within the week, there was more good news—this time from the West. Vicksburg had been taken, and the Union now had control of the lower Mississippi. Reading the newspaper accounts of the victory, Mary was impressed.

"Mr. Lincoln," she said, "this man Grant sounds as though he knew what he was about. If I were you, I'd keep an eye on him."

Mr. Lincoln glanced up over his spectacles. "You needn't worry, mother," he said quietly, "I intend to."

It wasn't until several weeks later that Elizabeth's letter came, telling Mary that both her brothers, David and Alex, had been killed fighting General Grant in Tennessee. Alex—with the red hair, who had played with Robert . . .

In midsummer there was a week of unexpectedly cool weather. Refreshed by the change, Mary took the opportunity to make several trips into town, to see about ordering some new linens and china for the White House. On the last afternoon, driving back to the cottage along the narrow shaded avenue, she was suddenly startled to have the horses rear and plunge into a reckless gallop. A sheet of paper had blown across the road and wrapped itself against one of the horses' legs—and before Tim could get control of them, they had bolted.

Thrown against the side of the carriage, Mary managed to cling to the seat while they careened down the road. But at the corner the horses clipped too close. The carriage swerved, throwing the back wheel into the ditch. Mary was pitched to the floor. She clutched blindly at the door handle, just as the carriage lurched again, twisting the handle in her grasp so that the door swung open with a force that pulled her with it. There was a spinning moment—she heard herself scream at Tim to stop—and the next she knew she was on the ground, struggling to get up while Tim, his coachman's tails flying, came running back along the road.

It didn't seem at first that she had been hurt beyond a

few bruises and a general shaking up. But the next morning Mary wakened to aching misery. Her lips were dry and her head felt swollen and feverish; when she tried to move, a pain like hot lead shot along her spine. She'd better see a doctor, Mr. Lincoln said anxiously. He promised to send one out from town.

The doctor looked Mary over gravely. So far as he could see, there were no bones broken. Quiet, and as much rest as possible, he said, was the best cure. "And no worrying, *if* you please."

Mary looked at him oddly. "Telling anyone not to worry in this house," she said to Mrs. Keckley later, "is like asking a fish to keep from getting wet."

She woke from a nap, late in the afternoon, to find Taddie by the bed, watching her with thoughtful curiosity.

"Do you hurt, mother?" he inquired with interest. "Maybe the doctor'll have to cut something off of you—like they do the soldiers over in the hospital."

After supper, Taddie came in again. He brought an armful of purple and pink asters and laid them on the bed. "John said to give you these and hoped you wouldn't mind," Tad said. John was the soldier with the game leg who had come to tea. "He picked them out behind the hospital, where he was sure no one would notice, only he said not to tell you that. He said to tell you if you could get some bear grease and rub on it was very good for taking out pains. And, mother, John showed me his knee, the one that was shot, and it had a regular hole in it—as big as this—where the bullet went in. He has the bullet too. He carries it around all the time in his pocket. I think John's nice, don't you, mamma?"

"Yes," Mary said; "very nice."

Taddie swung on the bedpost thoughtfully.

"Do you think papa could get a real bullet for me someday, mamma?"

"Well—I suppose so—"

"One that had shot somebody, I mean," Taddie said.

At first Mary had been quite certain that she would be up and well again before Robert arrived. But when the day came, her back was still too painful to let her move, and when Robert found her in bed and heard about the accident, he frowned.

"It seems to me you ought to be in town where you could have proper care," Robert said, "instead of being stuck in this place."

"Oh, but I'd much rather be here. I like it far better than town—and besides, it's so good for your father, dear. I wouldn't think of asking him to go back to the city."

"Well, no—I daresay you wouldn't." Robert's frown deepened. "But I should think Father would see for himself, even though he is so busy. A spinal injury isn't the sort of thing to be neglected. Father ought to realize that."

Mary's smile grew strained. It was novel and rather touching to have Robert so concerned about her—but all the same, she wished he had less of a knack for putting things in an unpleasant light. "Spinal injury" and "neglected" and "stuck away."

"Your father has certainly not been too busy to see that I have proper treatment, Robert," she said. "He insisted on having the best doctor out from town to see me immediately, and the doctor said it was nothing more than a strained back, and nervous shock—and that all I needed was a good rest."

Robert shrugged. "At least," he said, "you ought to have a proper nurse then, and I mean to tell Father so. Mrs. Keckley has too many other things to attend to—and I don't see how you can have much rest with Tad popping in and out of the room every five minutes and wearing you out with questions."

Mr. Lincoln seemed surprised but agreeable when the necessity for a nurse was pointed out to him.

"If you wanted a nurse, mother," he said, "you should have said so."

"But I didn't want one, Mr. Lincoln. It was simply a

notion of Robert's. He thought I wasn't getting the proper care—and with a spine injury, he says, one can't be too careful."

"Well, if it would make you feel any better, mother, I'll speak to the doctor tomorrow when I get to town, and he can send someone, I suppose."

Two days later, rather to her surprise, Mary found herself in the charge of a large-bosomed woman named Mrs. Sullivan, who had black hair and startlingly blue eyes that had a disconcerting way, Mary thought, of seeming to look right through her. But Mrs. Sullivan was also possessed of a comforting touch and an inexhaustible supply of lugubrious sickroom anecdotes, and she took an unfailing interest in other people's affairs that encouraged confidences and made conversation extremely easy. Within a few hours she and Mary were on the most congenial terms.

In the long days when Mr. Lincoln and Robert were in town and Tad was out playing, it was pleasant to have Mrs. Sullivan sit by the window, rocking. Not for a long while had Mary had anyone who would listen so attentively while she talked. Gradually, as she grew more certain of Mrs. Sullivan's sympathy, Mary found that she was telling things she wouldn't have dreamed of mentioning to anyone else—not even Mrs. Keckley. She spoke of the old days in Springfield, of her sisters and their husbands, of little Eddie who had died so long ago. They talked, long and companionably, about illnesses and births and deaths, and clothes and husbands and growing old.

One dark afternoon, when the rain drummed on the cottage roof, Mary told Mrs. Sullivan about Willie. She told about his pets. The pussy they had to leave behind when they came to Washington, and the black pony, and the kitten Willie had wanted on his bed when he was so ill. And the turtle that had been hung and come back to life. She told about the night Willie died, and the weeks afterward, and the way sometimes, even now, she could wake out of a sound sleep and fancy Willie had called her. She told it all without weeping, with a kind of quiet eagerness, knowing that there was someone to hear.

The next morning, when Mrs. Sullivan brought Mary's breakfast tray, there was an odd look in her eyes.

"Mrs. Lincoln," she said, "he was here last night. Did you see him?"

Mary looked up, puzzled. "Who was here?"

"*Willie—*" Mrs. Sullivan bent closer, her blue eyes burning with conviction. "He was here, the wee angel, begging to talk to you. He wanted to tell you he was happy . . . Now, Mrs. Lincoln, there's no need to go so white like that. It was only your own Willie. Sweet and pretty in his little white robes. You mustn't fear him when he comes so—there's nothing to be afraid of . . ."

Mary set down her cup, feeling her wrist gone suddenly limp. "I—want to see Mr. Lincoln," she said, her voice dry. "Please get him—bring him here."

"Now, now, you mustn't be all upset like this." Mrs. Sullivan lifted the tray away and eased Mary back, smoothing the pillow. "Mr. Lincoln's gone to town, an hour past. We won't talk any more of Willie if it riles you so. It's only because you're not used to it yet—and you're still too weak. But he'll come again—never fear."

Three days later Mary was enough better to be up and dressed, and it seemed unnecessary for Mrs. Sullivan to stay any longer. They had spoken no more of Willie, but before she left Mrs. Sullivan put a slip of paper in Mary's hand.

"It's the name of a medium in New York," she said. "If ever you wanted to go see her, she could help you talk to Willie."

After Mrs. Sullivan had gone, Mary took the paper and stared at it a long while. Twice she made a move to tear it—and the third time she actually did. But when the two fragments lay in her hands, she held them a moment, and then quickly she thrust them into a corner of the desk drawer, out of sight.

40

MARY FOUND IT HARD TO LEAVE THE COTTAGE, EARLY IN October. Hard to leave the quietness, and the trees that had begun to show red and yellow. The formal rooms in town seemed lonely and stiff, and in a house where there was nothing to do the old lassitude closed over her like a wave.

Mr. Lincoln was very busy. All day now, instead of office seekers, a new tribe of callers waited outside his door. The mothers and fathers and wives and sisters of soldiers who were reported missing or who had deserted and were sentenced to be shot. The desk in Mr. Lincoln's study was piled with letters, begging for clemency, for pardons, for stays of execution.

"I get them all day," he said to Mary. "Telegrams and letters asking me to sign the warrant to keep some boy from being shot. I don't see how we can kill any more—when so many are already dead."

Coming downstairs one morning, Mary found a man in the front hall. He looked at her out of eyes filled with bewildered grief.

"I came to ask for a pardon for my son," the man said, when Mary spoke to him. "Mr. Lincoln promised me he'd send word nothing was to be done until he gave orders. The boy was only fifteen when he joined up. He fought a year—but after Gettysburg, he ran away and came home. I don't know what to do now . . ."

Mary touched his arm. "You can go home," she said. "Mr. Lincoln will never give the order to have your son killed."

"We found a telegram today," Mr. Stoddard told Mary one morning, "asking for pardon in the case of a man who'd been convicted of three murders, out in Ohio. Mr.

Lincoln asked me to look up the papers, and when I found them I discovered that the fellow was hanged last Monday. I suppose it's likely to be the only execution that was ever carried out while Mr. Lincoln was in office." Mr. Stoddard shook his head. "The poor chap will never know what a narrow escape he had from being pardoned."

Just as Mrs. Keckley had predicted, Tad was restless and troublesome under the restrictions of town. A tutor had been engaged for him, but after the intoxication of doing as he pleased for a whole summer, Taddie took unkindly to Mr. Wentworth with his pale face and thick glasses and enthusiasm for the classics.

"You must be patient with him," Mary said, when Mr. Wentworth complained that his pupil was noisy and willful, and flew into tempers over having his mistakes corrected. "Taddie is a sensitive boy—and he's had so much to upset him."

Mr. Wentworth returned to his task, paler and more resolute than ever, but one morning, while Mary was at her desk writing to Robert, Taddie burst into the room and flung himself on her in a flood of tears. Mr. Wentworth had punished him, Taddie said—he had *whipped* him—just because Tad said his father was the President.

Mary stood up. Not waiting to quiet Tad, she sent for the tutor, and demanded to be told what had happened.

Mr. Wentworth arrived, breathing rapidly. Master Tad, he said, had hidden his eyeglasses, and refused point-blank to tell where they were when it was time for lessons. Mr. Wentworth had tried every possible means of reasonable persuasion—and when Taddie still refused, Mr. Wentworth had said that unless he returned the glasses, he should be whipped. Master Tad had replied that no one could whip him because his father was president of the United States, and would set the army on anyone who touched him.

"I saw nothing to do, Mrs. Lincoln," Mr. Wentworth

said, "but to take his hand and strike him six blows with the ruler."

Then, it appeared, Master Tad broke loose, howling with rage, rushed to the place where he had hidden Mr. Wentworth's glasses and threw them on the floor, smashing them.

While Taddie clung to her, whimpering and nursing his bruised palm, Mary listened to the story. Looking down to see fear in Taddie's eyes, Mary felt a sudden, overwhelming need to protect him. There in Tad she saw her one last link with happiness. Willie was gone—Robert grown up—Mr. Lincoln lost and changed by the burdens of care. Her own spirit was worn thin with disappointment, and bitterness and pain. Only Taddie was left—and here, suddenly, was this pale young man with his squinting, nearsighted eyes, like an embodiment of the fate that must strike at Taddie too. A furious, unreasonable anger seized her. Not so much at Mr. Wentworth as at life that must forever twist itself so that nothing can remain good but must somehow, inevitably, be hurt and ruined.

Mary looked up. "It's quite plain, Mr. Wentworth, that you are not fit to deal with this child. He's my son—I've known him since the moment he was born—and I've never seen him do a vicious thing. If Taddie hid your glasses, he meant it only as a prank. It wasn't until you frightened him with your bullying punishment that he turned on you and did the first destructive, malicious thing he has ever done in his life. You're to blame for that act, far more than the boy. If you hadn't deliberately provoked him—"

"Mrs. Lincoln—" the young man's voice was thick and stiff with resentment—"it wasn't I who provoked anything. I can assure you, I was entirely within my rights. By any reasonable code of discipline—"

Mary cut him short impatiently. His little pompous show of self-righteousness disgusted her. It was like him, she thought, with his narrow little bookworm's mind, to hurt the child and then trot out his own injured dignity as an excuse.

"I'm not interested in your reasonable code of discipline, Mr. Wentworth," she said coldly. "I am interested in my son. Taddie has the sweetest, most affectionate nature—and I will not stand by and see it ruined for the sake of your stupid notions of your own rights. Your rights, whatever they may be, certainly do not include the right to spoil this boy."

A flicker of a smile curved Mr. Wentworth's pale lips. "That, I think, Mrs. Lincoln, has already been quite adequately accomplished."

There was a silence; then Mary drew herself up.

"Your insolence is too much, Mr. Wentworth. You may consider yourself dismissed."

Once she had spoken, Mary had an instant of misgiving. She oughtn't to have been so hard on the little man perhaps—but curiously enough, Mr. Wentworth looked anything but crushed. For all his insignificant appearance, there was a cool gleam in his nearsighted glance.

"Since it was Mr. Lincoln who engaged me," he said quietly, "I should prefer my dismissal to come from him." He made a slight, ironic bow, and started for the door.

It was the last straw. For a moment Mary was speechless, then she called sharply. "Mr. Wentworth—"

He hesitated, at the door, but he did not turn back. A fresh wave of fury broke in Mary, sweeping away the final remnants of restraint. That this miserable little creature should dare to question her authority . . .

"Go to Mr. Lincoln, then!" Mary flung the words at Mr. Wentworth's narrow, stoop-shouldered back. "Tell him what you've told me—and you'll find he bears me out in every word. You'll see that you can't defy me like this. Mr. Lincoln won't stand for it. You'll see—" Mary stopped, half sobbing, to find that she was talking to no one. Mr. Wentworth had gone, and she was hurling the torrent of her torn, outraged spirit against nothing more than a closed door. The last bitter words died in her throat, and with them the strength of her anger seemed to melt, leaving her trembling foolishly. Everything was confused. She couldn't think, suddenly, why she had been so angry . . . Then she remembered Taddie. Sinking into a chair, Mary put out her hand. "Taddie—"

He eyed her silently.

"Taddie, come here. Come to Mother."

Taddie did not come. Instead, he edged toward the door, a strangely wary look in his eyes as he watched his mother's face. Seeing that look, Mary was smitten with a new terror. A few times, when she had been angry, Robert had looked at her with that expression. And once, the night in Springfield when they had quarreled about the turtle, she had seen the look in Willie's blue eyes. But never Taddie. Taddie had never watched her with that puzzled, uneasy glance, as though she were some strange and frightening presence. Dear God, it mustn't be this way with Taddie. Not Taddie. Please, please—not with Taddie. Mary forced her lips into a smile. Making her voice soft, she spoke again.

"Taddie, please come to me. I—want to tell you about a surprise, Taddie. Something nice, I've been planning . . ."

Taddie wavered. A faint gleam of curiosity came through the guarded look in his eyes.

"What kind of surprise?"

Mary heard the suspicion in his voice.

"Oh, you must come nearer, so I can whisper." Mary saw him hesitate, half tempted. She put her arms out, leaning toward him. "Come—don't you want to hear the surprise, Taddie?"

Taddie scrubbed his toe against the carpet, staring down at it. "No. I want to go out and play." The indecision was gone. An impish grin broke over his face. Without waiting for more, he bolted for the door and slammed it behind him.

Mary heard his whoop of freedom as he clattered down the hall toward the stairs.

"Taddie—wait, Taddie—" The words faded on her lips. Slowly her hands dropped into her lap, and she sat still, staring with puzzled eyes into the empty room.

Mr. Lincoln looked up as Mr. Wentworth came into his office. The young man had a peculiar look. Odd sort of fellow anyway, with his white face and stiff, thin shoulders. Without his glasses he looked queerer than ever. As if he were trying to see under water. There was something on his mind too. Mr. Lincoln knew that look well enough. He put down his pen.

It didn't take long to hear the story. While Mr. Wentworth spoke, Mr. Lincoln leaned back, listening without expression. Now and then he glanced at the paper on his desk. When the story was finished, Mr. Lincoln cleared his throat.

"What do you expect me to do about this, Mr. Wentworth?"

The young man drew back. "Well—I thought, sir, you ought to know what happened."

Mr. Lincoln looked at him fixedly. His eyes were still expressionless. Then he turned, deliberately, and glanced past Mr. Wentworth, out the window.

"Why?"

"Why, because—" Mr. Wentworth floundered, his self-assurance shaken—"because I've tried to do my work satisfactorily. And I felt, under the circumstances, that Mrs. Lincoln's criticism was—undeserved. I assure you, sir, I've done my very best with Tad."

"Yes. Yes, I'm sure of that. But the fact seems to remain that you have failed to please Mrs. Lincoln. If she has seen fit to dismiss you, I'm sorry—there is nothing I can do about it."

"But I thought, sir, if I explained the matter to you—you might see it differently."

Mr. Lincoln shook his head. "I've already told you, I

can do nothing, Mr. Wentworth. You must realize I'm a busy man. I have a war to fight—"

"Yes, sir, I do realize that. But in a matter concerning your own son—"

"I am concerned at present, Mr. Wentworth, with a thousand things besides my son. I'm sorry if you feel that you have been unfairly treated. Very likely you have —but you're not alone in that. People come to me all day long wanting me to right their wrongs. I can't do everything, you know. I'm not God. I can't make the whole world right."

"No, sir. Of course not."

"I regret this, Mr. Wentworth—but there is no more I can say."

As Mr. Wentworth turned, silently, and walked out of the office, Mr. Lincoln took up his pen and bent once more over the desk.

An hour later, having packed his belongings, Mr. Wentworth was ready to leave his room. He stood by the bureau, making a last, methodical inspection of the empty drawers, when someone knocked at the door.

"Come in."

Mr. Wentworth glanced up, and saw Mr. Lincoln standing on the threshold.

"Mr. Wentworth," Mr. Lincoln said, "I want to apologize for speaking to you as I did. You were quite right to come to me—and I shouldn't have turned you away. But it's a hard thing, Mr. Wentworth—" the lines around his mouth settled sharply—"when so many people come to you for help, and you can't give it."

"Yes, of course; I quite understand, sir." Mr. Wentworth smiled nervously. "I could hardly have stayed here, in any case, after what happened."

"No. No, I'm afraid not." Mr. Lincoln sighed. "I'm sorry, though."

Mr. Wentworth hesitated. "I shouldn't have troubled you—only, you see, sir, this position meant a great deal to me. I have my mother to take care of—and she depends entirely on me since my two brothers went into the army. I would have liked to go too—but one of us had to go on working. On account of my eyes, it seemed best for me to stay."

"I wish you had told me this before," Mr. Lincoln said. "Where are your brothers now?"

"One is in the Pennsylvania Fifth, sir, with General Sherman. The other was killed, a year ago at Antietam."

There was a silence. Then Mr. Lincoln said slowly, "I'm sorry. Very sorry. If you need help finding a new position—I'll do anything I can."

"Thank you, sir."

"And, Mr. Wentworth—"

"Yes?"

"I—hope you won't think too badly of us here . . ." Mr. Lincoln paused. For a moment he seemed lost in thought. "We are a strange family these days."

41

IN THE MIDDLE OF NOVEMBER, MR. LINCOLN HAD TO make a trip. Taddie had been in bed for a few days, with a feverish cold, and the night before he left, Mr. Lincoln came into Mary's room. He stood by the fire, his hands thrust deep in the pockets of his flowered calico dressing gown. For Christmas the year before Mary had given him a new robe of dark-red flannel, bound in blue, that had been ordered specially from Stewart's in New York. He had seemed pleased, and said it was just what he needed and very handsome—but to Mary's knowledge he'd never had it on his back. He clung, instead, to the old calico that dated from Springfield days when he had carried it in his satchel to ride the circuit, along with a venerable pair of leather slippers Mary had embroidered with his initials.

"Don't make me give them up, mother," he had said when Mary complained of the antiquity of the slippers. "They're the only shoes I ever had that I could think in. And besides—" he gazed down at them reflectively—"I might never find another pair big enough."

"I wish I didn't have to go tomorrow," Mr. Lincoln said now. "I don't feel up to much—but they're dedicating a new cemetery up at Gettysburg, and I promised I'd make a speech, so I suppose I must." He was silent a minute, staring into the fire. "It doesn't seem as though anyone would be much interested in listening to speeches. I don't know what sort of thing they expect me to say."

"Well, don't worry—" Mary leaned forward to stir the fire—"I daresay you'll think of something when the time comes, Mr. Lincoln."

Several times that night Mary went across the hall to Taddie's room. His cold seemed heavier, and he was restless and complaining. Papa had promised to take him along on the trip, Tad said fretfully, and now he was going to miss all the fun. And he'd *never* get another chance to see a battlefield and look for real bullets.

In the morning, before he left for the station, Mr. Lincoln came to say good-bye. He stood by Taddie's bed in his long black coat, his best hat in his hand.

"Be a good boy, now, and do as mamma says while I'm gone."

"Will you bring me a present if I do?"

"Well—I'll try."

Taddie's scowl vanished. "I'd like a cannon if you can find any they left," he said sweetly. "One that really shoots."

Outside in the hall, Mr. Lincoln patted Mary's shoulder. "You'll telegraph me if there's any change, won't you?"

She nodded. "I'm sure Taddie's all right," she said. She

was trying to sound reassuring, but she knew Mr. Lincoln was uneasy at leaving her alone.

The evening Mr. Lincoln came home, Mary was downstairs, waiting. Taddie was much better, she told him at once. The fever was gone, and he had been up and dressed that afternoon. She kissed Mr. Lincoln's cheek.

"How was your speech?"

"All right, I guess. It was kind of short—but Seward was there, and he seemed to think it was enough."

They went upstairs together, and Mary followed Mr. Lincoln into his room. She wanted to hear about his trip, but he seemed to have little to say.

"You know," Mary said, "while you were gone, I was thinking how it will be when all this is over and we can be at home again. I was trying to remember how it used to be—when you could be gone for weeks on the circuit, and I never worried. There was nothing to be afraid of then. Do you think those days can ever come again, Mr. Lincoln?"

He turned to look at her, and she saw the sadness in his eyes.

"I don't know, Mary—everything is so changed."

"But everything hasn't changed, Mr. Lincoln; surely there are some things that are the same. We can go back . . ."

He was still looking at her.

"There's so much, Mr. Lincoln—we can still go back . . ."

There was a tap at the door, light and discreet. Mr. Hay was there. He was sorry to trouble Mr. Lincoln, but there were a number of things in the office that had come up while he was away . . . Mr. Lincoln nodded. He'd be there right away. When Mr. Hay had gone, he turned back to Mary.

"I suppose I'd better see to these things, mother. We can talk tomorrow—when there's more time." He paused, touching her arm. "I'm glad you and Taddie are all right."

It was January before Mary got around to selecting a new tutor for Taddie. One thing and another delayed her—and after all, she said to Mr. Lincoln, with the holidays so near, and Robert coming home, what was the use of starting in with lessons? A little freedom never harmed anyone—and there would be plenty of time later for Tad to work.

"This time I mean to choose a man with the proper understanding," Mary said. "Taddie is far too sensitive to be turned over to the usual run of unimaginative, dry-as-dust teachers."

Mr. Lincoln, more preoccupied than usual, seemed glad enough to turn over the matter to Mary. After New Year's, when Robert had gone back, she made inquiries about the city and interviewed several young men for the position. None of them suited.

"The plain fact is," Mary said, "that the right man isn't to be found in Washington. I should do a great deal better in New York, I'm sure."

She planned to go, taking Taddie with her.

"There's no use hiring a tutor who hasn't seen the child," she said. "And it will be good for Tad to have a little change. That miserable affair with Mr. Wentworth upset him more than we realize."

Taddie was entranced by the prospect of a trip. Only the necessity of leaving his goats troubled him, but Papa promised to keep a close eye on them.

Once they were in New York, everything was wonderful.

"When I grow up to be president," Taddie said, over a breakfast of hot buns and marmalade in the hotel, "I'll change the Capital to New York. I like it much better here."

"So do I, Taddie." Mary smiled.

"People like us more here too," Taddie said, scraping his plate to catch the last bit of marmalade. "Everybody calls me 'sir.' "

It was nice to be away, Mary thought. There was no

hurry, surely, in finding a tutor, and in the meanwhile there were long, pleasant mornings, and brisk drives up Fifth Avenue through the winter afternoons. And the shops . . .

"This cape is the very thing for you, Mrs. Lincoln. If you'd just slip it on . . . There—see how it suits you. Not everyone could wear the style—but just notice the lines—you carry it to perfection. Mr. Stewart gave me permission to show it to you specially, he was so anxious for you to have it, even though it is a sacrifice at three hundred dollars—"

"I'll take it," Mary said . . .

Driving back to the hotel through the early dusk, Mary was conscious of a sense of comfort. A strain that she had hardly realized was there, seemed eased. She found Taddie in the parlor of their suite, his hair brushed slick and his face scrubbed to a shine by the maid who had been left to mind him.

"Has he been a good boy, Mamie?"

"A *lamb,* madam. We'd a nice walk in the park whilst you was gone, and fed the pigeons. It was ever so pleasant, wasn't it, Master Tad?"

Taddie, sucking on a lemon ball, made no reply. His face was filled with a consciousness of excessive virtue as he saw mamma's pleased look. When Mamie was gone, protesting that it hardly seemed right to take the dollar Mary slipped into her hand—"It was a pleasure, minding such a little gentleman"—Taddie went over to the sofa and sat down.

"Mamie's nice, isn't she, mamma?"

"Very nice."

"She didn't scold me at all."

"That's because you were a good boy."

Taddie looked thoughtful. "I wasn't, though. Not so very. I chased the pigeons with a slingshot and got my feet wet in the fountain when she told me not to."

"You shouldn't have done that, Taddie," Mary said. She spoke mechanically, but there was no conviction in her voice. It was nice being here—nice being where people didn't scold. She slipped her arm around Taddie's shoulder.

"Mamma—"

"Yes?"

"Why are people always nicer away from home?"

"I don't know, Taddie. Maybe they only seem nicer—because they're strangers."

Taddie reflected.

"You're nicer too, mamma—and you're not a stranger."

When they went down for supper, there was a telegram from Mr. Lincoln waiting. He was glad to hear they were enjoying themselves.

TELL TADDIE THAT FATHER AND THE GOATS ARE WELL. ESPECIALLY THE GOATS.

Mary smiled as she gave the message to Taddie. "You wouldn't want to stay away from home always, and leave Papa alone in Washington, would you?"

"Well . . ." Taddie considered. "We could send for the goats—and Papa too."

A tutor was found at length, and engaged. Such a nice young man—Mary approved of him immediately. He was from a good family, and had the most impeccable manners. Not in the least like the owl-eyed Mr. Wentworth, with his dreary insistence on the value of discipline and the classics, and his eternal worrying about his own dignity. Mr. Montmorency was plainly a gentleman—and he had some notion of wit too, Mary observed. Evidently his impressions of the interview were equally favorable, for he accepted the position without hesitation.

"Very well, then, Mr. Montmorency, we are agreed." Mary rose from the green plush settee in the hotel sitting room, and put out her hand. "You won't regret it, I hope . . ."

"How could I—possibly?" Mr. Montmorency bent over her hand gallantly.

"Well—at least it can't be said I didn't give you fair warning." Mary smiled. "Taddie can be a very spirited pupil at times."

"And I can be a very spirited teacher—at times."

"It's a fair match then."

"And may the best man win."

Mary laughed. "Taddie and I are going back to Washington tomorrow," she said. "We shall expect you to follow as soon as you conveniently can."

That afternoon Mary took Taddie with her for a drive. It had snowed, just enough to make a thin wet coating on the streets, and the trees showed feathery white in the light from the gas lamps that glowed on the avenue like a procession of yellow moons in the damp twilight.

Mary tucked the fur robe closer over her knees. The air was sharp, but it was good to feel it whip against her face—like a tonic after the flat mugginess of a Washington winter. It was good to be driving like this, with Taddie beside her—good to know that tomorrow evening at this time Mr. Lincoln would be on his way to the station to meet them. Smiling a little, she tried to picture what Mr. Lincoln would be doing now. Just coming down from the office, likely. He might have time to walk over to the War Department for the evening bulletins before supper. She could imagine how he would look, hurrying along in the early shadows. If it was raining in Washington, he'd no doubt forget his rubbers and umbrella—unless Mrs. Keckley remembered to remind him . . . She thought how pleased he would be to hear about the trip—and he was bound to approve of Mr. Montmorency . . .

She turned to look down at Taddie. "If you're a good boy," she said, "perhaps we might go to a theater tonight. As a special treat, on our last evening."

Coming into the gilt and marble hotel lobby, Mary blinked in the sudden light. As they walked toward the desk, the clerk bowed pleasantly, rubbing his plump hands together.

"*Good* evening, Mrs. Lincoln. I trust you and the young gentleman enjoyed your drive?"

Mary nodded, pausing to inquire if any messages had come.

"I believe there was one—ah, yes—*here* we are—and your key, Mrs. Lincoln—" He selected it, with its large brass tag, from the rows of pigeonholes behind the desk, and presented it with a neat flourish. "I hope you've found everything to your liking during your stay?"

"Yes, thank you—we've been most comfortable—everyone has been very kind."

"Not at all, Mrs. Lincoln. Not at all. We look on your visits as an honor, I assure you."

Walking between the double row of potted palms, toward the lift in its open cage of gilt scroll, Mary glanced at the envelope in her hand. It would be a telegram from Mr. Lincoln, no doubt, promising to meet them tomorrow. Taddie was asking something about the theater, and she answered him, absently, as she opened the message. She saw the signature—A. Lincoln—and the Washington dateline. And then the words between, that struck like a blow, cold and deadly.

. . . GENERAL BEN HELM . . . KILLED WHILE FIGHTING WITH THE CONFEDERATE FORCES . . . TENNESSEE . . .

The door of the lift clanged open. Mary realized that Taddie was pulling at her sleeve.

"Mamma—I said *are* we really going to the theater like you said we could?"

"Yes, Taddie—oh,—I don't know . . ." Mary closed her eyes. Slowly the dark wave receded, and she opened her eyes to see the potted palms again, and the plush carpet of deep patterned red. Strains of violin music came from the dining room across the lobby. She stepped into the lift, the cage door closed, and they trundled slowly upward—the music growing fainter.

Ben Helm dead. Mary remembered the morning he had left the White House on his way to New York. She remembered his face, young and earnest and troubled—and his letter a few days later. *Lee says he can never fight his own people—I cannot choose but follow.* . . . She thought of her sister Emilie going home from Springfield to marry Ben Helm. Emilie had worn a gray suit and bonnet the morning she left, Mary remembered . . .

"But why *don't* you know, mamma?" Taddie said insistently. "When you promised we could go to the theater?"

They were walking down the corridor, high and narrow, past the mahogany doors with their polished knobs and large brass numbers.

"Listen, Taddie—" Mary unlocked their door and drew Taddie down beside her on the green settee where she and Mr. Montmorency had sat that morning. "I've had a message from Papa with very sad news. Your Uncle Ben has been killed—fighting in the war."

Taddie looked at her frowning.

"You remember Uncle Ben, don't you, Taddie?"

He shook his head.

"Oh, but you must, dear. Uncle Ben was so fond of you. He used to play with you and Willie. Don't you remember when he came to visit—and brought the red whip for your pony cart? He was in the South when the war came—and he fought very bravely—until now—"

A sudden gleam of interest lighted Taddie's eye.

"You mean Uncle Ben was a Rebel?"

"Well . . . yes. But that doesn't matter now, Taddie. He fought for what he believed was right."

"Who shot him, mamma?"

"Oh, Taddie, it doesn't make any difference." Mary put her hand across her eyes, wearily. There was no use trying to explain—when Taddie couldn't even remember Ben. She went into the bedroom to take off her wraps.

She might as well send Taddie to the theater—since she had promised, and he'd be so disappointed. Mamie, the nice chambermaid, could take him, she supposed . . .

Mamie was willing, and Tad, mollified at not missing his treat after all, went off cheerfully.

Left alone, Mary looked vaguely around the sitting room. She had thought of writing letters—but now that she considered it, there was no one to write to. She would see Mr. Lincoln before a letter could possibly reach him—and even if she had known where to address Emilie, sending a letter through the lines to the South was out of the question. She could write to Robert, of course, or Elizabeth, but remembering Mr. Stoddard's warnings about mentioning news of her Confederate relatives, she hesitated to tell them about Ben. And she had no heart to write of other things. Besides, she recalled how queer Robert had been when she had told him about her brothers who had died fighting for the South. Almost as though she oughtn't to have spoken of them at all.

She sat down by the desk and took up an illustrated paper, glancing through the pages . . . there were pictures of soldiers and cannons and one photograph of a battlefield, strewn with dead. The ticking of the mantel clock seemed suddenly ominous and loud in the silence. Mary shut the paper abruptly and stood up. There was nothing to do—she might as well go to bed.

"Ben— Wait, Ben— Ben—"

It was the sound of her own voice calling that wakened Mary. She struggled up out of the heavy blackness into consciousness. *What was it?* What had made her call like that? There was no one there—through the half-open door she saw the lamp still burning in the parlor. Tad and Mamie hadn't come back yet. Gradually the dream began to loose its grip, and the terror, hammering and urgent, subsided. She could remember now. In the dream she had been in a strange house—not knowing why she had come or what person she expected to see, but only that someone had sent for her. She could remember going through the rooms, slowly at first, and then faster, trying to run—and the more she hurried the slower she went, as though some force dragged her back. There were doors, and long twisting corridors, and she kept finding herself in the same room, over and over again. But there was no one there. And then, all of a sudden, she had thought to look up—and she saw a balcony that was like an upper landing, and there leaning over the railing and watching her was Ben. She had seen him so plainly, looking down, his hands resting on the rail, his expression perfectly calm. She had known then that it was Ben who had sent for her. Of course—of course, it was Ben—how stupid of her not to have remembered. But when she tried to reach him, she found there were no stairs. She called him, but he made no answer, only stood watching while she hunted frantically for some way to get up to him. There was a way, she knew, only she couldn't find it—and all the while she was in terror for fear he would go away before she could get there. She saw him turn finally, not hurrying, his face still calm. And it was then she had screamed out—"*Ben— Wait, Ben— Ben—*"

Lying back, thinking of the dream, Mary tried to shake off the foolish conviction that Ben had really been there, wanting to tell her something. It was only natural that she should have dreamed of him. There was nothing strange about that, surely . . . But the feeling persisted. Long after Taddie had come in and was asleep, she stared into the dark, seeing that strangely calm look on Ben's face, watching her.

It was hours later when Mary finally got out of bed. Moving quietly in the chilly darkness, she went into the sitting room. There was no uncertainty now—she knew what it was she wanted. There on the desk lay her portfolio. She lighted a candle, and opened the portfolio, spreading out the contents. Bills, invitations, half a dozen notes she meant to answer—a letter from Robert and one from Mr. Lincoln to Taddie about the goats. She pushed them aside hastily. It must be here—somewhere. She could remember putting it there weeks ago, before they left the summer cottage. Yes—there, pushed back into a corner of the leather pocket, her fingers touched the two torn scraps of paper. She fitted the edges together, holding them close to the light. There was the name, written in Mrs. Sullivan's round, forward hand. *Mme. Asta d'Estignay.* And a number on Washington Square. Down at the bottom, Mrs. Sullivan had written: *Introducing Mrs. A. Lincoln.*

The yellow candlelight wavered with her breathing as Mary bent closer. She thought of the nurse's words. "If you ever wanted to go and see her she can help you—"

Mary straightened. There would be time, before they took the train in the morning, to drive down to Washington Square. Plenty of time . . .

42

A TELEGRAM CAME ONE MORNING FROM NASHVILLE. MRS. Emilie Helm, claiming to be a sister-in-law of the President, was being held at Fortress Monroe on her way from Atlanta to her home in Lexington. They could not allow her safe-conduct through the lines unless she took the oath of allegiance, and this she seemed unwilling to do. Would the President kindly wire instructions.

Mr. Lincoln brought the message to Mary.

"We must help her somehow," Mary said. "Couldn't you send word to let her be passed through the lines?"

Mr. Lincoln smiled. "I can do better than that," he said. He sat down at Mary's desk and wrote a single line. "Will this do for an answer, mother?"

He showed her the paper.

Send her to me.
A. Lincoln.

Mary looked up slowly. "But, Mr. Lincoln, how can you? What will people say if we have her here in Washington?"

"It doesn't matter what they say." Mr. Lincoln stood up. "You didn't suppose I'd leave Emilie there alone, did you? She must come here if she will, and we'll do what we can to help her."

The afternoon Emilie was to arrive, Mary waited at her sitting-room window.

"It seems queer," she said to Mrs. Keckley, "not to be meeting my own sister. But Mr. Lincoln thought it best not to attract attention to her coming—and I daresay he was right. I only hope Emilie will understand."

Watching for the carriage, Mary felt a growing tenseness. It would be strange seeing one of her family again—after so long. When the carriage finally came, she hurried down to the front hall. The door was open, and Edwards was showing in a small, tired-looking woman in mourning black. Mary felt a sudden shock of surprise. This, surely, couldn't be Emilie. She had pictured Emilie as she had been that last time in Springfield. Young and gay—in her bright summer frocks . . . She would have changed, of course, in five years. But not like this. Not this worn, sad, little creature with her thin face and shabby, dusty mourning crape.

"Oh, no—" Mary formed the words soundlessly. "No—no—"

She saw the woman look up at her, out of Emilie's eyes—large and dark-ringed. And with a second bitter shock, Mary realized that Emilie was staring just as she had—as though Emilie too could scarcely believe the change she saw.

"It's the war that has changed everything," Emilie said later, when they were alone upstairs. "After the things it's done to us—I don't think we'll ever be the same. Not any of us, Mary."

They talked guardedly at first—each careful not to

say the things that might be too full of hurt. But gradually the barriers faded.

"I've thought of you, Mary—so often . . ." Emilie said slowly. "Especially since Ben was killed. People have been kind to me—they sympathize, I know. But I kept thinking of you. It seemed to me somehow that you were the only one who would really understand."

They were strange words for Mary to hear. She looked at Emilie with a full heart.

On the second afternoon of Emilie's visit, Mary took her driving. They went along the river road. Coming home, turning into a section of town where the streets were narrow and crowded, the carriage swung round a corner just as a boy darted off the sidewalk after a ball, and plunged against the carriage wheel before Tim could swerve to avoid him. There was a jar—Mary screamed as she felt the jolt. The next moment the carriage had drawn up and she was out, kneeling in the street beside the boy.

He lay with one leg bent back beneath him, looking up at her. She felt her heart twist as she saw the pain and fear in his eyes.

"Tim, help me carry him. We must take him home."

Tim had jumped down from the box. Emilie was beside Mary, and together they bent over the boy.

"Wait, Tim—lift him carefully—this way—" Mary put her arms tenderly around the boy. "Don't be frightened. We're going to help you. You're all right—" She saw the terror in the boy's eyes subside. "Now then—"

"Just a moment, please—" A strange voice cut in suddenly.

Mary turned to look up. A bearded gentleman in a frock coat stood beside her.

"Aren't you Mrs. Lincoln?"

Mary nodded, not understanding. She still held the boy gently, feeling him cling to her arm. "There's been an accident. My carriage struck this boy, and we want to take him home—"

"I'm a doctor," the man said. "I think you'd better let me take charge, Mrs. Lincoln. If you stay here, I'm afraid there may be trouble."

Trouble? Mary frowned. "I don't think you understand," she said. "I want to help the boy. I must help him."

The doctor looked around, and following his glance, Mary saw for the first time the crowd that had gathered around them. She stared into the ring of faces—gawping, curious, a few hostile.

"Please, Mrs. Lincoln—" The doctor's hand was on her arm, quietly insistent. "You must leave, as quickly as you can."

"But the boy—" Mary shook her head—"he's hurt—" She stopped, hearing Emilie and Tim urging her to come. Slowly, Mary loosened the boy's arms and stood up. She looked at the doctor. "Can't I at least take him in my carriage?"

He shook his head. "My own carriage is here," he said. "It would be better if you let me take him."

Obediently, still bewildered, Mary nodded. But in the carriage she told Tim to follow the doctor to the boy's home. They waited outside until the doctor came out, and Mary spoke to him. It was nothing too serious, the doctor said. A broken leg. Two or three weeks and the lad would be as good as new. Mrs. Lincoln had better get on home.

"You see how it is," Mary said bitterly to Emilie. "They won't let me do anything."

The next day Mary drove to the house again, bringing a basket of fruit and a bundle of toys for the boy. The mother came to the door and took the things.

"I understand how boys are—" Mary said. "I have sons of my own. I know how these things can happen . . ."

The woman said nothing, watching Mary queerly.

"I—hope he's better today?"

"Yes—he's some improved, ma'am. Thank you."

Mary waited a moment longer. She had hoped to be

asked in, but the woman merely stood, waiting. Mary stepped back.

"Well, I—hope you'll let me know if there is anything you need. You will have a check, to take care of the expenses—but if there should be anything more—"

"Thank you," the woman nodded. "That's very kind, I'm sure."

"I'll—come again," Mary said. But as she went down the wooden steps, Mary knew that she would not come back.

It was late one night when Mary went down the hall to the room where Emilie slept. She hesitated a moment, for fear Emilie was asleep. Then she rapped softly.

"Yes?"

Mary went in. Emilie had been awake. She sat up in the big four-poster bed.

"Mary, what's the matter? You look so strange—"

Mary walked toward the bed, slowly. "Emilie—I had to tell you something. I haven't spoken of this to anyone —not even Mr. Lincoln—but I must tell you, Emilie." Seeing the puzzled alarm in Emilie's eyes, Mary smiled. "You mustn't be frightened when I tell you, Emilie. It's nothing to be afraid of . . ."

"Mary, what *is* it? Are you ill?"

"No." Mary went closer, bending down, so that the heavy braids of her hair fell across her shoulders. "It's something I've learned, Emilie. It's the only thing that brings me comfort now—" she paused. "Emilie—did you hear Ben tonight?"

"*Ben?*"

Mary nodded. "He was here, Emilie. He comes sometimes. Willie comes too. And Alec and David—even little Eddie. But it was Ben who came tonight. That must have been because you were here."

"You must be ill. You've been dreaming— Do you want me to call Mr. Lincoln, Mary?"

"No. Mr. Lincoln doesn't know. He wouldn't understand. But you understand, don't you, Emilie? They only want to comfort us, Emilie. Ben wanted to tell you he was all right. You mustn't worry if you didn't see him—he'll come again, and after a while you'll learn not to let it frighten you. It will seem like a dream—but he'll really be here, Emilie . . . They come because they want to help us. You'll learn . . ."

At breakfast next morning, Mary saw how oddly Emilie looked at her.

"I was thinking last night," Mary said. "It's time I saw to buying some spring clothes for Tad. He's grown like a weed this winter—I doubt if even Mrs. Keckley can make his last season's things do. I was wondering if you'd go with me, Emilie, down to the shops . . ."

Mary and Emilie were having tea in the south parlor one afternoon when callers were announced. Senator Harris and General Sickles had come to see Mr. Lincoln, and would like to pay their respects to the ladies while they waited.

Mary greeted the gentlemen pleasantly. She remembered General Sickles none too kindly from the trip to visit the army—but still, he had been nice to Taddie—and the senator she scarcely knew at all. She presented them to Emilie, and offered them tea.

Rather surprisingly, the general accepted. He sat down stiffly, and pointed to his missing limb apologetically. "Lost at Gettysburg, you know," he said. "I haven't got used to being a cripple yet."

They made conversation for a few minutes, pleasantly enough, when suddenly the general turned to Emilie. "I understand you're from the South, Mrs. Helm?"

Mary saw Emilie's thin face go white, but she nodded.

General Sickles smiled. "Quite so." He eased himself back in his chair. "Well, I expect it must seem quite a change for you, being here. We do things differently in the North. Talk differently, act differently—even fight differently."

"Yes, I suppose there are differences," Emilie answered calmly, but Mary caught the uneasiness in her glance. "I—haven't had much chance to notice really, general. My sister and I have been very quiet since I've been here."

"Ah, yes. Yes, of course. I keep forgetting that Mrs. Lincoln is a Southerner too. No doubt you've had a great deal to discuss—" The general's smile was genial. "Family matters, and so on? Well, you know the old saying, 'Blood is thicker than water.'" He turned abruptly to Mary, inquiring what she heard from Robert these days. "He's in good health, I trust?"

"Yes, quite."

General Sickles nodded. "Good, good. I'm glad to hear it. I'd wondered if it might be poor health that was keeping the boy out of the army—but I'm glad to hear that's not the case. I daresay he must have other reasons for not joining up."

Senator Harris shifted to the edge of his chair, murmuring something about getting on upstairs. But before he could rise, Mary stopped him.

"Just a moment," she said. "I should like to say, General Sickles, that if you have any doubts about the reasons for my son not being in the army—I must make it quite clear that the fault, if there is any, is mine. Robert has wanted to enlist for two years. He's only stayed on at college because I insisted. I thought—perhaps mistakenly—that his education should be finished first . . ."

"My dear lady—" Sickles shrugged—"no one said a word about any fault. I was only inquiring . . ."

"On the contrary," Mary said. "I think you came in here this afternoon with the deliberate purpose of criticizing my son. You sneer at my sister, because she happens to be a Southerner whose husband was killed fighting very bravely . . ."

"Look here—" Sickles's smile took an angry twist. "I don't propose to let you bulldoze me, ma'am. I'm not bound to take your lashings in silence, as your husband is."

Senator Harris stood up hastily. "I think—" he began.

"As for your sister," Sickles went on. "I shouldn't dream of sneering at her. She's hardly to blame, after all, if the Rebs are running away from a war they can't win."

Mary felt a flame of rage. "Sir, you forget yourself!"

Emilie stood up, quivering. "If our men run," she said, "it's because of the example your Union soldiers set them at Manassas and Fredericksburg and Chancellorsville. You can say our men are wrong if you like, general—but you daren't look at me and call them cowards."

The general heaved himself up, his face red with exertion and fury. "I've had enough of this," he said. "I don't come calling on ladies expecting to hear traitors' talk. The President will hear of this—you mark my words."

He stumped out of the room, followed by the senator, who scurried after him like a disconcerted shadow. Mary and Emilie stood watching them—listening to the angry mutter of their voices, and the stump stump of Sickles's crutch on the stairs.

"Mary—oh, Mary—" Emilie burst into tears. "I shouldn't have spoken so—in your house. What will Mr. Lincoln say?"

Mary shook her head slowly. "I don't know what he'll say, Emilie." An odd smile curved her lips. "But I shouldn't care to be in Sickles's boots just now."

That night at supper Mr. Lincoln told them. Sickles and Harris had come storming in, Sickles claiming they'd been insulted. He said Emilie was a Rebel and a spy, and demanded that Mr. Lincoln get her out of the White House.

"And what did you say?" Mary leaned toward him.

Mr. Lincoln rubbed his chin. "Well, I told Sickles he ought to have had more sense than to provoke a couple of Todd tempers. And I mentioned too that we were in the habit of choosing our own guests, whatever house we happened to be living in." Mr. Lincoln looked up. "Was that all right, mother?"

Next morning at breakfast Emilie told them she must start back to Kentucky. "I can't stay—though you've been so kind to me, both of you."

On the day she left, Emilie had a few moments alone with Mr. Lincoln when they said goodbye.

"I wish you could come back to us, Emilie," Mr. Lincoln said. "We're going out to the Soldier's Home in a few weeks now. If you could come for the summer, it might be a change for you—and it would mean a great deal to Mary."

Emilie looked down a moment. "I wish I could," she said, "but I—don't see how it's possible."

"No. No, I suppose not." Mr. Lincoln was silent for a moment. "I was thinking mostly of Mary—I'm troubled about her lately."

Emilie nodded. "I thought at first it was her grieving over Willie—but I don't know. There seems to be something more. It's as if she were frightened of something—without quite knowing what. She talks so strangely sometimes—about seeing Willie and Ben."

"Yes, I know. Though she never mentions it to me."

"She doesn't want to trouble you, I think, or admit that she's afraid. But if anything happened to you or Robert, I don't believe Mary could bear it."

Mr. Lincoln sighed. "Well, I'm grateful to you for coming," he said. "You've helped us more than you know." He paused. "I hope you don't hold Ben's death against me, Emilie . . ."

She looked up, straight into Mr. Lincoln's eyes. She didn't try to speak, but only reached up and put her arms around his neck. He touched her shoulder gently.

"It's all right," he said. "It's all right, Emilie."

43

THERE WAS SO MUCH TO GET BACK TO AT THE SOLDIER'S Home cottage that it seemed like coming home again. The cedar trees, and the low-ceilinged bedrooms, Mr. Lincoln's favorite rocking chair on the front porch—and the wicker swing that creaked on its moorings when Tad made it go hard.

Robert was to come for only three weeks, after his graduation at Harvard, and then he planned to go back to Cambridge to begin reading law.

John, the soldier with the game knee, was gone, but Taddie soon had a new friend to tag after. An Irishman named Joseph Greene who stood six feet two and said he was strong enough to pitch a bull over a fence. Mary believed him. She was puzzled, seeing Joseph's obviously perfect state of health, as to why he should be in the hospital.

Joseph explained one morning, leaning on his spade. He had been digging up a garden patch for Tad to plant.

"It was the noise, ma'am," he said. "They say it made me sort of daft. Came on me gradual like, it seemed to. First I'd only notice it just after a battle was over. It'd seem like crackers were going off inside my head for hours till I'd be near wild. Then it got so when we hadn't been fighting at all the least noise would feel like something had exploded right in my head. One night the lad next me dropped his belt and the buckle hit on the barn floor where we were quartered . . ." He paused, wiping his forehead, and smiled at Mary apologetically. "I don't know why it took me so, ma'am. A great husky like me, when there were little measly chaps could walk into a fight where the cannons were spitting—but they say noise can do that to some. Makes them dotty, they say."

Joseph spoke so mildly, and his manner was so sensible that Mary wondered.

"He's been here ever since Gettysburg," she said to Mr. Lincoln. "Why on earth should they keep him, do you suppose, when the hospital is so crowded?"

On Independence Day, Mr. Lincoln brought Taddie a package of firecrackers from town and Taddie rushed straight out onto the lawn to try them.

Half an hour later, going to call Tad for supper, Mary almost stumbled over the big Irishman. He was crouched by the back steps, his face white and drenched with sweat. Seeing Mary, he got to his feet, trembling violently.

"I—didn't want the boy to see me—like this—" He spoke painfully between chattering teeth. "It was the noise . . ."

As Tad appeared around the corner of the porch, Joseph cut and ran for the hospital. Mary looked after his lumbering figure.

"What's the matter with Joseph, mamma?"

"Nothing, dear; he doesn't feel very well, I think."

"But doesn't he want to see my firecrackers? I saved the biggest one to set off for him, mamma . . ."

It was a hard summer for Mr. Lincoln.

"I'm getting used to them, though," he said to Mary. "I wouldn't know what to do with any other kind."

It had begun with General Grant's long frontal attack on Lee's army, across the Rapidan into the Wilderness, down through Spotsylvania and Cold Harbor, and across to Petersburg. For a whole month Grant kept it up. Day by day, hearing the staggering losses the North was paying for its gains, Mr. Lincoln's face set in grimmer lines. Watching her husband, reading accounts of the daily slaughter, Mary's confidence in the new commander was shaken.

"In heaven's name, Mr. Lincoln, can't he be stopped?" Mary said. "The whole city is jammed with wounded and dying—and still they keep coming. This Grant is nothing but a butcher. He says he means to fight it out if it takes all summer—but does he mean to take all our men as well?"

"Grant knows what he's doing, mother."

Mary shook her head. "You've said that before, Mr. Lincoln—about every commander we've had."

"Yes, I know, but this time it's different. This is a frightful job Grant is doing—but it has got to be done and he's the one man who can do it."

And then there was the election coming along. Scanning the papers, Mary searched for some good word for Mr. Lincoln. But there was almost none. Even among the Republicans there were many who favored nominating a new man. "The Democrats will try to beat us by saying the war has failed," they said, "and they'll succeed unless we can get rid of Lincoln. People have got it in their heads that Lincoln is the Jonah of this war—and whether they are right or wrong, the party has got to face it."

"It's not fair," Mary said bitterly, "after all Mr. Lincoln has done—nearly killing himself with work, and suffering more in these four years than the men who criticize him could imagine in a whole lifetime."

When she spoke of it to Mr. Lincoln, he only shrugged. "Better not cry until we're hurt, mother," he said. "The politicians are like the preachers sometimes. They talk a lot about going to hell—but they never do much about it."

General McClellan was the Democratic nominee, and when Mary heard that, she felt better. "If Mr. Lincoln can't win over that little stuffed Napoleon," she said, "I'll be surprised!"

McClellan's platform was designed to appeal to those who were weary and sick of the war. "Call it a failure and stop throwing good money and good men after bad," he said. "The South will be ready enough to compromise now—we can make peace while there's still something left to make it with."

"If McClellan makes it," the Republicans said, "it will be a peace past anyone's understanding."

The news of Lincoln's renomination came from the Baltimore convention while he and Mary were having dinner. Mary put down her fork.

"I knew it, Mr. Lincoln. I knew they wouldn't fail you when the time came."

He looked up at her soberly. "Well, Taddie will be pleased anyway. Now if they'll just elect me, he can stop worrying about finding a new home for the goats."

"You know, Mr. Lincoln," Mary said one evening, "I heard a man say yesterday that no one except George Washington could serve this country as you are doing."

Mr. Lincoln looked up thoughtfully.

"I wish Washington would come and take my place awhile," he said, "so I could get a rest."

The troubles weren't over. At the end of General Grant's offensive Richmond was still untaken, and the Union had lost more than fifty thousand men—nearly as many as Lee had in his whole army. Down in Georgia, General Sherman was going for Atlanta.

Sitting on the porch at the cottage in the long afternoons, Mary worried about the election. A year ago, she thought, she might have been almost glad to think of Mr. Lincoln being free again. But she had come to realize that there was no freedom for them yet—that to leave now would only be to drag the chains after them wherever they went. A bargain with fate remained a bargain—and the things once sold could never be bought back.

When they were together, Mr. Lincoln spoke little of the future. But in spite of his weariness and the sadness that never left his eyes, Mary sensed in him the same fatal urge that drew him, past any hope of turning back, along the road he had begun.

"They talk of platforms and campaigning," he said once. "But there's only one platform people will believe in—and that's victory. There's no use my talking or promising—they know better than to listen to me. If the election is won—it won't be because of me. It will be because of Grant and Sherman and God . . ." He sighed. "And because the South can't fight forever with no supplies and outnumbered three to one."

It was that summer Mr. Lincoln signed the new draft bill, aimed to raise the reinforcements they needed to take the place of those who had been killed or wounded. But it still allowed for the hiring of substitutes by any drafted men who could pay the price of six or eight hundred dollars for aliens or underage boys to take their places.

"Sherman says we will get nothing much but a lot of riffraff and runaway lads," Mr. Lincoln said. "He says the North doesn't deserve to win when we are willing to pay so little for our victory."

It was a strange thing, Mary thought, that in the South the oldest families had been proud to send their men from the very beginning.

"They have given all they had, Mr. Lincoln," she said, "while we have to send out the militia to get our men to even answer the draft."

A few mornings later Mary opened the newspaper to find an article directed at the President's son. "He signs orders forcing other parents to give up their boys," it said, "while he keeps a son of his own in luxury at a university. He writes a letter to Mrs. Bixby, speaking of the nobility of her sacrifice in laying five children on the altar of freedom. Is the rail splitter's son made of porcelain—and Mrs. Bixby's boys of common clay?"

Mary showed the article to Mr. Lincoln and he read it in silence.

"This is my fault," Mary said. "Robert wanted to go—and you would have let him, except for me."

Mr. Lincoln put aside the paper. "Well, there's nothing we can do now, mother. He can't enlist before the election, or people will say it's playing politics. I don't know that it matters so very much—" he sighed—"except to Bob . . ."

44

IN THE AUGUST TWILIGHT THE SKY WAS BRIGHT RED. AS though the hot sun lingered, unwilling to give up after the long day. Daddy Joe Travers, limping a little, leaning on his oak stick, walked down the path from the contraband camp toward the dusty road. His grizzled head was bent, and his brown face lost in thinking.

Daddy Joe was worried. Worried and tired, and wondering what was going to come of all the folks in the camp back there. They'd come up from the slave states, all of them—just as Daddy Joe had come himself, walking most of the way from Carolina—and every day now more were coming. Daddy Joe and the others in the camp did their best to welcome the newcomers, giving them the best rations from the food they could scrape together, trying to keep them from finding out too soon that freedom could be a lonely thing when you had no place to go.

They didn't try to go, most of them. Just stayed, and got what they could out of being together. The ones that went on were mostly those whose families had been broken up long ago when they'd been sold separately. Husbands would come looking for wives, mothers for children. They'd stay awhile, asking for news, and then they'd wander on to the next place where there was a camp—hoping maybe there they'd find the lost ones.

Daddy Joe came to the end of the path and stood looking down the road. He always took a last look in the evening, for fear some traveler might be coming along and miss the turn-off in the fading light. He squinted down the way now, but there was no sign of anyone walking. Only a carriage coming along, the dust rising in small puffs on the road where the horses stepped. Daddy Joe waited while the carriage came near. There was a man in the back, and a woman, and a boy sitting between them who looked to be around twelve or so. They passed so slowly that Daddy Joe got a good long look. He could see the man's face, and the wrinkled black coat he wore. The woman was dressed much more finely—all in lavender and white, with a parasol and little short gloves, like the white ladies used to wear in Carolina. Daddy Joe smiled to see those gloves.

When the carriage had gone clear by, Daddy Joe went back, but he'd hardly got to the campfire when one of the women pointed down the path, and he looked around to see the same black carriage jogging along the wagon tracks toward the camp clearing.

"Who is it, Daddy Joe?" the woman whispered. Her eyes were bright and scared in the light from the fire.

Daddy Joe didn't know who it was. He stood waiting. "There's nothing to be afeard," he said. "We don't have anyone in the camp that's got to be afeard."

The carriage was almost up to Daddy Joe when it stopped, and the man in the black coat stepped out. He looked around at the circle of men and women by the fire, and they looked back, not speaking or moving until Daddy Joe came out slowly, leaning on his stick. He peered up at the tall stranger. He was about the tallest man, Daddy Joe thought, he'd ever seen. Lean as a rail, and with a plain, dark-skinned face and nice eyes. The way the man just stood there, not saying anything, made it seem as though he knew white visitors didn't come often to the camp. He was giving them a chance to look him over before he spoke.

Daddy Joe came a little nearer. He didn't hurry. He took his time about it, straightening his shoulders so his old blue shirt hung neater, and the raggedy trousers above his black feet that were gray with dust.

"I hope you don't mind our coming in," the stranger said. His voice was slow and easy. "We were driving past on the way back to the Soldier's Home—and saw your fire." He put out his hand. "My name is Lincoln—"

Daddy Joe stood a minute and just stared. Not believing it could be possible his eyes saw right and his ears hadn't fooled him. But he didn't forget his manners. The hand he put out to shake Mr. Lincoln's strong, square one was steady.

"It honors me to welcome you here, Mr. Linkum," Daddy Joe said.

Around the circle by the fire, Daddy Joe's words passed round in whispers. *It's the President, Daddy Joe says. Hit's Mr. Linkum hisself—praise the Lord. . . . It's Mr. Linkum stopped by to shake hands with Daddy Joe. . . .*

There was no excitement, no shout of welcome, no rush. Only a slow gathering around the tall, bareheaded man.

"Rosaleen," one of the women bent to whisper to the child beside her, "run back to the shanty and fetch out the others. Tell them Mr. Linkum's come."

"I hope you're getting along all right here," Mr. Lincoln said.

Daddy Joe nodded. "We do nicely, thank you. Nicely—" Daddy Joe spoke right up, good and clear. He saw the others standing near him bob their heads approvingly.

"I'm glad to hear that," Mr. Lincoln said. Daddy Joe saw how the smile lifted up his tired face. "Mrs. Lincoln and I have heard you singing sometimes in the evening, when we drove past. I wonder if you could sing a little for us now. If it isn't too much trouble."

"We'd be proud to, Mr. Linkum." Daddy Joe straightened his shoulders again. "Liza—"

A tall girl stepped out of the group, and Daddy Joe nodded. "This is Liza, Mr. Linkum." Liza stood looking down, her handsome head bent. "Liza starts the singing," Daddy Joe said. "She can sing the nicest of any of us."

Liza waited a minute, not looking up, then her voice came out of the silence, low and true.

Sometimes I feel like a motherless child . . .

The others sang with her until the last note ended in the purple dusk. There was a moment while Mr. Lincoln stood perfectly still, then Liza's voice led out again.

> Nobody knows de trouble I see,
> Nobody knows but Jesus . . .

All the while the lady and the little boy had been in the carriage, listening, and Daddy Joe turned to see the look on Mrs. Lincoln's face. She was sitting back, half smiling, her arm around the boy's shoulders. And while they sang, Daddy Joe could see her watching Mr. Lincoln's face.

Daddy Joe frowned. He was trying to remember what it was people said was wrong with Mrs. Lincoln. She was queer, some said, and had a mean bad temper. She wasn't as good to Mr. Lincoln as she might be, Daddy Joe had heard. But just to look at her watching him, Daddy Joe could see what a power she thought of Mr. Lincoln.

When the singing was done, Mrs. Lincoln leaned out of the carriage to smile at Daddy Joe and thank them all. Kind as could be, she sounded, Daddy Joe thought. Her voice cheery and nice like a lady's should be. She was looking down at a woman standing near the carriage with a baby on her arm, and the woman held the baby up, shyly, for Mrs. Lincoln to see.

"Is it a little boy?"

"Yes, ma'am."

Mrs. Lincoln smiled. "How old is he?"

"Just half a year now. He were born the week after I was free."

"He's a good baby to sleep so soundly." Mrs. Lincoln reached out to touch the round, dark head. "What's his name?"

"Abraham Linkum Jackson."

Mrs. Lincoln turned to the boy beside her. "Do you hear that, Taddie? The baby's named for your papa."

There was a murmuring and shuffling through the

group. A young girl, holding up her baby, said eagerly, "This here's one too, ma'am."

"I got me a little Abe—" called a voice from the back.

"Me'n too—"

Mrs. Lincoln shook her head. "I didn't dream you had so many namesakes," she said to Mr. Lincoln. "It must be a puzzle to keep the little Abe's sorted out."

Daddy Joe smiled. "We call 'em different," he said, "to keep 'em straight. This one here we call Fat Abe—and over yonder Mother Sally's got Skinny Abe."

"I got Long Abe."

"Mine's Puny Abe—" a mournful voice. "But just you wait, he'll grow up good as the others."

"We get kinder mixed up with all of 'em," Daddy Joe said, "but we don't keer. They'll all be proud, someday, to have the name."

Before Mr. Lincoln got back into the carriage he thanked Daddy Joe and Liza for the singing.

"If you should need anything, I hope you'll come and tell me," Mr. Lincoln said. "I don't live very far from here."

After the carriage was gone Daddy Joe turned back to the fire. It had almost died out now—there were only a few coals showing red under a gray frost of ashes. When he leaned on his stick just so, and remembered to take it easy, the stitch in his back didn't catch him so sharp. About this time of the evening, Daddy Joe's stomach could begin to feel right empty—but tonight he didn't seem to mind. After a while you got used to the feeling, and didn't notice any more, he thought.

And a man had to go hungry sometimes—to be free . . .

45

THROUGH THE DREARY WEEKS OF EARLY WINTER THE North waited to see whether General Sherman would bring his army out at salt water. Atlanta was taken—the news had come in time for the elections, and the day the returns came in, Mr. Lincoln brought a sheaf of telegraph messages into Mary's sitting room and laid them in her lap. He stretched out on the sofa and closed his eyes.

"They say we've won, mother."

Mary looked at him in silence. She remembered the other election day—when he had come home to the parlor at Springfield to tell her the news, and patted her shoulder while she clung to him and wept. She didn't weep now. There was too much in her heart for weeping. She only sat quiet, her hands in her lap, watching him. Thinking of all who had died since the November night four years before. Ellsworth and Ben Helm, and her brothers—Alex, with the red hair, and David and Sam. Willie was dead—and Mrs. Keckley's son whom she had never seen. The young Confederate soldier who looked so like Robert when she knelt beside him on the ground that afternoon in the square—and all the boys she had talked to—the ones who had come with their new regiments to march by in review and had stood in the East Room or on the lawn, drinking lemonade, shaking hands with Mr. Lincoln—telling Mary about their mothers and their sisters and their wives and children. There was no knowing how many or which ones out of the bright parade were gone.

Mary looked down at her hands. Death and suffering and time had claimed so much—more than just the boys—more than Willie and Ben and Alex and Ellsworth and all the nameless others. There were the other things that had gone with them. Hope and courage and faith had been alive in that November in the Springfield parlor. They still lived in Mr. Lincoln's face—beyond all the weariness and sadness. But in her own heart Mary found them no more. Only the fragments, twisted and broken, were left in the emptiness.

"Well," she said, "I'm glad, Mr. Lincoln."

Now General Sherman was gone—disappeared with his whole army into Georgia—and for thirty-three days, while Grant sat facing Lee's army at City Point, and Mr. Lincoln paced the floor of his study, and the country waited—there was no word.

Congress began to fume for news.

"I have none," Mr. Lincoln said. "I know what hole Sherman went into—but I can't tell you what hole he will come out of."

On the street one day, Mary heard Mr. Lincoln apologize to a friend for having passed him without speaking the afternoon before. "You must excuse me for not seeing you," he said. "I was thinking of a man down south."

Sherman's father-in-law wagged his head. "Cump will come out all right," he said. "What's all the fuss?"

One December night the wind blew a bitter gale. Toward morning the wind died, and the air grew mild. When Mary woke she looked out the window at the unbroken whiteness of snow.

"I can get my sled out and hitch up the goats, can't I, mamma?" Taddie asked. "Will papa come coasting with me, do you think, ma?"

"I don't know, dear. You can ask him."

When Taddie asked at breakfast, Mr. Lincoln shook his head. "I'm afraid I can't make it this morning, Tad. They've cooked up a special lot of work for me today—you'll have to make my excuses to the goats." He looked at Mary with a peculiar expression. "It seems as though there will be a Christmas after all, mother. I had word from Sherman this morning. He's in Savannah—safe with his army. He says the city is ours for a Christmas present."

The news was like spring tonic after the dreary dragging weeks. Washington came to life again. Sleigh bells jingled on Pennsylvania Avenue, the ladies put on their best bonnets and furs and came out to drive, and in the hospital wards the soldiers brightened with new hope and asked for pens and paper to write letters home.

In the sudden excess of Christmas cheer, hampers and boxes of gifts and food began to arrive at the White House. Mary loaded the baskets straight into the carriage to take them to the hospital.

"There's more than an army could eat," she said. "And enough wine and whisky to raise the spirits of the hosts of Egypt. They need cheering, poor boys—and they shall have it."

She stayed at the hospital all afternoon, sitting by the cots, reading letters aloud and writing answers for those who were too ill to write their own. Even the sickest had a cheerful word. One lad who had been blinded reached out and touched the sleeve of Mary's cloak.

"That's velvet, isn't it, ma'am? There was a girl I knew at home who used to wear a coat made of it."

Everyone smiled, everyone talked about going home. The war was bound to be finished now. Everyone said so.

When she got back to the White House, Mary met Tad flying down the driveway on his sled hitched to the goats. He waved and shouted at her, pointing to the harness decorated with gaudy streamers of red, white and blue.

"The goats have got new names, mamma—they're Tecumseh and Ulysses."

"Sherman and Grant ought to be flattered," Mr. Lincoln said, when he heard about the new names. "I doubt if even Napoleon and Caesar ever had two nannygoats christened after them."

New Year's was on a Sunday, and Mary had the East Room ready for the reception in the afternoon. It was the fourth time she and Mr. Lincoln had stood by the door to welcome their guests at the open-house on the first day of the New Year. Three times before she had seen the long room with the crimson curtains drawn and the candles lighted in the winter dusk, and watched the people filing by, strangers most of them, pausing to shake hands and say a word or two, or staring—awestruck—before they moved on to the dining room where the long tables were spread.

It was the same room, the same Marine Band played "Hail! Columbia" just as they had on other New Year's days—many of the same people were passing by to shake hands and pay their respects to the President. And yet everything seemed different. Mary saw it in their faces, in the way they spoke. There was jauntiness and good will in their voices.

She spoke of it to Mr. Lincoln, in a lull toward the end of the long afternoon, and he nodded.

"They act as though the war was already done," he said. "They're right, I suppose—but I wonder how they can forget so quickly."

It was past seven o'clock when the line of guests began to thin out. Mary saw Mr. Lincoln's hand drop at his side.

"That's about all, I guess, mother."

She nodded. Her arm was aching—the hand was swollen and stiff, and she glanced ruefully at her white glove. It was streaked and grimy, and three fingers were split.

They were just turning toward the door when a burst of voices from the corridor stopped them. One of the ushers appeared, hurrying to Mr. Lincoln's side to say something in an agitated whisper. Mary waited, seeing Mr. Lincoln look puzzled a moment—then he straightened up and the tiredness dropped away from his shoulders.

"Send them in," Mr. Lincoln said. "Send them in, of course." He turned to Mary. "It seems there have been some colored people waiting outside all afternoon, watching the carriages come up to our door. They want to know if they can come in and wish us a good New Year too."

The doors opened, and they came. All the Negroes in Washington must be there, Mary thought. Old and young and thin and fat and ragged and well-dressed. She smiled and nodded and tried to say how-do-you-do in a dozen places at once. She felt her hand wrung until she thought the bones would crack, and heard the voices, rich with feeling, all around her.

"God bless you, Mr. Lincoln—"

"I bless you, ma'am, and wish you happiness—"

There were tears in the dark eyes and on the brown cheeks.

"Bless you—bless you—"

"We pray for you, Mr. Linkum. We don't stop praying—"

Mary felt something stir in her that had lain a long while dead.

When they had all gone, Mary turned to Mr. Lincoln. He took her arm.

"Well, mother," he said, "I expect we ought to wish each other a happy New Year."

Robert was home from Cambridge for the holidays. The morning after his arrival he told Mary, quietly, that he wasn't going back to law school. If it wasn't too late already, he wanted to enlist. He looked at Mary all the while as though expecting her to burst out at him. But she only nodded.

"I should have let you go sooner, Robert. I—" she stopped. There was no way to say the things she felt. No way to explain the fears—the things she had dreaded so. Robert would only look at her as he was looking now. "I'm sorry, Robert."

The morning Robert put on his uniform it was Mr. Lincoln who seemed more shaken than Mary herself. It was odd of him to take it so, she thought. Robert was going in as a captain, on General Grant's staff. There couldn't be much danger, surely—when everyone said the fighting was nearly over . . . She looked at Mr. Lincoln, and saw how he sipped his coffee, holding the cup in two hands to steady it. He was like an old man, Mary thought suddenly. It was queer to think that of one's own husband. A strange pity stirred her heart.

"You look very fine, dear," Mary said to Robert. "Your father is proud of you, I know."

The fourth of March came, and Robert was given two days' leave for the inauguration. He and Mary and Tad rode together, while Mr. Lincoln went alone in the open barouche, in spite of a chilly, drizzling rain.

From the gallery where she had sat four years before, Mary heard Mr. Lincoln speak. There was no large party with her this time—only Taddie beside her. Robert sat on the platform with his father. There was no Mr. Douglas to hold Mr. Lincoln's hat. No pomp and show—none of the excitement of the first inaugural. The crowd was quiet, subdued, under a forest of black cotton umbrellas. Listening to Mr. Lincoln's words, Mary heard the strength, sure and final, in his tired voice.

When the speech was over, Mary rose. "Come, Taddie—" she held out her hand. No one stared at them as they made their way through the crowd, down the steps to the carriage.

The ball that night was in the East Room. There were the usual sightseers, noisy and pushing, but Mary was no longer surprised or shocked by their onslaughts on the refreshments, their gawping curiosity and shameless pocketing of souvenirs. She had learned a good deal in four years.

When the evening was over, Mary walked through the littered, disordered rooms. Not only silverware and napkins had been carried off, she found, but ornaments and even tassels from the curtains. Here and there she saw where bits of fringe had been snipped off the upholstery by the more enterprising collectors. She said nothing, until she discovered a hole nearly a foot square in one of the draperies in the East Room, where the crimson fabric had been hacked out.

"Someone must have wanted a new red kerchief," Mr. Lincoln said when Mary showed him the place.

Mary wondered what Mr. Montrose would have said to see his precious curtain. She had heard, the last time she was in New York, that Mr. Montrose had enlisted with a regiment of cavalry volunteers and had been killed at Cold Harbor, in his first battle. Poor Mr. Montrose. Mary sighed, remembering his elegant manners and the way clashing shades of colors could make him shudder and press his hands against his pale forehead. It was hard to think of Mr. Montrose as a soldier . . .

Mary let the drapery fall back, arranging the folds carefully so that the ragged tear was hidden. Later—when there was more time—she must see about having it mended.

Inauguration was over—and things settled down. Mr. Lincoln looked thinner than ever, and more worn.

"I wish you could rest, Mr. Lincoln," Mary said anxiously.

"I will, mother; don't worry. But we have a war to finish first." When that was done, he said, they might plan a trip somewhere. They could take Taddie, and go out to Springfield, perhaps, for a visit. He looked at her out of deep-shadowed eyes. "It's been a hard pull, mother. We must stick it out a little longer."

Mr. Lincoln was planning to go down to City Point, to see the troops and confer with Grant and with Sherman, who had come up from Goldsboro where his army had dug in. If they could manage to join Sherman's army with Grant's—the fighting would be over.

For all his weariness, Mr. Lincoln seemed hopeful of this final success, but Mary, hearing the plans for his trip, felt uneasy.

"Once you get off with those men, Mr. Lincoln, you'll

never get any proper rest. They'll wear you out—I know it. And you'll be ill."

"Now, mother, there's no reason to fret. They'll take good care of me."

Mary shook her head. She wouldn't have an easy moment without him. Why shouldn't she go too—and take Tad? Mr. Lincoln was doubtful. It was no sort of place for ladies. There might be action any minute, if Grant decided to move his men toward Richmond—

"If it's no sort of place for ladies," Mary said, "why is Mrs. Grant allowed to be there? And Mrs. Ord—and goodness knows how many others? If they can stay near their husbands, why can't I?"

"Well, mother, I'll see what can be done."

The arrangements were made, and Mary and Tad sailed with Mr. Lincoln on the *River Queen*, on a morning when the sky was full of light clouds that scudded before a sharp breeze.

"Are we going clear to Richmond?" Tad inquired. "And chase Lee out?"

Once they were at City Point, everything seemed to go wrong. There was only room at the dock for one boat as large as the *River Queen* to be moored and they arrived to find another boat already tied up. Mary asked what the other boat was doing there.

"Why, that's Mrs. Grant's boat. It's always tied up there."

Why, then, Mary asked, couldn't Mrs. Grant's boat be moved? Surely, when the President was visiting, he ought to be given that small courtesy.

Mr. Lincoln said it didn't matter—he wouldn't have Mrs. Grant disturbed. But the next morning the other boat was moved, and the *River Queen* was put alongside the dock. Coming out on deck, Mary heard someone on shore asking about the change.

"Oh—that's Mrs. Lincoln's boat," the man answered. "She was put out at not being in first place—so Mrs. G. had to move over and let her in."

Mrs. Grant was kind. She was quiet, unassuming and good-natured, and she kept insisting most carefully that Mary should take precedence wherever they appeared together. The officers, taking their cue from Mrs. Grant, treated Mary with consideration. They bowed to her, leaped up to offer her the best seat, made polite conversation, and arranged for her to go everywhere by carriage. But it was Mrs. Grant, Mary noticed, that they liked to talk to.

"I can't see what everyone finds so fascinating about Julia Grant," Mary said to Mr. Lincoln. "She hardly opens her mouth when I try to talk to her."

"Maybe she's afraid of you, mother. She seems kind of shy."

Mary bit her lip. "She's not too shy to talk to the gentlemen, I notice. General Sherman looks as though butter wouldn't melt in his mouth when he speaks to her."

The move on Richmond was planned, and Mr. Lincoln decided to stay on at City Point while General Grant took his army forward. Mary and Tad were to go back to Washington. Mary was glad enough to go, but when she was home again the house seemed empty and forlorn. She had thought of going up to New York for a few days, but she put it off. For some reason, the thought of the trip and the shops was less attractive than usual. And there was an uneasiness in the air—the old sense of waiting. She walked through the rooms, trying to plan changes here and there—fresh decorations, a new set of curtains . . .

At first she had no heart for it. In the midst of discussing some change with Mrs. Keckley, Mary would drift off and stand lost in some vague, disturbing thought. But gradually, as she began to plan for the new things, she grew more eager. There was no sense in brooding, after all, over unhappiness that was past and gone. It was the war that had made them all suffer so—and now it was nearly finished and they could begin again. Instead of only a few changes in the house, she thought of more, and more.

"I'm going to take down all those lace curtains," she said to Mrs. Keckley. "I've never liked them anyway—and every time I look at them they remind me of things I want to forget."

That was it—if only she could really make things different, break up the old patterns, they could forget . . .

"I must see about some new clothes too," she said. "Mr. Lincoln must be tired of seeing me in the same old things." She crossed to the mirror, and was startled for a moment to see how badly she looked. She hadn't given much attention to her appearance lately—but that could all be changed. She smoothed her hair. It was only being tired, surely, that made her look so old . . .

The following week word came that Richmond had been taken. The South was broken at last—it was only a question of settling the details of the peace now. Mr. Lincoln had gone on to Richmond, after the army, and a few days later he was back in Washington.

Mary waited eagerly to see him—to see how happy he would look—to tell him about all the plans she had made. They could really talk about the future—now that they were sure at last what the future would be. When she heard his carriage in the driveway she hurried out on the landing. She had put on a blue silk dress for dinner, one she knew he liked. Mrs. Keckley had dressed her hair in a new style and she wore her pearl necklace and bracelets.

"Mr. Lincoln—" Mary started down to meet him, her voice eager. "Mr. Lincoln—"

He paused on the stairs and looked up. In the light from the hall lamp, Mary caught sight of his face. The gray cheeks, the deep hollows around his eyes made her draw back in dismay. How could he look so? How could he—now?

He came up to the landing slowly, and crossed to his study. Mary followed. She stood on the threshold, watching while he sank down in a chair, as though he couldn't have taken another step. He sat slumped back, his arms hanging loosely, his head bent. Motionless.

Mary came toward him. There must be something wrong—something must have happened.

He looked up slowly, and took a long breath.

"It's over, mother." Weariness was like a leaden weight in his voice.

"Yes, I know."

He was silent a minute, then, as Taddie rushed past Mary into the room, Mr. Lincoln put his arm around the boy and his eyes lighted a little. "Well, Taddie—"

"Papa, did you go to Richmond? Did you walk right into the streets?"

"Yes. Yes, I did, Taddie."

"Did you see Lee, papa?"

When Mr. Lincoln shook his head, Tad looked disappointed for a moment, then he brightened.

"Is Lee dead, papa? Have they killed him yet?"

"No. Lee isn't dead—and they won't kill him, Taddie. They won't have to kill anyone any more now. The war is over."

"Oh." Taddie wriggled away from his father's arm and eyed him hopefully. "Then—can we go home again, papa?"

"Not for a while yet." Mr. Lincoln smiled. "But I have a surprise that may cheer you up. General Grant gave me a Rebel sword for you. One of his men picked it up in the field. I'll get it for you."

As Mr. Lincoln rose, he glanced at Mary. "You're all fixed up tonight, mother—" He sounded surprised. "This isn't any special occasion, is it?"

Mary turned away.

"No," she said, "nothing special, Mr. Lincoln."

46

IT WAS SPRING, AND THE STREETS OF WASHINGTON SEEMED to dissolve under the pale sun into thin, yellow mud. Stepping down from their carriages, the ladies held their skirts ankle high and trod carefully to avoid the squelching puddles. There were buds on the maples, raw and tender pink, and on the White House lawn the slender boughs of forsythia bloomed gold and waved softly in the April breeze.

On the Friday before Easter, Mary and Mr. Lincoln had gone for a drive. There was rain in the air, and a fine mist made the dusk seem earlier than usual. They stepped into the lighted hall to find a message from Mr. Hay. General and Mrs. Grant had sent their regrets for that evening. They were sorry—but being called suddenly out of town, they would be unable, after all, to join the President and Mrs. Lincoln for the theater.

"It's too bad," Mary said, "but it doesn't really matter, I suppose. I can get someone else in their place." She turned to Mr. Lincoln. "Perhaps you'd rather not go at all?"

Mr. Lincoln said they might as well, since they had planned it. If he stayed at home, he'd only work—and he'd heard the play was amusing. "Besides, people will be disappointed not to see Grant as they expected. We ought to give them something to look at, I suppose."

While Mr. Lincoln went up to his office, Mary sent off a note to Major Rathbone asking if he and his fiancée would join them for the evening. Then she pulled out a letter to Elizabeth she had begun that morning. It would be a good time to finish it, she thought, since there was no need to hurry about dressing. It would be an hour at least before Mr. Lincoln was ready for dinner. She took up her pen.

. . . We are all quite longing for a sight of you in Springfield. Taddie speaks of the old house always as *home,* and queries plaintively when we may go back and be a really truly family again. He is well, I am thankful to say, as are we all. Robert expects to be released from the army shortly and will return to his law work, secretly sorry, I suspect, to have to be so abruptly removed from these parts, for he is *much* in the company of a Miss Harlan these days, and shows symptoms of being greatly smitten. A sweet girl—such a lovely family. I quite approve, even though dear Robert does not dream for a moment that I even *suspect!*

Mr. Lincoln has spoken of the possibility of a trip to visit Springfield—a possibility which I ardently, but discreetly, *abet.* It would be a welcome rest, and a great treat to renew old days—though I fear we would all find many changes. Mr. L., however, is better these past few days than I would have thought possible after all he has endured. Mr. Seward remarked to me yesterday he believed the President looked ten years younger since this time a week ago, and I can agree and be most heartily thankful. As for myself, I am tolerably well, though the headaches still come. Still—I dare not complain. That we have come out of this frightful war as well as we have is enough to make all other tribulations seem of no account.

Write me soon, and send word of your young people. How dignified it must make you feel to be a grandmamma—a prospect I see in store for me before too many years, unless my mother's eye deceives me. You and Ninian must instruct us, when we meet, in the gentle art of being doting grandparents!

I must stop now, and dress, as we are off to the theater with some young friends this evening. With love as always, I am,

Your affectionate sister,

Mary L.

It was warm in the theater. Sitting beside Mr. Lincoln in the flag-draped box, Mary fanned herself occasionally. Mr. Lincoln was in the outside chair, where he could most easily be seen from the audience, and in spite of the interest in the play, Mary noticed the frequent glances in his direction. He sat absorbed, his head bent forward slightly, watching the stage. Now and then, when a line amused him, he laughed and turned to look at her. Young Major Rathbone and his fiancée sat in the front chairs of the box, and watching them, Mary felt a glow of tender approval. During the second act, her mind wandering from the play, Mary leaned toward Mr. Lincoln and took his arm. He patted her hand, not looking around. Mary leaned closer.

"I don't know what Miss Harris will think of me, hanging on you so—"

She saw Mr. Lincoln turn slightly.

"She won't think anything about it," he said.

Mary straightened, pulling back her hand. For some reason, she felt a little put off. As though Mr. Lincoln had chided her for thinking too much of herself. But he didn't mean it, of course. She opened her fan. It was made of dull-blue feathers, to match her dress. She moved it slowly.

The sound, at first, seemed to have no meaning at all. Only it was curious, not coming from the stage, but from behind her. A sharp sound—almost like a shot. Mary turned, but Mr. Lincoln was sitting quiet in his chair. Major Rathbone and Miss Harris had not looked around. Queer . . .

At that moment a figure, lithe and swift as something possessed, leaped from the back of the box and toward the railing. Mary saw Major Rathbone jump up—saw him struggle a moment, in silence, with the creature—and then there was a thud. The man had jumped over the rail onto the stage—shouted some queer gibberish—and was gone.

Mary shook her head. She could see Major Rathbone holding up his arm, and the blood dripping from it.

"Mr. Lincoln—" Mary started up—"Major Rathbone is

hurt—" She turned—and stopped. Mr. Lincoln sat quite still. There was something in the angle of his head . . .

A scream—Mary never knew whose it was—split the confused murmuring in the audience. "He's been shot. The President has been shot!"

Mary only stared—puzzled . . .

"*Mr. Lincoln—*"

There was no answer.

Confusion, panic, people climbing into the box from the audience, milling about. Miss Harris calling for water and brandy. Major Rathbone holding up his bleeding arm.

"Is there a doctor here? Isn't there a doctor?"

It was Major Rathbone's voice.

A young-looking man came into the box and looked at Mary.

"I'm an army surgeon," he said.

There were waves, dark and sickening, that swept over everything. Mary hung onto the box rail, onto the fan, crushed and bent, in her hand.

"Please take care of my husband . . . Please keep everyone else away . . ."

She saw them lift him out of the chair where he had sat so quiet, saw them stretch him out on the floor of the box. She didn't move. The young doctor was bending over him, kneeling down, opening his coat, feeling his shoulders, his neck, his head . . .

The doctor looked up, and spoke to Mary. "The wound is mortal," he said. "It is impossible for him to recover."

Mary sat down. She spoke quietly to Major Rathbone. "Please try to keep them away," she said. "Please—if you will . . ."

There was a stir in the back of the box, and Laura Keene, the actress from the play, came through. She was still in costume, her full hoopskirts seemed to fill the box.

"Please," Miss Keene said to the doctor. "Please—may I hold his head?"

The doctor nodded, scarcely looking up. Mary watched,

not moving, while the woman knelt down, spreading her skirts, and drew the dark head gently into her lap.

It seemed a long time that Mary waited. Then the doctor looked up at her. They might move him, the doctor said, if there were some place near by he might be taken.

"We can take him home—"

The doctor shook his head. He would die on the way.

Someone spoke. There was a house across the street. Mr. Peterson's. The doctor looked at Mary again. She nodded.

It took a while, getting the men, lifting him, carrying him out.

"Mind the steps here . . ."

"Be careful to keep the head level . . ."

"Take it carefully here—crossing the street . . ."

Mary followed, walking a little way behind. She felt arms around her, helping her, supporting her . . . She put them off.

"I can go alone—"

Across Tenth Street, between the lines of people. They were all looking at him. There were moans, prayers, cries, questions . . . Mary went in silence. Across, and up the narrow twisting steps onto the stoop, into a hall flooded with yellow light, smelling of kerosene. They carried him through a narrow passageway beyond.

"In here—there's a bed—"

Mary started to follow—but there were too many in the hall. She felt herself pushed into a dark little room, felt hands pulling her toward a sofa, easing her down.

"You must wait here—it will be best—"

She didn't know who it was that spoke. She sat still, in the darkness, and then someone carried in a lamp. She felt something in her hand, grinding between her fingers, and she looked down. It was her fan. The blue feathers stained with something dark and red that stuck to her fingers. She stared at it a moment, stupidly, then the waves of black swept over her and she fell forward. Choking, blinding, destroying—the truth tore through her . . .

Mary looked up. Someone was standing over her. A woman she had never seen was bending down, shaking her arm.

"Mrs. Lincoln—"

"Yes—"

"You'd better come, Mrs. Lincoln—"

The woman's arms were around her, leading out a door, down the narrow passageway filled with strangers.

"This way, Mrs. Lincoln—"

"Please stand aside—it's Mrs. Lincoln—"

"Will you let us by, please—it's Mrs. Lincoln—"

It wasn't a room at all where they had him. Only a sort of widened hall. He was lying diagonally on the spindle bed that was too short for him. His head lay back, his face was perfectly still.

Mary looked down. Weeping so deep that it seemed no part of her shook her. She knelt by the bed.

"Mr. Lincoln—"

There was no sound, no motion but his breathing, hoarse and slow.

"*Mr. Lincoln, please—*"

The arms were around her again, pulling her up. The hall, and then the little room, bare and chilly in the lamplight. Mary sank down, feeling the horsehair arm of the sofa cold and slippery beneath her cheek.

They kept leaning over her, talking about God, about the martyr, about sacrifice, country, freedom, peace, eternity. Mary heard them, but she didn't answer. She wanted to speak to Mr. Lincoln—freedom, sacrifice and God were nothing to her.

It was morning, just past seven o'clock, when they came in and said that he was dead.

"Come—" they said, "a carriage is outside. We'll help you—"

"Won't you give a hand here—it's Mrs. Lincoln—"

"Take her arm—"

"Here—careful of the steps—"

"Is this the carriage?"

"No. This one—"

"Who's going with her?"

"Her son is here—"

Robert's face, pale as wax. His hand on her arm. Mary looked at him dully.

"Please, mother—"

She tried to answer him—but the sobbing, dull and exhausted, would not stop.

Edwards let them into the house. He and Robert together helped Mary upstairs. She didn't know where Mr. Lincoln was. Down the hall, into her bedroom. A servant hurried in, turning down the covers on the bed.

Mary lay down. She saw Robert straighten and draw back. He stood a minute, waiting, but she didn't speak. She saw him turn.

There was a voice outside in the corridor, crying.

"They've shot my papa. They've killed my papa."

That was Taddie. Mary heard it dimly, but still she didn't move.

"Madam—"

Mary looked up. Mrs. Keckley was leaning over her. Mary stirred—put out her hand. There was some comfort, at last.

"Please don't leave me," Mary said. "Don't go away . . . Don't leave me . . ."

The days ran together like beads falling into a box, all alike, jumbled together without sequence. Lying in her room, Mary watched the morning light come to noon, to afternoon, to night. She watched the darkness deepen, steady through the long night—pale and blanch into day again. People came and went. Brought her meals, sat by to talk. Tried, at first tearfully, then with a shade of firmness, to rouse her. There was the house to be got ready and turned over to President Johnson. Plans to be made. Trunks to pack. There was Robert, standing by so manfully. There was poor Taddie—wandering over the house disconsolate. Taddie coming into the downstairs parlor one day and finding a sightseer who had strayed in helping himself to a book that lay on the table. Taddie flying at the visitor, kicking his shins, screaming at him to put down the book—it was his papa's book. There were these things to think of, they told her, and Mary listened, not answering. They looked less persuasive then. They shrugged, or pursed their lips, or shook their heads. There was life, they said firmly. Life had to go on.

Mary nodded. She knew what they said. She heard and understood when they whispered outside her door or looked across the bed at each other, their eyebrows raised meaningly. She heard, she knew, she kept meaning to answer. When Mrs. Keckley was there she would try sometimes, sitting up a little, beginning carefully. She must tell Mrs. Keckley what it was that she had wanted to say to Mr. Lincoln.

"You know, Lizzie—you understand, don't you?"

Mrs. Keckley would reach out and take her hand.

"Yes, I know, madam. I know."

Mary would try—try to think. Only there was something so strangely wrong. Something that kept her from remembering. After a while she would lie back again.

"Later, Lizzie. I can tell you later."

"Yes, madam."

Later she would think. Think what it was she always meant to tell Mr. Lincoln. She never could tell him now—but it was important to remember. Terribly important . . .

The first day of June. Summer was in the air, shimmering and bright. Mary stepped into the carriage, her black dress and long crape veil feeling out of place and wintry in the hot noon sun. Old Edwards was by the carriage, handing her in, piling the luggage in after her, looking up to say good-bye, gruff and awkward.

Robert and Tad were beside her. Mrs. Keckley was sitting on the small seat facing them, all in decent black, with her gray hair smooth, and neat cotton gloves.

Robert gave the order to Tim, and they started down the drive. Mary looked back, and saw Edwards on the step watching, alone, his gnarled face squinting in the sunlight. She saw the house. The portico, the wide front door, the edge of the crimson draperies at the long East Room windows. The lace curtains . . .

Mary sighed, troubled and vague. Then she remembered. She started to speak—to tell Robert. About those curtains. About having them changed. That must be what she had meant to tell Mr. Lincoln . . . About changing the curtains and making everything different.

"Robert—"

He was looking straight ahead, his face set, not seeming to hear.

Mary hesitated. The carriage swung round the corner down the avenue, past Willard's, toward the station. Mary sat back, letting her hand fall into her lap.

No matter whether he had heard or not. It was too late.

Part Four

47

MARY SAT AT THE SMALL, RICKETY DESK IN HER ROOM ON the second floor of a London boardinghouse, writing letters. The light was poor, and her back ached from leaning over so long—but still she must keep on until the letters were done. There were so many of them, and it was so important to finish in time to catch the post for the boat train in the morning.

She came to the end of one and straightened up a minute, easing her back. The desk faced a window that looked down on the small grass court. How many windows just like this one, she thought, she had looked out. Windows with curtains of coarse lace, starched stiff as iron without ever being really clean. In boardinghouses, pensions, family hotels. And nearly always the windows looked down on gardens just like this one, with close-clipped grass and a neat bordering hedge, and a round center bed of canna lilies that bloomed with plump red or yellow blossoms. Little boys in the boardinghouses were always forbidden to play on the grass. When they disobeyed, the manager would come out and scold them. Or here in London it would be the manageress, who would rap on the window with her gold and ruby ring and shake her head. The manageress wore a plain-front black alpaca shirtwaist with a gold watch fastened by a fleur-de-lis pin, and eyeglasses on a snap chain. She looked severely at all her guests, but especially at the little boys. Mary always felt sorry when the little boys were scolded for playing on the grass. A few years ago it might have been Taddie . . . Now Taddie was lanky and long-legged and despised being reminded that he had ever played on a lawn.

The dining rooms in the boardinghouses were like the grass plots, all alike. The same white tablecloth, fresh twice a week. Vinegar cruet and salt and pepper for the centerpiece. The same elderly ladies, who had been guests for years. The same crusty bachelors. Each guest provided his napkin ring. Mary had her own, left from boarding-school days, but she had given Taddie one that had belonged to Mr. Lincoln, with the initials A. L. engraved in flowing script. It had lain, in the last five years, on walnut sideboards in Chicago, in New York and Florida and Paris—for a little while in Robert's house on Wabash Avenue after he and Mary Harlan were married. Mary would find herself in the midst of a meal sometimes—not eating, staring at the napkin ring by Taddie's plate.

The rooms, often, were different. Some were wide, some long, some dark, some sunny. There was always the bed, true. Always the same spread of woven white cotton, drawn smooth so that it looked like a slab. And the dresser, maple or pine, with the scarf, the pincushion, the round-holed container for combings. And always the desk—always rickety. Mary had found a way to steady the legs, propping one with a book. She used the volume of Shakespeare that had been Mr. Lincoln's, that she always carried with her. She could imagine what he would say to see it used so.

"Well, mother, I don't suppose Shakespeare would object to finding himself of some use."

But there wasn't much time to stop and reflect on such things when there was so much to be done. Always so much. And it was all so difficult. From the very beginning, back in Chicago when she and Tad and Robert were all together, the troubles had begun. Troubles about money. Robert had tried his best. He kept sorting things out, making long columns of figures, sitting down with her and trying to explain. Father had left this much. Enough for them all to be quite comfortable if they lived carefully. But Father had left no will, which was very odd, and under the law, Mary was to have one-third of the estate, the other two parts going to Tad and Robert.

She listened to Robert. She tried to be patient. But there was so much he didn't understand. He couldn't know what it meant to be left with so little—he kept saying it was enough—but that was only because he didn't understand. He couldn't know what it cost to live properly—and with prices so outrageously high after the war.

Mary didn't like to trouble Robert—that was why she wrote the letters without telling him. And then when he found out, he would talk to her again—go over the whole matter—make the columns of figures. Explain.

Mary would look at him sadly. He couldn't understand about the letters. He couldn't understand after he was married why she and Taddie had to keep traveling—going from one place to another.

There had been the time when Mr. Williamson wrote to her. First about the public subscription they were going to raise. A dollar from every patriotic American to be made a trust fund that would ensure security for Mr. Lincoln's family as long as they lived. People would regard it as a privilege to contribute, Mr. Williamson had assured her, but Mary hadn't said anything to Robert. Robert was so sensitive—and he had never really understood how the public had felt about his father. Robert found out about the plan when the newspapers took up the story and printed such lies that the subscription couldn't be raised at all. Only the newspapers never bothered to tell that Mr. Williamson turned out to be only an agent for Stewart & Company and Lord and Taylor in New York. He'd been hired by the shops to raise the money so they could claim it in payment for debts.

Debts. It was such an ugly word. Surely, in the days when Mary had shopped, and the clerks had been so kind and polite—so anxious for her to have their nicest things—there had never been any words like that. But everything changed. Everything changed so terribly.

Once Mary knew about the debts, she had realized something must be done. That was why, when a firm of merchants on Broadway had written, suggesting that she might wish to allow some of her belongings to be sold, quite discreetly and privately of course, she had consented. Though Robert mustn't be told—for fear he might misunderstand. Going to New York, with trunks and boxes and barrels—meeting Mrs. Keckley there, who had promised to help her—Mary had felt so hopeful. She remembered how it had been, staying at the small hotel with Mrs. Keckley. It had been difficult going over the old things—unpacking dresses and furs and fans and gloves she hadn't seen since the days in Washington. She remembered how she had sat holding the pearl necklace and bracelets, weeping over them. But, of course, she had been doing it for Mr. Lincoln. He would have wanted her to sell them. He never could abide the thought of a debt.

The morning the papers came out with the dreadful story about the President's widow holding an old-clothes sale, Mary's first thought was of Robert. But Robert had been very kind, really. When she got back to Chicago, he had said scarcely anything. They had driven up from the station together—it was snowing, she remembered, and the lake was gray under the swirling flakes. To the boardinghouse where she and Taddie were living. Robert had got out of the carriage with her and helped her in with her luggage. He'd stayed to talk for a few minutes, and when he was ready to leave, he reached over and patted her arm and said he hoped she'd stay home now for a while and not go gadding. They couldn't have her getting spoiled with city life, he said, and running off to marry some duke or earl.

Sometimes, really, Robert was surprisingly like his father.

Mary never told Robert about the incident on the train coming home from New York. When she got off at a station restaurant to have a cup of tea. There were other passengers from the train, lined up at the long marble counter, but she had been careful to keep her veil down, shadowing her face. It was when she reached for the sugar bowl, and her hand collided with that of a distinguished-looking gentleman beside her that she had looked up, taken off guard for a moment, and found herself looking at Senator Sumner. They both stared, astonished, for a moment, then he greeted her kindly. They spoke of the weather, he inquired about her health and about the boys. He spoke with the same courtly gallantry she remembered from the old days. Helped her back onto the train, left her politely, with good wishes. But all the while, in his eyes, she saw the pity and embarrassment. She knew he had seen the papers—and when he was gone, she sat staring at the closet door of the compartment. It wasn't until after the train started that she had wept, pressing her hands against her eyes, feeling the tears run down between the fingers of her shabby black gloves. *Mr. Lincoln—oh, Mr. Lincoln. Mr. Lincoln* . . .

Mary finished writing her letter and blotted it carefully. She read it over, underlining a word here and there, adding a comma. There, it was done, ready to seal. She laid it with the other three she had written and rose from the chair, a little stiffly. The pain in her back was sharper—but the letters must be written. Everything depended on the letters now. The men in Congress who were working for the pension bill Senator Sumner had introduced must be written to. When they were doing so much for her, she must at least let them know her plans—how grateful she was. And there was so much she could tell them about how to proceed. Things that only she could know. The debate over the pension had been so bitter—and she could tell them why it was that certain people were opposing it. Out of revenge, of course. They were the men who had been jealous of Mr. Lincoln—she was careful to point that out in the letters. It had been painful to set down again all the old grievances. More painful still to discover new ones.

When General Grant had been elected president, Mary had hurried to write to Senator Sumner, to Judge Davis, Mr. Logan and Senator Harlan, Robert's father-in-law.

> One word from President Grant will put my pension safely beyond this haggling *political* controversy. After the close relationship between my husband and Grant, I am confident that he cannot possibly wish to refuse his help . . . These men who are trying to block the pension by spreading lies and insults about me are moved by the pettiest and meanest of motives. But once General Grant is in the White House the slander will stop. He was too devoted to Mr. Lincoln, and is himself too gentle and too just a man to allow this public abuse of me to continue. . . .

When Mary heard that the new president had let it be known he had nothing to say in the matter of the pension, she was first stunned, then bitter.

"They are schemers, all of them," she said darkly. "I've always known it. I knew it years ago in Washington. I used to tell Mr. Lincoln then they weren't to be trusted, any of them—and Grant was no better than the rest."

There were others, besides Grant, who had proved false. Billy Herndon, with his lecture tours, going about the country taking money for his reminiscences about Mr. Lincoln. And that story he had invented about someone named Ann Rutledge. He told people that Mr. Lincoln had been engaged to marry Ann Rutledge before she died—that he had always been in love with her, and that Mary had led him a dance with her tempers and selfishness—all because she had been jealous of the memory of Ann Rutledge. Mary had never heard of Ann Rutledge until Billy Herndon began his lectures. But people listened.

Bitterest of all had been Mrs. Keckley's book. Her memoirs of the White House and the Lincolns. Mary remembered how Robert had tried to hide the book from her when it was first published. But she had found it in a shop. She had stood by the counter, reading it. Reading what Mrs. Keckley had written about her. The false sympathy, the patronizing kindness. The lies she had twisted out of things Mary had told her in confidence—telling about the time Mary had tried to sell her things, magnifying her debts, making a fool of her. Standing by the shop counter, reading the book, Mary had thought of the time in the sewing room when Mrs. Keckley had said, "I never think of being anywhere but here, Mrs. Lincoln. I feel as though I belong with you."

Mary had never told Robert that she had seen Mrs. Keckley's book.

Mary gathered up her letters and took them downstairs to put them in the post. There was no time to lose if they were to catch the first boat sailing. In the hallway she met the manageress, who greeted her with unaccustomed deference. There was a gentleman calling, she informed Mary, in lowered, modulated tones. He was waiting in the parlor and had presented his card. After carefully inspecting the card, the manageress handed it to Mary.

Mary looked at it. *General Adam Badeau, Consul General of the United States.* She nodded to the manageress, smoothing her hair hastily before she went into the fusty, genteel, fringed parlor with its gloomy hangings and persistent faint odor of camphor and boiled cabbage, where Mr. Badeau waited.

She saw him rise and come forward politely. His face was dimly familiar. No doubt she had met him before, in Washington. Mary sat down, straightening the lace collar on her plain black dress. Mr. Badeau has only just learned of her presence in London, he said. He trusted she had found everything agreeable in the city? Mary nodded. If there was anything he could do to make her comfortable, she was to be assured that he was at her service. Would she remain long?

Mary shook her head. Probably not. She was expecting

to go to Germany in the autumn, where Taddie would enter school. Her plans were necessarily vague, owing to the uncertainty of waiting for word from Washington, where her pension bill was still pending before Congress. Everything in her future and Tad's education depended on that. Mary spoke quickly, warming to her subject, but when she saw Mr. Badeau beginning to look uncomfortable, she stopped. She must learn to remember, she thought, that people were distressed and embarrassed by any reference to her lack of funds. She turned the subject, inquiring politely for Mr. Badeau's family—and saw the relief in his face. He rose at once. His family were well, very well. He hoped that Mrs. Lincoln would do them the honor of coming to dine. One night the next week?

Mary stood up. "I appreciate your kindness, Mr. Badeau," she said, "but Taddie and I are living very quietly. I'm afraid it's impossible for me to accept any social engagements—just at present—" She offered him her hand. "I'm glad you called—"

He took her hand and bowed low over it.

Going upstairs, Mary was pleased. It had been difficult receiving Mr. B. in that wretched parlor—but all the same, having the consul general call would show the manageress and some of her boarders who were inclined to smile, not too covertly, at Mary's references to her former position, that she was someone still. It would be something to tell Taddie, too, when he came home. And something to write Robert, and Elizabeth.

Mary went to the mirror. She didn't look too badly . . .

48

MARY WAS DRESSING WITH EXTRA CARE, WATCHING THE onyx clock on the mantel of her room at the Grand Pacific Hotel. She had been in Chicago several weeks—and this morning Robert was calling for her. Something special, he had said. She was to be ready at nine, and he was going to take her downtown. He hadn't said just where. A matter of business. She must be ready promptly—and dressed to go out. She put on her black silk, with lace at the neck and sleeves, and laid out her ostrich boa and fresh gloves. And her newest bonnet.

She glanced at the clock again. It was pleasant to be waiting for a definite appointment, instead of only looking aimlessly, to see how much time had passed in the slow days. She was ready now. And Robert would surely think she looked well, and be pleased. It would be nice to see him pleased. He had looked so troubled lately, poor boy. He tried to hide it from her, she knew, but she could see he was worrying—she knew it must be over money, though he kept saying not. Only yesterday, when he had told her about this business appointment they must keep, he looked so strange and white—almost as though he was going to weep. Mary had comforted him.

"You mustn't worry, dear. I can provide for us better than you think." He'd been surprised when she told him how cleverly she had managed to keep a part of her estate out of the hands of those wily lawyers who claimed to be handling her affairs. She had bent near him, whispering. "See what I have here, Robert. No one knows I have them—I carry them with me every moment." And she had opened her purse and showed him more than fifty thousand dollars in securities. They were hers—she'd got them all to herself, safe from the lawyers' clutches . . . Robert had jumped up, his face whiter than ever, and tried to take them—but she had put them away quickly. "You needn't worry, dear. You see, I *can* take care of us—better than you think."

She was glad now she had come hurrying home from Florida when she had. At first it had been rather upsetting when she arrived. Robert hadn't seemed to understand at all why she had telegraphed Dr. Isham that Robert was ill and must be cared for at once. He was perfectly well, Robert kept saying when he met her at the train in Chicago. She'd tried to explain to him, and to Dr. Isham, about the dream she had had. But, though they were polite, it was plain they didn't believe she really had the dream at all. And then they had been so odd about the man on the train who had tried to poison her. They acted almost as though it wasn't true—though she explained quite carefully how the man had recognized her as Mrs. Lincoln—and then how he had changed her coffee cup when he thought she wasn't watching. She'd seen him, though, and when she tasted the coffee and found it bitter she had known for certain. But it had been a mistake, probably, to tell Robert. Robert was so like Mr. Lincoln in some things. Trusting everyone, poor thing.

No doubt this business appointment where Robert was taking her was concerned with some trouble he had got into by trusting people. But she would be able to tell him who the false ones were, once she had a look at them. Hadn't she always been able to tell Mr. Lincoln? And Mr. Lincoln had relied on her so—trusting her judgment over any other in the world.

When Robert came to call for her he had on a new black suit, and his face was very set and tense. He treated her with extra kindness on the way downtown, but Mary could see he was worrying. When the carriage stopped, she looked out astonished.

"But, Robert, this is a courthouse—"

Robert said nothing, helping her out. He looked so queer and stern she hardly liked to question him any more, but just before they came to the door at the end of the long bare corridor he turned to her suddenly.

"I couldn't help it, mother," he said, and turned to lead her in.

She couldn't think what on earth he meant. A large woman in gray came and took Mary by the arm, led her to a seat on one of the back benches. Mary looked around, frowning, puzzled. Good heavens, she did hope Robert wasn't in any sort of trouble with the law. The jury filed in and sat down, and then the judge.

Down in front, sitting near Robert, Mary saw Dr. Isham. Now, that was odd. And beside him that other doctor—was it Danton? Danforth?—that Dr. Isham had brought to see her about her headaches. That had been nearly four years ago, just after Taddie died. Why in the world would he be mixed up now in anything Robert might have done?

They were getting on with the case. The judge said everything so fast Mary could scarcely understand the words. Something about the case of Mary Lincoln, widow. It seemed an odd way to speak of her. Dear heaven, why did the man have to chew his words so? She leaned forward.

The witnesses were being called. First Dr. Isham. Telling that whole story about her telegraphing from Florida that Robert was ill, and making it sound absurd. Then Dr. Danton—no, Danforth, that was it. He told about visiting the defendant in her rooms at the Clifton Hotel. Finding her a victim of hallucinations and nervous debility. She had told Dr. Danforth there was an Indian pulling wires through her eyes, and removing the bones of her face. On another occasion, a year later, she had said steel springs were being taken out of her head.

She'd only been trying to describe the headaches, but to hear him tell it, Mary thought, you might suppose she was insane. The lawyer was asking something about that. Unsound mind, he called it. Yes, Dr. Danforth said, in his opinion the defendant was of unsound mind.

There were a great many other witnesses. Clerks from the shops where Mary had gone. She heard them tell about the things she had bought. Three hundred dollars for soap and perfumes. A hundred yards of moiré silk. Jewelry, fans, gloves. Six hundred dollars' worth of lace curtains . . .

"May I put a question to Mr. Lincoln, please? Has defendant any permanent home at this time?"

"No, she has none." That was Robert's voice.

"Defendant has no reason, then, for a purchase of more than sixty pairs of lace curtains."

"No. No reason."

"Thank you."

It seemed a queer way to put things, Mary thought. Making so much of it only because she liked being in the shops, liked having the clerks speak politely, say kind things, make a special fuss over her when she bought a great deal. If they had only asked her, she might have told them those things. But they never asked her.

There were several witnesses from the hotel. Gus, the man who ran the elevator at night. Mary remembered how he had told her about his daughter's baby who was sick—and now he was saying something ridiculous about her going down in the elevator not properly dressed, and Robert having to follow and bring her back. But that was too absurd. She could see from their faces even the jury didn't believe it. The man must be unsettled, poor old soul, from so much trouble.

Then the chambermaid. Mary was surprised to see how pretty Stella looked out of her drab gray uniform. She was rolling her eyes at the jury box. Yes, she was employed at the Grand Pacific Hotel, had attended to the defendant's room for the past four weeks. She found defendant pleasant as a rule, kindly spoken, but on occasions had heard defendant employ peculiar language and speak of dreams, etc., in which the dead appeared. Defendant appeared happy about this rather than despondent, but on other occasions was extremely depressed, spoke of imminent death, wishing same, but at the same time accusing various persons of plotting her end. Defendant was never guilty of unseemly conduct. Given to fits of weeping, tempers over small incidents, suffered from headaches and seemed unduly concerned over money matters, insisting that the management was overcharging her, falsifying her accounts, etc., etc.

"That will be all, thank you."

Stella stepped down from the witness chair, smoothing her skirts primly. Just to think, Mary reflected bitterly, that she had given Stella a dollar only the day before.

"Mr. Robert Lincoln, please."

Mary watched Robert get up and walk to the witness chair. He looked at the lawyer, his face deathly white. He was telling his name, his age, where he lived.

"You are the son of Abraham Lincoln, deceased, President of the United States?"

"Yes."

"Defendant, Mary Lincoln, is your mother?"

"Yes."

"In your opinion, Mr. Lincoln, has the testimony of these witnesses given an accurate picture of your mother's erratic state of mind?"

There were more questions but Mary didn't hear most of them. She was looking at Robert's face—thinking of the night in the Globe Tavern when he was born. She thought of Mr. Lincoln, sitting by her bed in the summer twilight. Of his saying, "We must have a regular home now, I suppose, for the little boy." She was remembering how dreadfully Robert had cried that first year. Especially when Elizabeth and Ninian were there. How he took colds, and had such a delicate chest, and she had rubbed him with camphorated oil. For some reason, she felt very sorry for Robert.

The woman in gray sitting beside Mary leaned toward her, solicitously. Would she like a drink of water? Mary shook her head. Did she feel faint? Would she care for smelling salts? No—no. "Do be quiet and let me hear."

The judge was speaking to the foreman of the jury. He turned to the court. *"Verdict of the court—the defendant is of unsound mind, incapable of handling her property and conducting her affairs . . . Remitted to the Belleview Sanitarium at Batavia in the State of Illinois, in accordance with arrangements to be made by Mr. Robert Lincoln. Case dismissed . . ."*

Mary stood up, quite steadily. Robert was out before

her, waiting at the door. She took his arm, starting down the corridor. There were people standing about, but they were quiet, respectful. Robert kept his head down—hurrying her along. He'd always hated so to be stared at. Mary looked back at the faces . . . It was a long while since they had crowded around her like this—pressing close to the carriage while Robert helped her in. Mary looked out the window—saw them still watching. She was glad she had worn her best black dress . . .

When Taddie had died—so suddenly of pneumonia, the year they came home from Europe—Mary felt that she had lost the last of Mr. Lincoln. Tad had been eighteen years old, but she always thought of him as the little boy Mr. Lincoln had loved so much. And in the hopeless, empty misery of the months that followed his death, it was almost more for Mr. Lincoln that she grieved than for Taddie.

Sitting beside Robert in the carriage, as they drove back from the courthouse, Mary felt for the first time as though a corner of that loneliness had been eased. He had spoken so kindly about her when they questioned him in the courtroom. Robert had never been affectionate—neither shyly, like Willie, nor tempestuously, like Tad. He was always so reserved, so hating any show of feeling. She had been surprised to hear how troubled and sad his voice sounded.

When the judge asked whether his mother had made her home with him, Robert had said he wanted her to—but she had refused because she fancied his wife didn't wish to have her. Mary wished Robert hadn't said that. It wasn't true, of course. She hadn't ever wanted to quarrel with Robert's wife. Hadn't she loved her like her own daughter? It was only when she saw that his wife wasn't taking proper care of Robert and the babies that she had tried to set things right. It was only natural—any mother would have done the same. But she was glad Robert had said in court that he wanted her to come and live with them . . .

Robert went up to her room with her when they got back to the hotel. There was a woman, in a blue and white uniform, waiting for them. Some sort of nurse. Mary wished she would go away—but Robert was arranging things with her. About packing—about taking the train next morning. He was being so kind . . .

It wasn't until Robert was ready to leave that Mary opened her purse to look for her handkerchief—and saw that the package of securities was gone. For one frightful, chilling moment she stared into the purse. Then she emptied the contents on the floor—kneeling down, rummaging through them, searching . . . They were gone. She had been robbed. She tried to tell Robert what had happened. It must have been that woman in the courtroom who had stolen them—she had sat so close—leaning over Mary . . . But the more she tried to explain, the less Robert listened. The nurse had Mary's arm now, trying to quiet her. They kept saying nothing had been stolen—that the money was quite safe. But they didn't understand. The nurse was a fool—and Robert couldn't understand, possibly. He was such a child about these things.

All at once Robert was holding something out to show her—and Mary saw that he had the securities. All of them. He had taken them from his pocket. He was going to put them in the bank for her, he said, where they would be safe. Mary was blank for a moment—blank with the shock of realizing what Robert had done. He had stolen them from her. Stolen them out of her purse behind her back. She shouldn't have let him know she had them—she shouldn't have trusted him. She couldn't trust anyone—not anyone—not her own child.

She flew at Robert—trying to take them back from him. The nurse was holding her—Robert, his face like ashes, was pushing her back— There were footsteps running in the hall outside, someone knocking at the door—

Mary's strength failed, and she sank back on a sofa, trembling.

Robert was explaining. The nurse explaining. *Send for*

the doctor. Get her water—brandy. . . . No one would listen when Mary tried to tell what Robert had done. They were all in league with him. Plotting against her—

Mary put her hands up to her face, shutting out the sight of Robert. She could never trust anyone again. Never.

"If Mr. Lincoln were here you wouldn't treat me so," she said. "You wouldn't dare. He'd never let you . . . never . . ."

49

THE STATEROOM ON THE LOWEST PASSENGER DECK OF THE steamer was cramped and stuffy. It was a pity, Mary thought, that they couldn't have showed enough consideration to let her have a more suitable cabin. Even though she hadn't had the money, at the moment, to pay for a better room, one would have thought they owed her that much courtesy. She had explained quite carefully, at the steamship office in Cherbourg, who she was. She had told the young clerk, who listened civilly, that she was ill—that she had had a fall, and injured her spine, and was going back to New York for medical treatment. The clerk hadn't seemed to understand. He had only said, quite politely, that the ship was crowded and they had no other accommodations at their disposal. If Mrs. Lincoln cared to wait for one of the smaller boats, they might be able to suit her better for the same price . . .

But she had wanted to come on the *Amérique*. It was the largest and the fastest ship—and she must get home. After nearly four years away, she felt suddenly that she must be in her own country again. She had written Elizabeth, before she left the south of France, explaining about the accident, and the dreadful pain she had suffered. The

French doctors said there was nothing to be done—but she wanted to get back to America. She didn't trust the foreign doctors. They were a tricky lot—only after money.

Elizabeth had cabled, saying she was to come at once. Robert would meet her in New York—see that she had the best doctors there—and when she was better she was to come to Springfield and stay with Elizabeth.

So she was coming.

But she was nervous about seeing Robert. It had been so long. He had written regularly, telling about his work, and the children—especially his little daughter who was named for Mary. The letters were always kind—but there was a stiffness in them that made Mary realize he had never quite forgiven her for not staying longer at the sanitarium. She remembered how Robert had looked on the day of the second trial. Standing in the courtroom so stiffly while Ninian Edwards testified that Mary had been paroled from the sanitarium in his custody for eight months, and during that time had lived at his home in Springfield and given every sign of being mentally recovered.

The judge had turned to Robert.

"*Have you any objection to this proceeding, Mr. Lincoln?*"

"*No. None.*" Robert's face had been white.

"*Then it is the judgment of this court that Mary Lincoln, who was heretofore found to be insane, is restored to reason and is capable to manage and control her estate.*"

She had fought back the shadows, after all.

But all the same, Robert hadn't approved. Mary could see that. If it hadn't been for Ninian and Elizabeth to help her, she might have stayed on at Batavia, in the large, square room with ruffled curtains that couldn't quite hide the barred windows. The bars had made patterns on the floor at night, when the moon shone . . . It was strange to think she had Ninian and Elizabeth to thank for being free. She wondered sometimes what Mr. Lincoln would have said. He would have smiled, probably, and made a joke out of it somehow. Still—he had always been kind to Ninian and Elizabeth. He was always like that—never wanting to believe anything but the good in people, but never being surprised by the bad.

Well, she had got her freedom, though she had wondered sometimes, in the five years, whether it had been worth all the loneliness. It might have been simpler just to stay on at the sanitarium. Where she could rest, and not worry about things, and the nurses were so friendly and would listen for hours while she told them about Mr. Lincoln and the boys, and how devoted they had been to her. It was hard, nowadays, to find anyone who cared about listening. They were all so busy. Still—no matter how much easier it might have been to stay on at Batavia, it had been the thought of Mr. Lincoln that made her know she must get out, somehow. He would have hated the bars on the window. Besides, she never wanted to have anything about her that would disgrace his memory.

Once she was on the ship, she began to feel better. The pain was less—though she was still weak and ill—and after the second day she felt able to go up on deck. She had hesitated about it at first—for fear people would stare at her too much. The stewardess said the ship was full of Americans—and they would recognize her, of course. She hated to have people see her when she looked so badly. Her clothes were in wretched condition. But she had gone finally, and got a deck chair in an obscure corner. She had explained to the deck steward that she must have a place where she wouldn't attract too much attention—and he had been very kind about it.

In the dining room the steward had been helpful too, giving her a small side table, near the door. She was careful to go to meals early, so she could slip in quietly without being noticed. She spoke to her waiter.

"You must be careful, please, not to let people hear you

call me Mrs. Lincoln. It always attracts attention—and I'm not well enough to meet strangers just now."

He had been careful.

On the last morning before they landed, Mary was in her deck chair. She had a rug over her knees. The October sun was bright on the sea, but there was sharpness in the air. People walked past, briskly—promenading on the deck. Laughing, talking. Mary watched, careful to keep her face shaded. A group of children came along. Two noisy little boys tried to climb into a lifeboat and were scolded by the steward. When the steward had gone, Mary beckoned to the two boys. They came over curiously, a little doubtfully. She smiled, encouraging them. Their cheeks were very round and red and they wore blue serge suits with stiff white collars.

"I like little boys," Mary said. "What are your names?"

They mumbled their names, glancing at each other sideways.

"Are you brothers?"

They nodded.

Mary looked at them a minute in silence.

"I had two little boys like you once," she said.

They didn't answer.

Mary beckoned them closer. "Do you know what my name is?"

"No—" They hung back, embarrassed.

"My name is Mrs. Abraham Lincoln—" She waited, but the boys said nothing. "You know who Abraham Lincoln was, don't you?"

The younger boy looked blank, the older one frowned a little. Finally he shook his head.

"But you must have heard of President Lincoln. Don't they tell you about him in school?"

"We don't go to school. We live in Paris and our papa has a tutor for us. He teaches us in French."

"Oh." Mary understood then. "Do you like your teacher?"

The boys turned to stare at each other a moment, then they burst into giggles.

"No, we hate him. He has popped-eyes, and Tommy pulled a chair out when he was going to sit down once and he went bang on the floor—like this. He was mad."

"You oughtn't to tease your tutor," Mary said. "When you get to America I expect you'll go to school. And then you'll learn about President Lincoln—and you can tell your teacher Mrs. Lincoln talked to you—and told you Mr. Lincoln was very fond of little boys—even when they were naughty. You won't forget—will you?"

The boys stared a minute longer—then suddenly the little one made a dive at his brother and turned to run—and they pounded off down the deck and around the corner, whooping.

Mary sat looking out across the sea. After a while, when it was time for lunch, she got up and folded her rug and went inside.

The boat was due to dock at noon. Mary was ready by eleven, her bags packed, her gloves on. She had spent a long time dressing. Arranging her hair carefully, so the streaks of gray wouldn't show too much—adjusting her bonnet, dusting her face with rice powder to hide the lines around her mouth and eyes. It would be a pity to have Robert find her looking old. Because, of course, sixty-three wasn't really old at all. It was only being miserable and ill that made her look so haggard.

She stood up and looked once more in the mirror. A last, careful glance around the stateroom. She must be so careful to have everything in order—so Robert would see how well she managed alone. Going up on deck, she stepped cautiously over the high sills. She must find the nice deck steward and make arrangements with him for letting her down the gangplank as soon as possible. It would be so awkward if, after all her care, word got around at the last minute that she was on board, and a crowd gathered.

She looked down over the rail—the ship was just being made fast. But her heart sank. There was a crowd, already. Heavens, the dock was jammed with people. Milling and shouting and waving handkerchiefs as they all craned up to stare onto the deck. Mary stepped back quickly and pulled down her veil. Robert would hate it so if there was any fuss and staring. She looked for him, scanning the upturned faces through her veil. There he was, standing alone, toward the back of the crowd. Dear goodness, he looked almost old—with all that brown beard. But so tall and distinguished in his black suit and hat. She started to wave—and then remembered not to. She must find the steward now—get him to help her down quietly.

There he was by the rail—they were just lowering the gangplank. She started toward him—but at that moment a surge of people pushed her from behind—there was a commotion—someone called out.

"There she is—there she comes now—"

Mary looked around, startled. People were standing aside, making a clear space on the deck—and a young woman came through, all in gray, with flaming red hair and a small, very white face with enormous, beautiful eyes. She was laughing, waving her hand—calling out something in French.

"*Sarah Bernhardt*—"

Mary heard the name, and then she remembered. The stewardess had said something about her being on the ship, and all the other passengers making a great to-do over seeing her.

It was Bernhardt's first trip to America, the stewardess had said. She was stepping onto the gangplank now—starting down, and the crowd below was wild with excitement. She stopped and put out her arms—still laughing—blowing kisses.

"The divine Sarah," someone said, back of Mary. "Have you never seen her? Oh, she can make you weep, that woman. She can play such tragedy as you never knew existed."

Mary stepped nearer the gangplank, trying to see Robert. She had lost him in the crowd.

"Excuse me, madam—stand back there!"

Mary heard the voice without really noticing it. She was still searching for Robert. The voice spoke again.

"You, there—stand back, please. No one allowed off yet."

There was a hand on Mary's arm—and she realized suddenly that the words were being spoken to her. She turned, looking up into the face of a police guard who had come up from the dock.

Mary didn't step back. "I'm looking for my son," she said with dignity. "My son is Mr. Robert Lincoln. I am Mrs. Lincoln—"

The officer moved on down the line, pushing people back. "The rest of you will have to wait," he said, "until we can handle the crowd down there."

Mary looked after him. He didn't seem to have heard her name.

By the time she got off, the crowd had mostly left the dock, and she found Robert easily. He came forward, his hat in his hand, and bent to kiss her cheek.

"Well, mother . . ."

Mary looked up. He was smiling, looking pleased to see her. She took his arm, and they turned away together. It was nice being home again. She felt stronger already. Surely the doctors would be able to cure her now—and she must be very careful to say just the right things to Robert. Not to have any trouble again. She turned to look up. He would see how she had changed. He would see everything would be better now. Everything would be different.

Near Chicago
June 8th 65.

My Dear Mrs Wilson.

Your very kind and sympathizing letter, was received a few days since, pray, receive the grateful thanks of my deeply afflicted heart for the words of affection & comfort it contained. My precious Boys & myself, are left very desolate & brokenhearted, the deep waters of affliction have almost overwhelmed us and we find it very difficult, to bow in

are very dear to us -
Please present, my
kindest regards to
your husband & to
[illegible]
your [illegible] remain
[illegible] always
your [illegible] Mary Lincoln